Be a Better Pilot

Making the Right Decisions

Paul A. Craig

TAB Books
Division of McGraw-Hill, Inc.
New York San Francisco Washington, D.C. Auckland Bogotá
Caracas Lisbon London Madrid Mexico City Milan
Montreal New Delhi San Juan Singapore
Sydney Tokyo Toronto

pbk 4 5 6 7 8 9 10 11 12 DOH/DOH 9 9 8 7 6 5 4
hc 2 3 4 5 6 7 8 9 10 DOH/DOH 9 9 8 7 6 5 4 3

Library of Congress Cataloging-in-Publication Data

Craig, Paul A.
Be a better pilot : making the right decisions / by Paul A. Craig.
p. cm.
Includes index.
ISBN 0-8306-2053-2 (h) ISBN 0-8306-2047-8 (p)
1. Airplanes—Piloting. I. Title.
TL710.C73 1991
629.132'52—dc 91-11564
CIP

Acquisitions Editor: Jeff Worsinger
Book Editor: Tracey L. May
Director of Production: Katherine G. Brown
Series Design: Jaclyn J. Boone

PFS
3675

Dedication

This book is dedicated to all those who have helped me make good decisions:

Floyd and Anne Craig, my parents, who recognized the dream of flight in me and helped to strike the spark.

Dorothy, my wife, who has made so many sacrifices in order to see me follow the dream and, in doing so, turned the spark to a glowing fire.

And to some very special people: William Gehres, Mel Romine, Dewey Patton, Gene Jack, Wallace Maples, Oyvind Berg, Ken Futrell, Mike Cooper, Paul E. Garber, Don Culp, Ken Vojta, Johnny Henley, Thomas Wahab, John Benton, and 467 aviation students.

P.C.
June 1990
Winterville, North Carolina

Other Books in the TAB PRACTICAL FLYING SERIES

ABCs of Safe Flying—2nd Edition *by David Frazier*

The Pilot's Radio Communications Handbook—3rd Edition
by Paul E. Illman and Jay Pouzar

Aircraft Systems: Understanding Your Airplane *by David A. Lombardo*

The Art of Instrument Flying—2nd Edition *by J.R. Williams*

The Aviator's Guide to Flight Planning *by Donald J. Clausing*

Mountain Flying *by Doug Geeting and Steve Woerner*

Avoiding Common Pilot Errors: An Air Traffic Controller's View *by John Stewart*

The Beginner's Guide to Flight Instruction—2nd Edition *by John L. Nelson*

The Pilot's Air Traffic Control Handbook *by Paul E. Illman*

Ocean Flying—2nd Edition *by Louise Sacchi*

Mastering Instrument Flying *by Henry Sollman with Sherwood Harris*

The Pilot's Guide to Weather Reports, Forecasts and Flight Planning
by Terry T. Lankford

Improve Your Flying Skills: Tips from a Pro *by Donald J. Clausing*

General Aviation Law *by Jerry A. Eichenberger*

Flying in Congested Airspace: A Private Pilot's Guide *by Kevin Garrison*

Good Takeoffs and Good Landings—2nd Edition
by Joe Christy, revised and updated by Ken George

Cross-Country Flying—3rd Edition *by R. Randall Padfield*

Flying VFR in Marginal Weather—3rd Edition *by Daryl E. Murphy*

Contents

Acknowledgments

BOOK PROJECTS ARE NOT THE PRODUCT OF ONE'S WORKING ALONE. THIS book could not have been possible without the help and encouragement of several people. In particular, three students at the Center for Aviation Education of Lenoir Community College, Fred Nauer, Phil Heitman, and Paul Curlee, were instrumental for their advice, critiques, and editing skills. Fred is Air Force cool and even. He flew F-4s and now Cessnas; General Aviation is better off. Phil is passionate, a lover of the Warbirds,their pilots , and their stories. You would not want an entire class of him, but having one is great. Paul is the competitor. If he is not taming the waves on a sail-board, he is teaching the tricks of the air. These three represent the future of Aviation and the essence of Airmanship. The future is in good hands.

Also thanks to Otto Keesling, FAA Air Traffic Representative, for his constant help in understanding the complexity as well as the simplicity of the national airspace system. Thanks to Don Hedstrom, North Carolina Accident Prevention Specialist, and Larry Lambert, Raleigh FSDO, for help on this project and over the years.

Special thanks to the staff at the Leesburg, Virginia Automated Flight Service Station, the Washington Air Route Traffic Control Center, the Seymour Johnson Air Force Base, the National Air and Space Museum, and the NASA Langley Research Facility.

Thanks to Craig and Associates and InHouse Publications for advice and graphics . . . and thanks, Zig, for letting me use your room.

Introduction

IT IS JUST AFTER MIDNIGHT WHEN THE TELEPHONE RINGS AT THE FIELD office of the National Transportation Safety Board. An accident investigator answers the call. There has been a small airplane accident. The investigator calls together his "Go Team" and within minutes they are on their way to the scene.

Resting upside down in a thick forest are the remains of a once proud and beautiful airplane that had been cared for inside and out by trained mechanics and loving hands. It is now a mass of smoldering, twisted, undefined scrap. Inside lay the bodies of a pilot and his family.

The "Go Team" is a group of specialists, each person trained in a different area in the investigation of engines, structures, air traffic control, avionics, and human factors. The team hikes their way through the thicket in search of the airplane wreckage. The sun is now rising and the sky, which had been threatening the night before, is now clear and calm. One of the investigators thinks about what a great day it will be for flying. Then one of the searchers cries out, "Over here!" The plane and its passengers have been found.

The pilot who died that night was a good pilot. The flight instructor who taught him to fly the year before said that his student was a quick study. His coworkers felt he always displayed good judgment and was cool under pressure. He was a real high achiever, someone who would never settle for second best. He was excited about flying and wanted to learn all he could to be a better pilot. He had attended an FAA safety seminar just the month prior to the accident and was always reading up on new avionics systems, new airspace rules, and good maintenance practices. He was going to start working on his instrument rating soon.

It was a real mystery. How could a pilot who had excellent training and was flying one of the best equipped airplanes find himself in a position that he had no control over? What led him into this fatal situation? Why do good pilots make bad decisions?

These questions have no easy answers. More than half of the fatal accidents involving general aviation aircraft are attributed to a bad decision made by the pilot. An accident rarely is the result of one factor. The pilot, when contemplating a flight, must make countless decisions, each decision then influencing the next decision. If a chain of bad decisions is established, it will soon follow that an otherwise good pilot can make a critical mistake. The pilot in the story may have had pressures on him to make the flight that tainted his ability to make a safe final decision. He may have rationalized the situation and went against his training and judgment.

In an airplane cockpit, your decision-making skills are constantly put to the test. There are very few times in a person's life when he is totally and completely in charge; but in an airplane, the pilot in command has total authority. The pilot is the first and final decision maker in his airplane. The Federal Aviation Regulations are quite clear on who is in charge. Regulation 91.3: "The pilot in command is directly responsible for, and is the final authority as to, the operation of the aircraft." This places a great responsibility on the pilot/decision maker. The decisions made must be consistently without flaw.

To be better pilots we must be able to identify a bad decision chain and break it. This identification will take a great deal of knowledge, skill, and experience. This book has two primary purposes: to deal with the knowledge that affects the decisions and to teach ways of stepping back from a situation and taking a look at the bigger and safer picture.

This book is primarily written for the student, private, and instrument pilots who enjoy flying and want to improve their airmanship skills. Pilots should be eager to maintain and improve on their ability to fly and to work in today's air traffic system. The better decisions a pilot can make, the better pilot he will become.

1
Why We Fly

WHEN ASKED THE QUESTION, "WHY DO WE FLY?" MOST PILOTS WILL answer, "Because it is fun!" We pilots are truthful when we say this, but we are also hiding behind it. The real reason we fly is much more complex than mere enjoyment, but most of us have a hard time expressing our inner feelings about flying. The reason may be so complex that even we do not fully understand it ourselves.

The urge to start flying must have been very strong in me. Like many other pilots I know, I am afraid of heights. But I did not start flight lessons to confront my fear face-to-face. I am not afraid of flying; I am afraid of the possibility of falling. An airplane flies because of the laws of nature, and I believe in them; therefore, I perceive no possibility of falling. However, I cannot walk out on a hotel balcony 30 floors up. You cannot see how that thing is hooked on, and that mystery leaves enough doubt in my mind to allow for the possibility of falling. I can easily fly over a 2,000-foot television tower, but I would not climb up the ladder to the top of that tower for a million dollars.

THE PILOT PERSONALITY

Overcoming fears is a strong motivation to start flying. But the real reason is very basic: We fly because we need it. There is something inside us that thrives on the challenge, control, and uniqueness that flight has to offer. Flying just fits our personality. In 1974 two psychologists, Joseph Novello and Zakhour Youssef, conducted a study about the personality of both male and female pilots. They discovered what we knew all along: general aviation pilots have personalities that are distinctly different than the personalities found in the general public. In 1990 I conducted my own survey of both male and female pilots to see if this uniqueness was still alive and well. See the appendix. The answers I got offer some insight as to who pilots really are. The survey helps us understand what makes a pilot tick and what about flying is so motivational. From this understanding, a better idea can be formed about why and how pilots make decisions.

Using the same personality factors used in the Novello and Youssef study, I asked 83 pilots questions to determine what personality traits they displayed.

The survey questions were designed to bring out from the pilots some of their feelings and to thereby establish a key to their collective personality. Specific questions judged the pilots on their level of achievement need, exhibitionism, dominance, and the need for change. Other questions aimed at the pilot's spirit of adventure and need to do new and challenging things. There were also questions designed to show a pilot's level of deference, sense of order, endurance, and stubbornness. The following is an analysis of the data collected.

Achievement

Pilots tend to be very goal oriented. A pilot sees a difficult task and enjoys working toward mastering that task. A private pilot once told me he wanted to accelerate through his flight training and get his instrument rating and commercial pilot certificate as soon as possible. He said he was on a "mission." Working to achieve a piloting skill, which we perceive as difficult, feeds our need for personal reward. Most pilots, when asked questions involving personal progress toward predetermined objectives, gave answers that reflected a high degree of achievement need. The "Pilot's Personality" then involves the strong drive to aim at and accomplish difficult tasks. The more difficult the task, the greater the reward. Pilots believe that because they have accomplished the difficult task of becoming a pilot, their level of achievement is superior to the common man-on-the-street. The pilot's ego then places itself above mere ground dwellers.

Exhibition

Pilots not only want to achieve where others fail; they want recognition for the effort. The movies have painted a "romantic hero" image of the pilot. Real pilots know there is little romance in electrical systems, weight and balance forms, and performance charts, but we would still like to be seen in a romantic light. We want non-pilots to believe that we alone have what it takes to brave the heavens, to cheat death, and to reach out and touch the face of God. Pilots really like to talk about their own experiences, and certainly exaggeration is just part of that art. When non-pilots would not listen to our heroics, we turned to other pilots and "hangar flying" was born. "There I was at 30,000 feet, flat on my back, all hydraulics had failed, it was at midnight in a thunderstorm, the air traffic controllers were asking me for advice. Then at the last minute I pulled things back together, hand pumped the gear down, and made a perfect landing without spilling my coffee." For a person with the Pilot's Personality it is usually not enough just to please themselves; they must also put awe into the hearts of others. What endeavor other than flying can do that so readily?

Dominance

Pilots really like the control that flight gives them. There are very few situations in real life that give a person total and complete authority like the responsibility of being pilot in command. While on the ground, there are many people who control me: my employer, my banker, my family, my insurance agent, to name a few. But when I am at the controls of an airplane in flight, I am in command. I have power over the situation. The Pilot Personality needs to feel in control, needs to dominate the surroundings. This can make flying an escape because nowhere else can such power be obtained better than in the airplane.

Change

If you like the security of doing the same thing every day, in the same way, on the same schedule, then you are a little too conservative to be a pilot. Pilots tend to enjoy doing new things. If you really want to frustrate a pilot, make him or her do the same task repeatedly on an assembly line all day. The Pilot Personality is bored with repetition. Here again the task of piloting an airplane feeds this need. While in flight the situation is constantly in a state of change. Every flight, every landing, every instrument approach is different from the one before. A takeoff from runway 23 today might require superior cross wind technique, whereas yesterday a takeoff from the same runway might have required no wind correction at all. A pilot sees each flight as being a completely new and different challenge that must be met and overcome.

Adventure

When the pilot group was asked what they would rather do, A) tour historic Europe or B) sail around the world solo, they overwhelmingly liked the idea of one person against the ocean. Several other questions dealt with the desire to do the unusual, or face a seemingly insurmountable challenge. In each case pilots were more likely to seek adventure. Why climb Mount Everest? Because it is there! Pilots have this "because it is there" spirit. The thought of taking an airplane up against the elements, flying to distant places, and seeing things the average man only dreams of, this is what drives pilots to the airport.

THE DARK SIDE

Flying offers the opportunity to satisfy our need for achievement, exhibition, dominance, change, and adventure. We fly because it fits who we are. A person who needs a goal set before him, or likes to talk about personal adventures, or will push for his point of view, that person can quench those cravings in an airplane. We fly because our inner, complex self is not happy with anything less. Flying has all the right ingredients.

But there is a dark side to all this. The Pilot Personality carries with it some potentially unhealthy baggage. A pilot is an intricate total person that contains a mix of good and bad traits. In a pilot the good traits are usually not alone; they are accompanied by traits that could lead a pilot to disaster. How a pilot thinks and reacts to these traits influences every decision he makes.

From the survey, I learned that pilots today have within them the potential for faulty decision making that goes beyond poor judgment; it is actually part of their personality.

Deference

Pilots do not like to yield to another person's judgment or will. The Pilot Personality would rather take charge than be submissive. Pilots with a low degree of the deference trait do not take criticism well; it goes against their grain. If you are in need of constructive criticism, then obviously you do not have complete control. Because you want and need control, you reject the criticism or argue against it. This trait can lead to real problems for pilots. If a flight instructor makes the suggestion that you shallow out your VOR intercept angle, your first reaction may be that he is only picking on you and that the angle you have selected is satisfactory. Doing what the instructor has suggested is giving away your much-needed power. All the good advice in the world will not help.

Recently a private pilot was killed in an airplane accident that occurred less than 24 hours after he earned his pilot certificate. He wanted to fly over his girlfriend's house (exhibitionism) and show her he was now a pilot. He got too low and too slow and lost control of the airplane. There are many stories of brand new pilots who have gotten themselves into trouble by getting in an airplane after completing the check ride and doing something foolish. Why did they get themselves into danger after they had just been taught to make good decisions? They got their license and for the first time they were no longer "under the thumb" of their flight instructor. Statistics show that the most dangerous pilot is a private pilot with between 100 and 300 flight hours. Part of the reason for this is inexperience, and part is personality.

Order

Pilots as a group are not as interested in orderliness as the general population. They are not necessarily sloppy people, but putting things in the "proper" order is just not a very high priority for them. This trait could lead a pilot to overlook details on a preflight or to only partially complete navigation plans. The decision to get into the air may take priority over organizing the cockpit for efficiency. Details become trivial. Items are easily overlooked or rationalized so they become less important.

Endurance

Because the Pilot Personality likes change, it follows that anything that remains unchanged for long periods of time would be uncomfortable. Unfortunately, much of the knowledge and skills of flying require the learner to show endurance over the long haul. Pilots must "stick to it" in order to gain any ground, but more often pilots will put aside a task when the first diversion comes along. There are many more student pilot certificates issued by Airman's Medical Examiners than private pilot certificates issued by Pilot Examiners. The adventure-seeking traits that first bring the potential pilot to begin flight lessons may be overshadowed by his lack of endurance and the would-be pilot never reaches the goal.

Do not get the impression that because you are a pilot you are an uncaring, sloppy, easily diverted, hard head. But these traits, both good and bad, are part of what motivates us to fly. This illustrates an inconsistency in the Pilot Personality. The same traits that first interest a person in flying can also be what lead him to make poor decisions. A pilot needs to be both drawn to fly and capable of making tough decisions, but the personality profile says that both are not equally contained within the pilot.

Deep within the Pilot Personality then are the reasons why flying is so much fun. We need to fly because flying satisfies and nurtures our personality. But also planted in our personality are the seeds of poor decisions. The same forces that bring us to the airport may also be our undoing. To be safe pilots, we must recognize when personality overshadows good judgment. If we can do that, then flying will always be fun.

A 1987 Federal Aviation Administration "Back to Basics" study of poor decision making pointed out that a person's attitudes and personality have a large impact on what decisions the person makes. The study identified five attitude characteristics that are incompatible with good decision-making skills.

Anti-Authority

If a person feels that he knows it all, he will rebel against any suggestion that he needs to improve. An excessive amount of the dominance trait found in the Pilot Personality can lead to cockiness and anti-authority feelings. Suggestions made by a flight instructor, a weather briefer, or an air traffic controller will not be heeded because the person feels these outsiders are a threat. Good operating practices and regulations only apply to the "other guy."

Impulsive

A person who reacts to a situation without thinking will often make poor decisions. In this case, no actual process to arrive at a good decision is undertaken. The impulsive person feels that time has run out and that there is no opportunity to reason out the problem.

Invulnerable

An attitude that nothing bad could possibly happen to me implies a belief in one's invulnerability. "All those statistics about poor decisions leading to airplane accidents do not really affect me." A person who feels invulnerable to danger will take risks that go against good judgment.

Macho

A macho person is one who pushes ahead without looking at the total picture. A person with this attitude may decide to fly without checking to see if the weather along the route of flight is safe. He feels that he can control any situation that comes along. "Because I am in charge, there will be no problem."

Resignation

Resignation is an attitude where the person feels powerless to change anything. A pilot may think that nothing he can do will improve the situation so what is the use of trying. He resigns himself to indecisiveness and can be swept away with the current of what is taking place around him.

All the attitudes listed require that the pilot before each flight make a self evaluation. You must ask yourself what motivations or pressures are present at the onset of each flight. Recognition of personality and attitudes is the first step in recognizing and breaking a bad decision chain.

2
Acquiring Airmanship

I ONCE HEARD AN AIR TRAFFIC CONTROLLER DESCRIBE HIS HANDLING OF an inflight emergency. A pilot was forced to make an emergency landing at night when his engine threw a rod. Spotting an airport's green and white flashing beacon, he safely landed his airplane under the worst of conditions. The controller said, "That pilot showed a great deal of airmanship that night."

Airmanship is a compound idea. It is hard to describe precisely, but it is one of those things that you "know when you see it." It involves a high level of skill on the part of the pilot, but there is more to it than that. It also involves a high level of judgment and knowledge. Judgment and knowledge are partners: You cannot fully command one without the other. Being told you have airmanship is a great compliment. It means you can be depended upon in the air to handle any situation. It also means you are a good and reliable decision maker. You confidently and consistently make decisions that keep yourself and your passengers safe. You have a foundation of knowledge on which to base safe decisions, and you know how to gather information to safely make future decisions (FIG. 2-1).

Today the pilot is not merely the operator of controls. He must become an information manager. He must receive, process, interpret, and make decisions about information from many sources at the same time. This constant flow of information from the flight instruments, air traffic controllers, charts, and outside observations keeps the pilot aware of his immediate environment. The more he knows about what is going on around him, the less likely he will be to have a problem. Problems that exist are diagnosed early and corrected. Having this total situational awareness is airmanship.

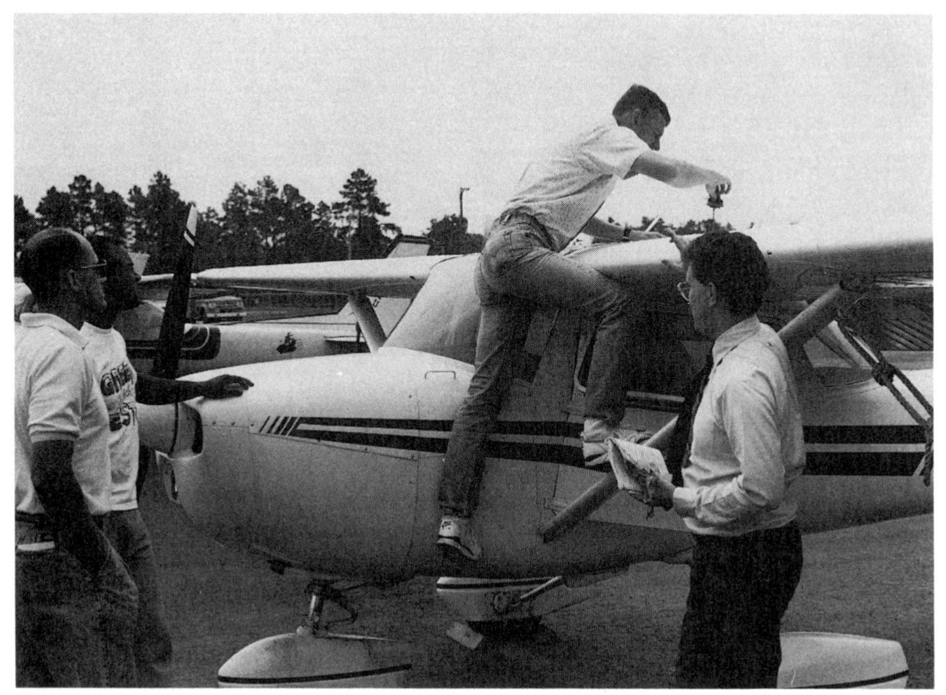

Fig. 2-1

IMPEDIMENTS TO ACQUIRING AIRMANSHIP

No pilot certificate that is issued by the Federal Aviation Administration guarantees airmanship. Airmanship is earned by experience, corrected mistakes, and a healthy attitude toward safety. In fact, airmanship is not something you ever hold; it is more something that you always strive for without actually achieving. Airmanship is excellence. The great football coach Vince Lombardi said, "Perfection is not attainable. But if we chase perfection, we can catch excellence." Airmanship is, therefore, the pursuit of excellence in flight. Every pilot should be interested in catching some of it!

Airmanship is also partially the poet's dream of flight. Many people fly to feel the freedom of flight but are poor pilots because they cannot or will not see the technical side of flying. Other pilots see only the regulations, performance charts, and the fact that it is just another job. Airmanship, however, is the place where art and science meet. The pilot who is learning the lessons taught by the school of airmanship has the proper respect for both sides.

Peer Pressure

I was a completely different pilot in 1974. I was young and was the proud holder of a private pilot certificate. None of my close friends knew how to fly, or even had an interest, so my flying made me a novelty. I enjoyed that. I was in the business of building flight time, so like most inexperienced pilots I was using my license-to-learn in all sorts of ways. The best way was to exploit the "share expenses" regulation and have someone else help pay for the flying. I flew with cost-sharing passengers all over the southeastern United States, mostly to basketball games, beaches, and parties.

I was the classic overconfident, underexperienced private pilot. I thought I knew all there was to know about flying. I had graduated from flight training and no longer cared about check rides, flight instructors, and study. The acquisition of skills was behind me now, I had arrived, I was a pilot. I was what the National Transportation Safety Board statistics would call an accident waiting to happen. A private pilot with 100 flight hours is more likely to get himself and his passengers killed than any other pilot, according to all accident records.

It was Spring Break, and two friends and I were flying to Destin, Florida, for a great weekend on Fort Walton Beach. I picked up a third friend in Auburn, Alabama, (one more to share expenses) and flew toward the fun in Florida. Unfortunately, the weather did not cooperate and when we approached Destin with no flight plan filed, we discovered a fog-covered airport that even IFR pilots were avoiding. All traffic was diverting 30 miles north to Crestview. We landed there and rented a car for the beach. But just as the airport had been covered with fog, so was the beach, and instead of a bikini-dominated landscape we saw only an elderly couple scanning the sand with metal detectors.

It was suggested that the beach idea should be replaced by a quick flight back to Auburn for a party that we could still attend. Here is where the pressure started to set in. My fellow travelers had no idea of the dangers of flying unprepared into marginal weather. I had inadvertently placed myself in a position to make a series of very unpopular decisions or take some risks I was not comfortable in taking. I called the Flight Service Station when we arrived back at the airport and discovered that the entire area had decreasing ceilings and visibilities. If I had received a weather briefing like that at home, there would have been no question about making the flight. I would have stayed on the ground. That would have been the best decision, but now I had other factors to consider. Factor number one: We had no money for a hotel and must therefore fly to Auburn for the night. Factor number two: My friends had used up a lot of money on this trip and wanted a good time to show for it. The nearest good time was in Auburn. Factor number three: I was the pilot, and being the pilot, was superior. If I now said that I could not fly, what would my friends think of me? With the pressure of all these factors in my head, I made the decision to chance the flight. We took off from Crestview as the Sun's last light disappeared.

The first 20 minutes were great. The weather was not as bad as predicted, and I was feeling pretty good about pulling this plan off. Then it happened. An eerie green glow on the right wing caught my eye. I swung my head around and saw that the left wing was enveloped in a red halo. I did not know what was happening. I quickly turned on the landing light. The intense beam of light threw itself against a white murky fuzz. Then in a rush, many things came back to me. This was IFR! I had run into a cloud that could be hundreds of miles long and thousands of feet deep. I knew of the statistics of VFR pilots who were where I was now and never made it out alive. I figured I had only a few seconds to live. "The 180-degree turn may save your life someday," my first instructor had told me, so I slowly rolled into a left turn. Within a minute, I was back in the clear. I was shaken. I saw the rotating beacon light back at the airport from which we had taken off, and nothing was going to keep me away from returning to the safety of that airport. My friends never knew there was a problem until I announced that we were staying overnight in Crestview, Florida, whether they liked it or not. I was lucky.

We slept outside that night around a campfire we built on a drainage ditch. We were cold and uncomfortable, but the bad decision chain had been broken. We were alive!

The Federal Aviation Administration calls the sickness I had that night "get-there-itis" (similar to "get-home-itis"). I had taken a situation in which good judgment said one thing and I had talked myself into a completely different decision. At several times during the pre-takeoff planning, I could have seen that the decision to go was flawed, but I was caught up in the moment. Instead of saying "no-go" to myself and my passengers, I said, "It will probably be all right; nothing bad would ever happen to me!" I let peer pressure rather than good aeronautical judgment determine my decision, and I almost paid with my life. To have made a better decision at that time, I should have separated the aeronautical information and passenger pressures. Aeronautical information includes weather, airplane performance, suitable equipment for a night flight, terrain to fly over, etc. This category would take into consideration all the safety factors of the actual flight. The pressure from my passengers led me to make the most popular decision. The correct decision, however, would have required me to separate in my mind the safe and the popular. That night I did not make the separation; I still had more lessons to learn before achieving airmanship.

There are other factors that if not recognized can prevent the acquisition of airmanship. Each pilot must make a self-evaluation on each flight. The personality traits and attitudes discussed in the first chapter can prevent a person from making clear, safe decisions. A person with airmanship will recognize early any interference with good judgment.

Stress

The introduction of stress into the mix can easily contaminate good judgment. Stress is an outside interference that affects the thought process. This interference will lead to poor decision making. When you are flying an airplane, you must act in "real time." You must be totally consumed by what is taking place around you at that very moment. If anything mentally or physically gets in the way of the job of piloting, then you are not operating safely. If you take your problems aloft when you fly, you are taking a risk. A pilot must have a mental toughness that can switch attention to a particular situation and prevent outside interference.

Stress manifests itself in four forms. Each form can cause a good pilot to make bad decisions. The four types are:

- Physical Stress—If your body's well-being is threatened, you cannot perform at your best. The lack of oxygen, cockpit noise and vibration, exhaust contamination of the heater vents, temperature, any of these factors can turn the attention of the mind from decision making to self-preservation.
- Physiological Stress—If you attempt to fly when your body is not prepared, you will leave yourself open for problems. You would never take an airplane into the air without first verifying that it was completely ready to fly, yet many people do not check themselves by the same standards. If you work all day and then head for the airport to get an early start on a weekend trip, you will have a higher fatigue level and be less alert than you would be under optimal conditions. Lack of sleep or a recent illness can also bring down your ability to recognize and solve problems.
- Psychological Stress—The emotions you have on the inside dictate what type of action you will take on the outside. If, when you approach a high density airport you become worried about your level of preparedness for what lies ahead, you can turn small problems into large ones. You could worry yourself into missing a radio call, and the fact that you are now apprehensive has gotten you behind the airplane.
- Sociological Stress—When you take problems with you into the cockpit, only problems can result. You cannot do the proper job of situational awareness if your mind is cluttered with concerns about marriage, family, employment, or finances. Airmanship requires that you separate all "Earthly" problems from aeronautical decisions.

THE FOUNDATIONS OF AIRMANSHIP

If attitudes, peer pressures, and stress tear down or prevent airmanship, what exactly builds it up? Airmanship has its foundation on good judgment. Good judgment can be defined as a timely decision arrived at through evaluation of any given situation based on aeronautical knowledge, skill, and experience (FIG. 2-2).

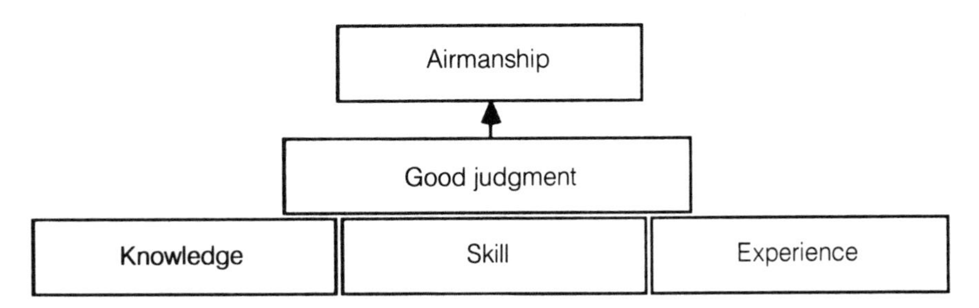

Fig. 2-2

Knowledge

Your aeronautical knowledge is first determined through written testing. You first have to pass a "pre-solo" written exam given to you by your flight instructor. This test covers basic flight and safety rules as well as information about the local airport and practice areas. Then you take an FAA written test. This test covers much more material and requires much more study. Then you prepare for the oral exam that is part of the flight test. Your flight instructor, together with study guides and test reprints, will guide you to the basic knowledge. But aeronautical knowledge is not just what you acquired to pass the FAA written tests; it must be ongoing. You must develop a standard for yourself that goes way beyond the stated requirements. You must get into the habit of using a personal checklist to increase your knowledge.

1. Ask Questions Constantly. Your flight instructor is a primary source of information, but don't stop there. Talk to other pilots, airplane owners, air traffic controllers, weather briefers, airport managers, and A & P mechanics. If you have a question about anything, do not leave the airport without getting an answer.

2. Read. The regulations, equipment requirements, pilot certification procedures, and airspace are changing almost monthly. There is no way you can keep up with the changes if you are only exposed to instruction on a periodic flight review. You should read aviation books and magazines and get on the list to receive FAA Advisory Circulars. Your local Flight Standards District Office has free copies of the "Advisory Circular Checklist." Using the checklist, you can shop the available circulars. The FAA will mail you up to 10 free previously published circulars if you write to the following address:

U.S. Department of Transportation
Utilization and Storage Section
M-443.2
Washington, D.C. 20590

To receive future Advisory Circulars, ask to be placed on the mailing list by writing:

U.S. Department of Transportation
Distribution Requirements Section
M-494.1
Washington, D.C. 20590

Before the FAA makes any changes to regulations or airspace, they first ask pilots what they think of the new plan. You can get on the mailing list to receive all new proposals and make comments on them before a final decision is made. To get on this mailing list write to the last address given (M-494.1) and ask to receive regulations proposals. You need to ask for a specific part of the regulations, such as proposed rules for Part 61 or Part 91.

3. Attend Safety Meetings. Every FAA office in every state has an Accident Prevention Specialist. The Specialist's job is to promote safety in his area. This is accomplished in many ways, but the most visible are scheduled safety meetings. These provide opportunities to meet with and talk to other pilots and to hear the latest news. The AOPA Air Safety Foundation also holds meetings and seminars on current events and safety issues.

4. Never Accept Second Best. Decide early in your flying activities that you will not settle for minimum standards. You should be eager to learn all you can at all times.

Skill

Even though your pilot certificate is issued without an expiration date, you cannot exercise the privileges of a pilot unless you keep your skills sharp through practice. The regulations require you to make three takeoffs and three landings every 90 days in the category and class of aircraft you intend to fly to be able to carry passengers. To stay current at night you must make three takeoffs and three full-stop landings after dark. The regulations never require you to practice anything else, but airmanship is a higher calling. You should practice all maneuvers. Flight skills deteriorate rapidly with disuse.

The FAA completed a study entitled "Private Pilot Flight Skill Retention 8, 16, and 24 Months Following Certification" (DOT/FAA/CT-83/34). The object of the study was to determine how fast a pilot loses pilot proficiency. All the subjects of the study were, at one time, competent enough to earn a private pilot certificate. After time intervals of 8, 16, and 24 months, the subjects were again tested to see if they could again meet private pilot standards.

TABLE 2-1 tells the story. During the time after the subjects became pilots, but before they were required to take a Biennial Flight Review (24 months), only 51% of the subjects could correctly perform the task of landing at an uncontrolled field, or make a short field landing. Only 38% could hold a specific rate of climb or properly execute a steep turn, and only 33% remembered how to do a magnetic compass turn. TABLE 2-2 ranks the tasks in the order of least retention. Simply stated, use it or lose it. Flying cannot be just a hobby; it must be something that is always taken seriously and practiced often.

The Accident Prevention Specialist can help you get your "Wings." In an attempt to encourage pilots to practice more often and to do more than just the three takeoffs and landings every 90 days, the Pilot Proficiency Award program was established. If you attend an FAA-sponsored safety meeting, you will get a program application card. Have the speaker at the meeting sign your card and then take it to a flight instructor. After you receive three hours of refresher dual instruction, you will be sent a Wings lapel pin. The three hours must consist of one hour of airwork instruction (stalls, minimum controllable airspeed, steep turns, etc.), one hour under an IFR hood, and one hour of landings (cross wind, short field, soft field). The Wings pin is nice, but you should want to do it for your flight proficiency first. As of 1991, participation in the Wings Program can satisfy the requirements of a biennial flight review.

Table 2-1. Percent of Correctly Performed Flight Tasks

Task	On Private Check Ride	After 8 mos.	After 16 mos.	After 24 mos.
1. Engine runup/takeoff checklist	100	98	100	94
2. Takeoff and departure	95	74	64	60
3. VOR tracking	79	68	48	50
4. Straight & level flight	72	74	76	65
5. Minimum controllable airspeed	83	62	37	39
6. Takeoff and departure stall	99	77	79	71
7. Approach stall	98	84	80	76
8. Constant altitude turns	79	54	51	38
9. Accelerated stall	90	51	52	57
10. Simulated engine failure	92	88	67	77
11. Forced landing	95	74	67	76
12. Traffic pattern (uncontrolled)	89	70	52	56
13. Landing (uncontrolled airport)	94	68	56	51
14. Short field takeoff	95	75	56	56
15. Short field landing	90	67	54	51
16. Soft field takeoff	94	80	65	61
17. Cross wind takeoff	93	89	53	75
18. Cross wind landing	93	81	58	63
19. S-Turns across a road	88	54	53	41
20. Turns about a point	83	52	52	41
21. Constant rate of climb	84	56	62	38
22. Magnetic compass turns	74	51	40	33
23. Unusual attitude recovery (hood)	97	66	70	66
24. 180-degree turn (hood)	90	79	63	52
25. Go-around (balked landing)	100	90	85	78
26. Landing (controlled airport)	94	68	65	54
27. Communications	100	93	87	74

Experience

Experience can be hard to come by. The pilot examiner who gave me my private pilot certificate said as he handed me the temporary white certificate, "Here is your license to learn!" I did not fully know what he meant at that time. The more flight time you put in your logbook, the smarter you get. When you expose yourself to new situations, you learn the decision-making process. You gain experience in good judgment. But flying airplanes is not cheap, and if you must always pay for your experience it can come slowly. Look for every way to increase your experience and widen your challenge each flight. Ask a flight instructor if you can observe an instrument or multi-engine flight lesson from the back seat. In this situation you will not be able to log the flight time, but your experience will grow with exposure to new procedures and maneuvers.

Table 2-2.
Flight Tasks with the Greatest Skill Loss

1. Landing at an uncontrolled airport
2. Traffic pattern at an uncontrolled airport
3. Short field landing
4. Accelerated stall
5. Constant altitude turn
6. S-Turns across a road
7. Turns about a point
8. Constant rate of climb
9. Magnetic compass turns
10. Minimum controllable airspeed
11. Short field takeoff
12. Cross wind landing
13. Landing at a controlled airport
14. VOR tracking
15. Cross wind takeoff

Acquiring airmanship is a lifelong pursuit. Working toward better piloting skills and personal satisfaction should never have an end. Making good decisions all along the way makes your flying safer and more enjoyable. A good decision maker is a good airman.

3
Information Gathering—Preflight

THE FEDERAL AVIATION REGULATIONS MAKE IT QUITE CLEAR: IF YOU ARE the pilot, you are responsible for anything and everything having to do with the flight. FAR 91.3 says: "The pilot in command of an aircraft is directly responsible for, and is the final authority as to, the operation of that aircraft." This means that along with the power and authority of being a pilot comes the tremendous responsibility of being pilot in command.

If an air traffic controller gives you instructions to fly a heading of 320 degrees, but if in doing so you will come dangerously close to a television antenna, you must reject the instructions. If you do not reject the instructions and fly too close to the antenna, you could find yourself violating a regulation and putting yourself in danger. If this happens, the pilot would be solely to blame even though the controller told him to fly that heading. It would seem only right that the controller should share some of the responsibility for the error, but the law says he does not. It is the pilot's responsibility to analyze the correctness of a controller's instructions and reject any instruction that would violate a law or jeopardize safety. The pilot, not the controller, is the voice of authority in any situation. Because the pilot stands alone in judgment, it is essential that he have all the knowledge and information necessary to make the correct decision.

A pilot must recognize a bad situation and take charge to rectify it. If your A & P mechanic forgets to properly attach the exhaust manifold of your plane after an inspection, and you take that airplane into the air, you are responsible for the fact that the plane is unairworthy. Even though you are not trained as a mechanic, you as PIC are the final decision maker as to whether or not that airplane is fit to fly. If this mistake were to cause a fire in flight that endangered you and your passengers, you would have some strong words for that mechanic; but the ultimate responsibility is still clearly on the pilot in command. The pilot is accountable.

If you are willing to take on the authority and responsibility of pilot in command of any flight, then you must be ready to properly prepare for that flight. FAR 91.103 says: "Each pilot in command shall, before beginning a flight, familiarize himself with all available information concerning that flight." This regulation is written to cover anything and everything! This law says that the pilot in command must know ahead of time everything that there is to know about every facet of this flight. Imagine how much information that includes. The pilot must be prepared to make decisions based on a seemingly unlimited amount of information.

Nobody can know it all. But before you climb in behind the controls and yell "CLEAR," you must make an honest and responsible effort to get as many facts as possible. Good decisions are based on good information. The more you know about a particular situation, the better your decisions are likely to be. So the goal is: Get the information!

The information that will be needed to make good decisions in an airplane falls into two groups: information about the aircraft and information about the environment in which the aircraft will operate.

AIRCRAFT INFORMATION

You must know the plane you fly. You must understand what it can and cannot do. No matter whether you own or rent an airplane, you should become completely familiar with what makes it work and its limitations. For this you do not have to be a mechanic, an engine designer, or an aerodynamicist. But you do have to be a curious investigator always asking "what if." What will happen if the speeder spring in the propeller governor should break? What will I do if the left wheel brake catches fire after a short field landing? What should I do if the Ammeter shows a continuous discharge on a cross-country flight? If you contemplate the "what ifs" while on the ground and come up with the best action to take in any particular situation, then decision making in the air will be easier and faster. You cannot dream up every situation that could possibly happen and predecide what you would do if caught in that situation; but by asking "what if," you will discover what makes the airplane work. Armed with this type of knowledge you will have a better chance of figuring out the best course of action. Good information leads to good decisions.

The pilot in command must have trust in who services the airplane. Trust will help fill the credibility gap that exists between what an A & P mechanic knows about the airplane and what the pilot knows about the airplane. Remember, the pilot must make airworthiness decisions as if he were a mechanic. The pilot may not be able to fix what is wrong, but he must recognize that something is in need of fixing (FIG. 3-1).

Fig. 3-1

Routine maintenance is important, but the unexpected maintenance may be more important. When a defect is found in an airplane by inspection or during an accident investigation, the FAA may issue an Airworthiness Directive (AD). An AD is a recall. Sometimes the problem is so serious that the plane should be grounded until the recall item has been corrected. Other times the item may be relatively minor and the repair can wait until the next routine inspection. Once issued, an AD is sent to each registered owner. The owner's registration certificate informs the FAA of who owns which airplanes and therefore who should receive AD notices. But if you rent the plane you fly, or you are flying another person's plane, how will you know if all outstanding ADs have been corrected? The answer is, you may not know. Another credibility gap exists between what the pilot must know to assure the plane is safe versus what is possible to know about a particular airplane. You can review the maintenance logbooks for an airplane; but if the mechanic is unaware of an outstanding AD, the entry will not appear and you will not know the problem exists.

Let's say an AD is issued on the airplane you are renting concerning the heater shroud. Investigation has determined that carbon monoxide could leak into the cockpit if the shroud is not replaced. But the mechanic is unaware that the AD has been issued, and the old faulty shroud is still in the airplane. You take the airplane into the air, also unaware, and because of this breakdown in communication between the FAA and the airplane operator you become light headed and pass out from carbon monoxide and crash. You the pilot (or your estate) would be liable for damages to property and injuries or death of passengers. The pilot is always responsible. The moral of the story is to rent from a reputable owner and ask many questions. The more you know, the better chance you will have to make a good decision about renting the airplane.

Once you assure yourself that you have done all you can do to determine the airplane's basic airworthiness, you need to look at the demands on the airplane for a particular flight. Is the airplane's performance equal to, or greater than, the situation? FAR 91.103 also says that for any flight, the information the pilot must familiarize himself with includes: aircraft performance under expected values of airport elevation, runway length, runway slope, aircraft gross weight, wind, and temperature. The pilot must then consider these variables and their effects on takeoff and landing distance.

Using the performance charts is often a pilot's least favorite task. But predicting performance can eliminate problems later. Making the correct decisions during preflight planning can preempt the need for emergency decisions later. The questions should not stop when the law is satisfied. Will the airplane climb high enough to clear obstructions along my proposed route of flight? Will this flight require supplemental oxygen? Does the airplane have the correct equipment required for this flight? Fly the flight in your mind before you ever leave the planning table. By doing this, problems that you would have encountered in the air can be considered on the ground. On the ground you can turn your full attention to the problem; in the air you will be constantly distracted and your decision will be hurried (FIG. 3-2).

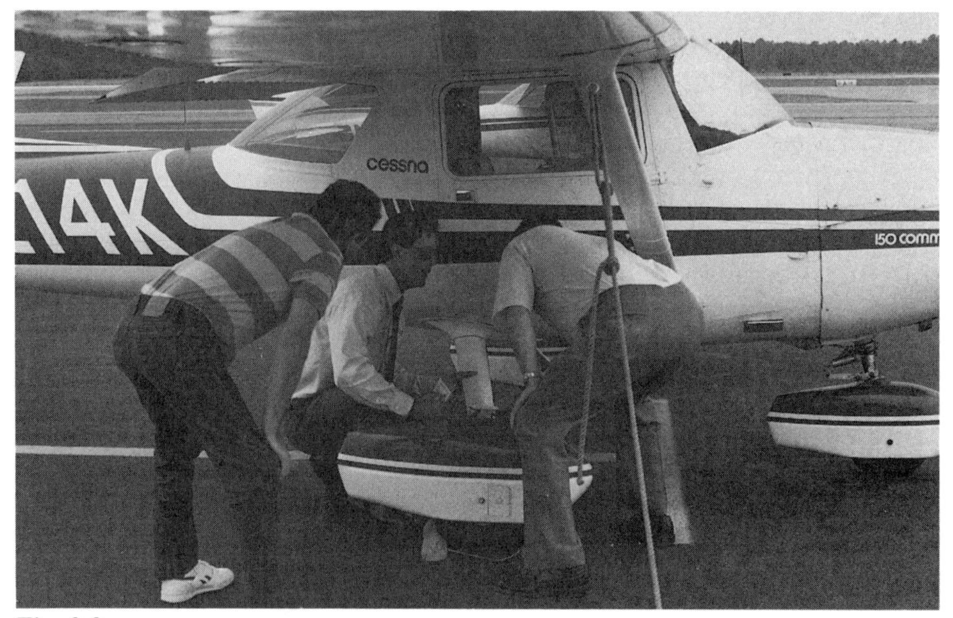

Fig. 3-2

You learned to make a preflight inspection of an airplane during your very first flight lessons, but do not think of this as something for beginners only. A preflight inspection is your last opportunity to detect a problem before leaving the ground. Once a problem is identified, its importance must be determined. Is the problem something that should keep this airplane on the ground until a qualified mechanic has made an inspection? Or is this problem not really important to airworthiness? Decisions made on the ground have more options than those made in the air. The pilot's options on the ground include: flying the airplane as it is, changing airplanes, delaying the flight for repairs, or canceling the flight. The options a pilot has in the air may be limited to choosing a corn field in which to attempt an emergency landing.

A checklist is not something you use until the day that you have it memorized. Checklists are used throughout aviation, from Cessna 150s to Space Shuttles. Use the checklist, but do not restrict yourself to it. In fact, most of the manufacturer-provided checklists just include the bare essentials. A preflight inspection that keeps you out of trouble in the air will go beyond the checklist on the ground. You simply need to check everything.

I know a pilot who climbed into a single-engine airplane for a local night flight. He had gone over that airplane carefully with his flashlight and determined that the plane was safe for the flight. One thing he did not do was look under the pilot's seat. Looking under the seats is not on the checklist. He started the engine and taxied for takeoff. It was a brilliant moonlit evening. He took to the air alone in the sky. But he was not alone. While at 3,500 feet he felt something touch his leg. A rattlesnake had somehow gotten into the plane while it sat in a grass tie-down area and had been sleeping peacefully under the seat. My friend made a great "no rudder" landing, and now he always pokes his navigation plotter under the seat as part of his normal preflight inspections. To get more preflight ideas, ask another pilot or a flight instructor to inspect the airplane and see how many different items they consider important. Ask an A & P mechanic what he thinks are important items to check before committing to the air.

If you really consider "all" factors pertaining to the airplane's readiness for a flight, you will have a big job. But it is time well spent because, as stated before, a pilot has big responsibilities.

ENVIRONMENT INFORMATION

"For a flight under IFR or a flight not in the vicinity of an airport, the pilot should familiarize himself with weather reports and forecasts, fuel requirements, alternatives available if the planned flight cannot be completed, and any known traffic delays." This paragraph from FAR 91.103 instructs the pilot to understand the environment under which the proposed flight will be conducted. This is a direct challenge to gather as much information about the flight as possible before takeoff. The regulation does not offer any suggestions as to where to look for this information, just that you are responsible for getting it. If there is a direct connection between the acquisition of accurate, timely information and good decision making, then clearly, the FAA expects you to be a good decision maker based on the information you are expected to receive.

Better information means better informed decision makers, and a better informed decision maker is a good decision maker. So where is this information, and how do you gain access to it?

THE INFORMATION BANK

The transfer of weather information goes from observer, to an information bank, then to the user. When a weather observer in Huntsville, Alabama, sees rain falling from the sky, that observer does not directly tell his findings to the people who will ultimately use the information. The observer makes a deposit in the information bank.

Information comes to the bank from four different sources: Surface, Radar, Satellite, and Upper Air Observations.

1. Surface observations are personal accounts, using weather instruments and educated guesses to report what the weather conditions are at the time of observation. Today most of the observations are made by people, but the future calls for more automated weather observations (discussed later in this chapter).
2. Radar observations are taken from weather radar scopes from across the country. Flight Service Stations and the National Weather Service (NWS) use a real-time radar display provided by the new Radar Remote Weather Display System. This allows a weather briefer to display on a color screen the actual radar echoes from a given radar station.
3. Satellite observations are taken from two weather satellites currently in a "parking" orbit over the equator, and together they cover the United States. The pictures from the Geostationary Operational Environmental Satellite (GOES) are excellent for predicting weather trends. By showing a series of pictures each taken at a different time, a "motion picture" can be developed of large, surface-weather patterns.
4. Upper Air observations are taken from radiosonde balloons and pilot reports. Many stations across the country send up weather balloons twice a day that record and send back information on temperature, humidity, pressure, and winds. Pilot reports are the only direct source of information pertaining to turbulence, icing, and the height of cloud tops.

The information from all these sources is gathered together. Then NWS and Flight Service Stations prepare and deposit the information so it can be used by the decision makers: the pilots.

Pilots must then make withdrawals from the information bank. To general aviation pilots, the information bank is the Flight Service Station (FSS). Very few pilots ever walk into an FSS to look at the weather charts and computer printouts before takeoff. In the 1980s 95% of the information withdrawals about the weather went out over FSS telephones. In the 1990s the percentage will not be that high, not because pilots will begin making more visits to Flight Service Stations, but because there will be more efficient ways to withdraw information than by the telephone.

Still, the most often used, and for now the most convenient way to gain weather information is by calling a Flight Service Station. The telephone numbers to FSSs are usually toll free and can be found in the phone book under "United States Government." The plan is to make all FSS telephone numbers nationwide the same number: 1-800-WX-BRIEF.

When you call an FSS, you must know what to ask. If you do not ask the right questions, you may not receive any information that you can really use. The briefer is usually very busy, and the more efficiently you use his time, the more pertinent the information you will receive. When the briefer answers the phone, first tell him your airplane number. The FSS uses airplane numbers for two reasons. First, it is an accounting system. They know how many weather briefings they have given by how many aircraft numbers they collect. Ultimately, this helps the FAA determine staffing levels for the facility. Second, there may be a need to determine if you ever received a weather briefing prior to your flight. If you are involved in an aircraft accident, part of the investigation into the accident will include whether or not you obtained weather information as part of your decision-making process.

Next, tell the briefer whether you are planning a VFR or an IFR flight. Doing this early in the conversation will save some time. If the briefer puts you on hold to research your flight then comes back with a five-minute talk about low ceilings, poor visibilities, and weather advisories, and then you say, "Did I mention I have to go VFR?" this will not make the briefer your friend. The briefer forms an individualized presentation just for you based on your needs. You will get more useful information when they know what you need.

Tell the briefer where you are. Chances are extremely good that you are talking long distance to the FSS and the briefer has no idea where you are calling from. As the Flight Service Stations consolidate, the individual stations will be responsible for a wider area. The weather across their area could be very different. Again, they cannot give you what you want until you give them all the facts.

Tell the briefer where you are going and when you propose to make the trip. The FSS has all types of current weather sources and forecast weather sources; the time and route of your flight will determine where the briefer looks first. How far in the future you plan to take off has something to do with the nature of the briefer's report. There are three types of briefings: Outlook, Standard, and Abbreviated.

Ask the briefer for an "Outlook" briefing when the time of your proposed takeoff is more than six hours from the time of the briefing. The briefer will then give you basic forecast information. If you are limited to VFR weather, the briefer can give you a good idea of whether the flight is possible. This type of information should be considered as only a first look at the weather for your flight. Later, when the time to fly is at hand, you will need to call again for more specific information.

The specific information for flight planning purposes and real decision making is given when you ask for a "Standard" briefing. This briefing will be an "all-there-is-to-know" discussion of the weather. When the briefer starts talking, sometimes it is hard to keep up with him. It is easier if you know the format. Here is how the briefing is conducted:

1. Adverse Weather Conditions. The briefing begins with the bad news. It is done this way so that, if within the first few sentences you realize the weather is not good for the flight and the rest of the briefing is pointless, you can stop the briefer and save everyone valuable time. If you hear, "A line of thunderstorms is moving in your direction," you will probably not need to listen to the rest. You get information about SIGMETs, AIRMETs, and Center Weather Advisories here.
2. VFR Advisory. If you originally told the briefer you were proposing a VFR flight, the briefer may at this time make the statement, "VFR flight is not recommended." The briefer makes this statement only after becoming fully familiar with the ceilings, visibilities, and weather advisories along your proposed route of flight. As always, the pilot is solely responsible for the flight. The FSS briefer cannot tell you not to fly, but his advice usually should be heeded.
3. Synopsis. The synopsis is a broad-brush description of the current weather. It will include type, location, and movement of large weather patterns like fronts and air masses that may affect the flight you intend to make.
4. Current Conditions. The briefer will collect information from all sources reporting what is taking place at that time. This includes current weather observations made at your departure and destination airports, observations made at airports along your route of flight, pilot reports in the area of your flight, and current weather radar information. If you call more than two hours before the flight, this information might be omitted from the briefing since this information will be obsolete at the time of the flight.
5. En route Forecast. The briefer will look at all available forecast material for your route of flight. Usually he will give you information in chronological order. The briefer will discuss forecast weather at your departure point at the proposed time of departure. Then, en route forecasts pertinent to your flight.
6. Destination Forecast. The briefer will give you an outlook for weather conditions during your descent and landing at your destination at your estimated time of arrival.
7. Winds Aloft. The briefer will give the predicted winds at various altitudes above the ground. Remember, the winds at the surface and the winds aloft can be very different both in velocity and direction. You should use the winds aloft when determining en route ground speed and fuel consumption. The winds aloft are given at nine different levels from 3,000 feet MSL to 39,000 feet MSL. When a station's elevation is within 1,500 feet of one of these predeter-

mined levels, the wind is not forecast. This is why some stations will have less than nine forecast wind levels. The briefer may assume that you need only the lower wind levels in the briefing. Make sure you ask for other levels if you think they will be considered in your flight planning.

8. Notices to Airmen (NOTAMs). Specifically the NOTAM(L) and NOTAM(D) types. The "L" refers to Local information. The Flight Service Station collects NOTAMs in an area within approximately 400 miles of the station. This information includes runways being closed and construction on or near the airport. The "D" refers to Distant Dissemination beyond a particular FSS's 400-mile area of responsibility. This information can include radio navigation facility closures, service interruptions of instrument approaches or radar, or even entire airports being closed. There is a common problem here, however: The briefer will not include "D" NOTAMs if they have already been printed in the "Notice to Airmen Publication." If you do not have the publication, you will need to ask the briefer for NOTAM(D) specifically. Also, FDC (Flight Data Center) NOTAMs are not normally included in a weather briefing. FDC NOTAMs refer to regulation changes or changes to aeronautical charts and instrument approaches prior to the next scheduled publication date of the chart. The briefer should be able to give you any NOTAM information if you specifically ask for it.
9. Air Traffic Control Delays. If the briefer knows of any reason why the flight cannot be handled by air traffic controllers at the time you propose the flight, he will inform you. This basically pertains to IFR traffic, although IFR congestion at a busy airport would certainly affect a controller's ability to handle VFR traffic. The controllers would much rather have you sit and wait at the end of a runway than have you perform holding patterns in the air. If traffic is routinely being "held for release," the briefer should advise you. A release will come when a "slot" opens up either en route or at your destination.

If you are not getting as thorough a weather briefing as this format indicates, then you are not using the right language. The term "Standard Briefing" unlocks the flood gate of information. In addition to what is in the format, you can ask the briefer for specific information about military training routes, MOAs, restricted airspace, density altitude, stability of the atmosphere, air traffic rules, U.S. customs services, and search and rescue procedures.

If you wanted to check one last item about the weather before your departure, you could call the FSS and ask for an "Abbreviated Briefing." Provide the briefer with the necessary background information, and then ask specific questions. This type of briefing should be requested only after you have received weather information from some other source prior to this call. The other source might have been a Standard Briefing that you previously received or one or more "mass dissemination" outlets (covered in this chapter). The Abbreviated Briefing should be seen as a supplemental information source, never as the only information source.

THE NEW AUTOMATED FLIGHT SERVICE STATIONS

The demand for weather information and other services provided to pilots is on the rise. The FAA feels that in order to handle the future demand, some changes must be made. The system that pilots learned prior to and during the 1980s will soon be replaced by a more consolidated and automated system. From the pilot's point of view, local Flight Service Stations will be closing. The FAA has chosen to take a regional rather than a hometown approach. Four or five Flight Service Stations at a time will be shut down and swallowed up by an Automated FSS somewhere in your area. The FAA has determined that there is no need for face-to-face communications with a briefer. Gone will be the one-on-one human touch, lost in the name of progress. This is not to say that you cannot go and talk personally to a weather briefer, but you may have to travel a long way to do it.

One of the biggest objections raised about Automated FSSs is that computer-generated briefings require the pilot to turn his push-button telephone into a computer keyboard. We still do not completely trust computers. When we file a flight plan over the phone to a living human being, we hang up and envision that person going right to work for us. Giving the same information to a computer seems cold, like talking to a telephone voice recorder. We know that it may be a long time until a human gets the message. The FAA is hoping these objections are just temporary problems of acceptance and troubleshooting. The FAA has done and is doing several things to convince pilots that this is the way to go. By the year 2000, there will probably be no need for something called a Flight Service Station. We will all have computer access, and weather information will therefore be readily available in our homes, cars, and airplanes. We already have it in our airports.

The positive side to Automation is access to more, better, and faster information. This will put more burden on the pilot to keep up with the flow. The pilot will have to become an information manager. We now depend on an FSS weather briefer to pick out what bits of information might be pertinent to our flight. In the future, we may have no one on whom to rely but ourselves. We will have to become translators of vast amounts of incoming information. The computer will just be the bank; we must figure out from which account to withdraw.

If the Automated FSS will swallow up many smaller observation stations, who will be making the weather observations in the future? The answer is: robots! Well, not a robot with arms and legs, but an automatic machine capable of taking weather information. Currently the Automated Meteorological Observation Station (AMOS) is in operation at approximately 90 locations. These stations may operate without any human assistance or may have part-time people to assist the robot. AMOS is a solid-state machine that measures and reports temperature, dew point, wind direction and velocity, altimeter setting, and precipitation accumulation. In addition to the information listed here, future AMOS stations will automatically report visibility, cloud coverage, and ceiling.

The Automated FSS will manage more "mass dissemination" outlets. In other words, there will be more ways to get weather information without actually talking to a human. The FAA would like a transition period where pilots use more of the mass dissemination outlets and less personal contact. For example, you get detailed weather from a recorded message over the phone and then for quick details you call the FSS and request an Abbreviated Briefing. If you do this, you should tell the briefer, when you finally reach one, which mass dissemination outlet you have used. This will help the briefer fill in the gaps. This, in theory, will free up the briefers to handle more calls.

MASS DISSEMINATION OUTLETS

Anything new will always be greeted with skepticism. But the more you know about the new system, the less frightening it is. Many of the new ideas are available now or will be in your area soon.

AM Weather

Although not a new idea, pilots' television weather certainly reaches the masses and deserves mentioning. Check your local television listings for a program called "AM Weather." It is usually broadcast on a public television station and comes on in the morning. AM Weather is a good source of "outlook" weather information. The show lasts 15 minutes and is very fast paced. The forecast weather for that day is covered, including IFR and Marginal VFR areas, icing conditions, turbulence levels, and winds aloft. Areas of possibly severe weather are also depicted. AM Weather should never be used instead of a Flight-Service-Station-generated pilots weather briefing. The show ends with a disclaimer and encourages you to call an FSS for a personal briefing.

Pilots Automatic Telephone Weather Answering Service (PATWAS)

Pilots Automatic Telephone Weather Answering Service (PATWAS) is not a new service. Usually this service is found at nonautomated Flight Service Stations. PATWAS are several telephone numbers, each assigned to different information. When you call the number, you will hear a continuous loop recording of aeronautical and meteorological information. Your call might catch the recording in the middle, so it becomes like going to a movie late and then staying over for the beginning of the next show just so you will not have missed anything. The recordings normally contain a summary of data for an area that is within 50 nautical miles of the "parent" station. PATWAS is certainly a general, nonspecific outlook at the weather. At best it is used to determine whether IFR or VFR weather exists, and if you are a VFR pilot you can make a "go or no-go" decision strictly from PATWAS. If you decide to "go," you will need additional and more specialized information. In this way, the VFR pilots are "weeded out" of an IFR system. VFR pilots make the decision not to fly without ever speaking to anyone, and the briefers that stand ready to give more detailed information are available to those who will ultimately need it.

Telephone Information Briefing Service (TIBS)

Telephone Information Briefing Service (TIBS) and PATWAS are very similar, but TIBS provides area and route briefings and is provided by an Automated FSS. The telephone message is continuous and may also contain airspace information and special announcements. There is a different recording and therefore a different telephone number for various routes originating from the FSS. For instance, routes to the Northeast, Southeast, Southwest, Northwest, and Local would each have their own numbers. The objective of TIBS is to save the time of FSS personnel. The telephone numbers can be found in the Airport/Facility Directory under the FSS and National Weather Service sections.

Telephone-Transcribed Weather Broadcast (TEL-TWEB)

The Telephone-Transcribed Weather Broadcast (TEL-TWEB) has been around for a long time. Usually it is considered an in-flight weather advisory, but what is new is that at some locations the TWEB can be accessed by telephone. The service allows you to listen in on the broadcast that is being transmitted on an NDB or VOR station. TWEBs will be discussed further in chapter 4.

Direct User Access Terminal (DUAT)

Once you become computer literate, a home computer can offer the best opportunity for weather services short of a personal visit to a Flight Service Station. You will need a computer with a modem. A modem is a device that enables one computer to talk to another by way of the telephone. A modem can be built into your home computer or come separate as an attachment. In addition to a modem, you will need a software program that sends commands to the modem and lets you dial the telephone number from the computer keyboard. You will also need the knowledge to translate the computer-coded weather reports. The codes have been around for a long time, but most pilots never saw them except on written exams. When pilots call the FSS, the briefer, who is at a computer, will call up the weather information and then translate it for you over the phone. In the past the pilots never actually saw the reports. With the personal computer in your home or office there is no briefer to translate, so you must learn the language. The Federal Aviation Administration publishes the Aviation Weather Services Handbook, which has a key to all the different weather products and their codes.

At first the National Weather Service computers were allowed to be tapped into by private vendors. These vendors acted as the information go-between. The individual user, the pilot, would call the vendor on the computer using the modem. The vendor would pass on the computer information that they received from the National Weather Service. The pilot had to pay for the time that his computer talked with the vendor's computer. On top of that, the pilot may have had to call long distance just to allow the computers to communicate, so the pilot had a big phone bill as well. If the FSS is a bank of information from which pilots make withdrawals, then the computer is the Automatic Teller Machine. The analogy is very real. Weather vending machines started to appear in Fixed Base Operators' flight planning rooms. Some of the computer weather products were provided free to the user pilots, but the FBO was still paying the vendor. In other places the computer weather products were available only after the pilot keyed in his Visa or Mastercard number. The idea was good, but the drawback of cost kept the systems from being widely used. The FSS is still the number one source.

Today the FAA is changing its game plan. If computers will be the major access to weather information in the future, it makes sense to educate the users early. If pilots do not widely accept the new systems, then the FAA's automation plans will be slowed. Initially the major obstruction to acceptance of the new systems was cost. Why would a pilot pay for weather information that is uninterpreted when he could get a personal and well-explained briefing for free? The FAA had to make the computer free as well.

After competitive bidding, two companies were chosen to be Direct User Access Terminal vendors. Now the FAA, not the pilot, pays for the time that the pilot's computer speaks to the vendor's computer. Even the telephone call is a toll-free 800 number.

In DUAT's infancy there were many problems. The vendors who won the bids were large computer companies with little or no experience with aviation needs. The programs were not practical. If you wanted to fly from Denver to St. Louis, you could not get weather information about points in between. Finally, with many comments from the aviation community, the DUAT is growing up and becoming more useful.

The basic package of weather is free, but the vendors also offer impressive software packages so that your computer can reproduce weather charts and forecasts and look in on the color weather radar reports. The software packages cost the user extra. Now even flight plans can be taken in over the computer terminal.

The following are DUAT-approved vendors:

Contel Federal Systems
12015 Lee Jackson Highway
Fairfax, Virginia 22033
1-800-345-DUAT

Data Transformation Corporation
559 Greentree Road
Turnerville, New Jersey 08012
1-800-243-3828

One of the biggest advantages of DUAT is that, with a printer, you can put your weather on paper. This allows you to take the actual weather report with you in the plane. Also, once on paper, it can be read at your own pace and you will get a more complete picture than you did when you tried to copy a briefer's spoken words. Usually you got down only about half of what the briefer had passed on to you. If you can read the computer codes, then there will be less miscommunication.

I was recently demonstrating to some student pilots the computer access to DUAT and all the weather information it can bring to the screen. One flight student watched in determined silence for 15 minutes, then said, "This stuff is the same stuff the guy on the FSS telephone sees when he talks to you." "That is exactly correct," I replied. Then he said, "Well then we don't really need those FSS guys anymore." We still need them, but we need to use them more efficiently.

The biggest potential disadvantage is that now pilots have to make all the judgment calls. Even though the FSS briefer is supposed to give you only facts and not try to influence your "go no-go" decision, the voice at the other end can help you lean one way or the other. The computer will not say, "VFR is not recommended." Also, if you receive all your weather information by way of one or more of the mass dissemination outlets and never speak to a briefer, there is no record that you received any weather information at all.

An FSS weather briefer once recommended to me that I use the "remarks" block of the standard flight plan form to record this information. If when planning a flight I called the nearest PATWAS number and then took weather information off the computer, when I filed the flight plan I should list under remarks: PATWAS & DUAT WX BRIEF. This at least puts me on record and helps verify that I kept my commitment to consult "all available information" pertaining to that flight.

There is no shortage of information sources. The tools to make good flying decisions are as close as your telephone or home computer. The burden is still on the pilot to take this flow of information and use it well. If good decisions are a by-product of knowledge, pilots should be better decision makers in the "information age." We must now learn to use the new tools.

4

Information Gathering—Inflight

THERE ARE PILOTS WHO METICULOUSLY PREPARE THEIR NAVIGATION LOG for a cross-country flight and then once in the airplane ignore their valuable plans and pitch the nav log in the back seat. The airplane is not a place where information gathering stops. In fact, the pilot in flight has the greatest need for accurate and real-time information. Takeoffs are always optional. If in your preflight information gathering effort you decide that the flight should not be made, then you elect to cancel the takeoff. But once airborne a landing somewhere is mandatory. The pilot in flight sits at the point of decision. The best decisions are made only with the best information, so the pilot must be able to reach information pertinent to the flight from the cockpit.

Recently a pilot on a cross-country flight ran out of fuel and made a controlled crash landing in a grove of trees. During the investigation, the pilot was asked why he did not stop for more fuel before he ran out. "I have made this flight many times before on one load of gas; the wind just must have been stronger today," he replied.

If the wind was stronger than anticipated, why didn't he know that fact ahead of time and change his plans accordingly? The job of decision making does not end at the runway; the airborne decisions become even more urgent.

Information available to the pilot for inflight decision making comes from two sources: inside the airplane and outside the airplane. The inside information you must prepare before you leave and have available at your fingertips in flight. The outside information comes by way of the airplane's radio.

INSIDE INFORMATION

Developing a plan before you fly is essential. There are many things a pilot can do before takeoff that will make the job of piloting easier when aloft. Your first line of defense is good organization. First, organize your thoughts. Do not rush into a flight with your mind racing. You will miss small details that can lead to larger problems. Next, organize your cockpit. Have you ever needed your navigation plotter but it was in the back seat in your briefcase? The airplane may end up doing unintended aerobatics while you attempt to retrieve that plotter.

The inside of a light general aviation airplane is not usually very large, but if you do not prepare the cockpit before you start the engine, the space inside the plane will start to grow. You must turn everything within arms length of the pilot's seat into a personally tailored office. The airplane designer spends a lot of time placing the flight instruments, engine instruments, flight controls, and engine controls in places where they maximize efficiency. You must do the same with aeronautical charts, flight computers, navigation plotters, and IFR approach charts. One of the toughest things to do in aviation is to unfold a sectional chart while you are flying the airplane. Before you locate the proper place, you seem to end up wearing the chart!

Some of the "glass cockpit" designs of the 21st century will eliminate the need for you to juggle all these items on your lap. Futuristic plans have the charts appearing on a television screen and you flying a "video game" to you destination. For now though, you will need a simple clipboard to hold your charts, flight plan, and navigation log. It is a good idea to take along a scratch pad so you can easily jot down weather information and controller instructions. Tie a string to a pencil and attach it to your clipboard so it cannot get away from you.

Think through the flight before you start the engine. Ask yourself what material you will definitely need to access while on the flight. Do you have all the proper frequencies for ground control, control tower, nearby Flight Service Stations, Flight Watch, and Air Route Traffic Control Centers (ARTCC)? What about airport runway and taxiway layouts? What about Area Charts, Standard Instrument Departures (SIDs), and Standard Terminal Arrival Routes (STARs)? You might need all these items on a flight. The fact is that if you need these things, you probably will need them fast. You will not have time to rummage through your flight bag looking for an important piece of information.

Collision avoidance is the top priority for a pilot. The more organized you are, the more time you will have to look out the window. Remember that even on an IFR flight plan you are still responsible for collision avoidance whenever you are outside instrument meteorological conditions (IMC). The more familiar you are with your office-cockpit, the quicker you can retrieve valuable information and go back to your primary function of avoiding other aircraft.

The data you collect and the books and charts you decide to take along on the flight should be very familiar to you. You should not have to look up chart symbols during a flight to know what they represent. You should know the way approach chart books and the Airport/Facility Directory are arranged. Years ago the NOS approach charts were arranged alphabetically by the name of the airport. This meant that if you were flying to Rome, Georgia, you had to know that the airport's name was the Richard B. Russell Airport. If you did not know the name, and who can remember them all, you had to go to a separate directory to look up the airport name in that city, then go looking for the actual approach chart. This took up valuable cockpit time. The designers of the charts became aware of the inefficient layout of the book and changed the format so that now airports are listed alphabetically by city name. All this to improve cockpit organization and save time so the pilot can look outside more often.

In the airlines this concept of making the cockpit an efficient and safe place to work is called Cockpit Resource Management (CRM). When pilots and information sources work together as a team, the ability to control the airplane safely is greatly improved.

Cockpit organization comes down to: develop a good plan, then efficiently carry out the plan. Like a computer that receives faulty data then gives an incorrect result, your preflight plan must not be faulty or your inflight decisions will be faulty. The garbage-in/garbage-out theory applies in aviation.

OUTSIDE INFORMATION

When in flight the pilot has available to him many different radio sources from which to acquire information. It is safe to say that if you have sufficient altitude to ensure line-of-sight Very High Frequency (VHF) transmission, then you have the power to access inflight information if you know where to look. Some of the information is given to the pilot in the form of recorded messages that he can tune in and listen to. The most common of these is the Automatic Terminal Information Service (ATIS). ATIS is a continuous audio tape recording that is broadcast on a VHF frequency. An ATIS frequency will be found at most airports that have a high degree of activity. Essentially the ATIS is a time-saving device for the pilots and controllers when they use the radio. The ATIS recording will give information concerning runways in use, instrument approaches in use, weather, and pertinent remarks like a runway being closed. If the controller had to tell every pilot this information individually, the controller would have no time left over to handle the traffic. ATIS passes the information along to the pilot, freeing up the controller to do his job.

If you are inbound to an airport that has an ATIS frequency (some ATIS information is broadcast on VORs), you should listen to the recording and copy down the information. You may need to listen to the recording more than once just to make sure you have the correct information. Each ATIS recording is coded with a letter from the phonetic alphabet. The beginning and end of the recording will say ". . . this is information Charlie." The next recording that is issued and put on the radio will most likely be "information Delta." When you first talk to the approach control, you will tell the controller that you have "information Charlie" and the controller will assume that you are aware of all the information contained in the current recording. When a new recording is issued, the approach controller may say, ". . . attention, information Delta is now current." The controller is actually telling you to update your information. In this case, if you had two radios you could place the "both" switch of your audio panel to the speaker (or headset) position. This would allow you to listen to the new ATIS information while remaining in contact with approach control to avoid missing an important call. This same technique works well on IFR flights when the Air Route Traffic Control Center (ARTCC) or other agency hands you off to your destination airport's approach control.

ATIS is a good source of information even if you are not inbound to the airport at which the ATIS originates. While passing through the area on a VFR flight, listening to ATIS can give you an idea of what the weather is ahead. Do not be worried, however, if you are flying VFR and hear about IFR approaches in progress. IFR approaches can be used regardless of the weather, so listen specifically to the ATIS broadcast that pertains to weather information. ATIS will tell you ceiling, visibility, obstructions to vision, temperature (Have you ever heard an airline captain say, "Welcome to Kansas City. The temperature here is 72 degrees"? Where do you think he got that information?), dew point, altimeter setting, and wind direction and velocity. If the visibility is greater than five miles and the ceiling greater than 5,000 feet, these items may be omitted. The wind information, since this is a surface observation, will be given in degrees magnetic.

The altimeter setting that is given is also very helpful to ensure that you are maintaining the proper altitude en route. The Airman's Information Manual recommends that you update your altimeter setting with stations that are within 100 nautical miles of your route of flight. ATIS is the easiest way to accomplish this.

ATIS is only found at larger airports, but real-time weather information can be received from smaller airports as well. Currently more "robots" are being installed at smaller airports to provide weather information similar to that of ATIS. These robot weather machines are called Automated Weather Observing Systems (AWOS) and Automated Surface Observation Systems (ASOS): AWOS at uncontrolled airports and ASOS at controlled airports. These machines are different from AMOS. AMOS reports weather to an FSS or other information-gathering bank. The pilot gets information from AMOS on the ground by way of a weather briefing. The AWOS reports weather by voice directly over a radio frequency so the pilot can receive the information while in the air.

The AWOS system has four levels of service. AWOS-A broadcasts the local altimeter setting. AWOS-1 reports altimeter settings, wind data, temperature, dew point, and density altitude. The report is given by a computerized voice synthesizer. The voice sounds like a human, but don't try to carry on a conversation with it. AWOS-2 is currently under approval and will give all the AWOS-1 information plus visibility. AWOS-3 reports, in addition to all AWOS 1 and 2 data, the cloud coverage and ceiling data. The AWOS transmitter allows pilots who are closer than 25 miles out to hear the information. The wind information from AWOS will allow you to plan ahead for the traffic pattern. Knowledge of the traffic pattern will mean better collision avoidance. The AWOS message lasts between 20 and 30 seconds and is broadcast once per minute. Many AWOS messages can also be accessed by telephone. The Airport/Facility Directory will list the telephone number if telephone access is available.

Today the only source of weather information at uncontrolled airports is the unicom operator. Unicom operators usually know very little about the weather outside the FBO office, so installation of more AWOS systems will be a great improvement. NASA has even experimented with robot controllers for uncontrolled airports. A radar antenna spots airplanes in the traffic pattern, and a computer voice reports their positions. If you were inbound to the airport and heard the computer announce that an aircraft was on downwind to runway 6, this would alert you to the runway in use as well as to where to look for traffic when entering the pattern.

The ATIS and AWOS systems give information only for the immediate area around the airport from which the recording is broadcast. En route information is recorded and broadcast over Transcribed Weather Broadcasts (TWEBs). You can listen to a TWEB on any navigation facility that displays the small solid box in the lower right corner of the facilities information box. Figure 4-1 shows how the TWEB is depicted on a sectional chart. The TWEB can be broadcast on Nondirectional Radio Beacons (NDB) or VOR stations. The TWEB will give information about winds aloft, current weather conditions, hazardous weather advisories, and NOTAMs along individual routes. The TWEB may not describe your exact route, but you can listen to information that pertains to your general direction. TWEB routes have a numbering system just as interstate highways do. If that pilot who ran out of gas fighting strong headwinds had listened to a TWEB recording about winds aloft, maybe his flight would have turned out differently.

When severe weather begins to develop, pilots who are in the air must become immediately aware of hazardous situations. Flight Service Stations record pertinent messages alerting airborne pilots of the location and intensity of the danger. The warnings come in many forms. AIRMETs warn of weather hazards that concern mainly light aircraft, such as moderate turbulence or moderate icing. SIGMETs are warnings of dangerous conditions that are of concern to all aircraft. Convective SIGMETs warn pilots of thunderstorm activity and squall lines. AIRMETs, SIGMETs, and Convective SIGMETs are all reports of current conditions.

A Center Weather Advisory (CWA), instead of originating from an FSS, comes from one of the Air Route Traffic Control Centers and is a report of existing or forecast hazardous weather. When any of these reports are necessary, they will be broadcast over all FSS frequencies except the emergency frequency (121.5 MHz). AIRMETs, SIGMETs, and CWAs are broadcast at 15 and 45 minutes past the hour. Convective SIGMETs are broadcast on the hour and at 15, 30, and 45 minutes past the hour. Air Route Traffic Control Centers broadcast these alerts once when they are issued over all their frequencies (except the emergency frequency) if any part of the hazard is contained in their airspace.

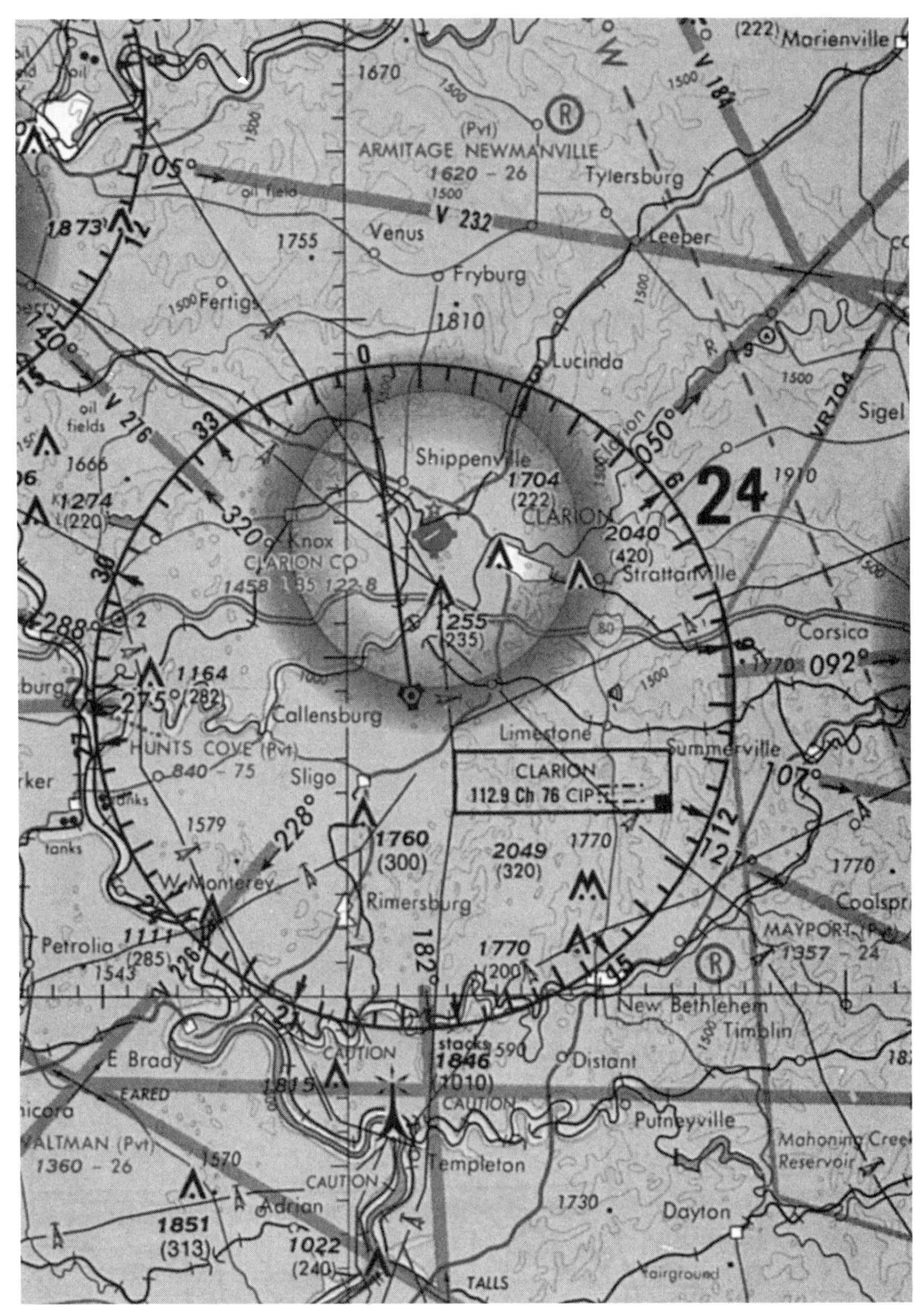

Fig. 4-1. *The small box in the lower right-hand corner notes that a TWEB is broadcast from this facility. This TWEB broadcasts over the Clarion VOR, but TWEBs can be broadcast from Nondirectional Beacons (NDB) as well.*

Many VFR pilots use their radios when departing an airport, but then the radio goes essentially unused for the remainder of the trip. Pilots then fly across the land listening to downwind reports at distant airports and idle chatter on the unicom frequency when vital information passes them by on the FSS frequencies. Before takeoff, write down the FSS frequencies that you can receive along your route of flight. Then while inflight, monitor the frequency that will do you the most good. In this way vital decision-making information will come to you. You will not even have to go scrambling for it!

If the weather broadcast in the AIRMETs, SIGMETs, and CWAs are so important, why are they only broadcast at certain intervals allowing for the possibility that a pilot would miss an alert? This question is being answered by a new system that brings all these alerts under one umbrella: the Hazardous Inflight Weather Advisory Service (HIWAS). HIWAS is a continuous broadcast that summarizes information from all existing AIRMETs, SIGMETs, CWAs, and PIREPs. When a HIWAS alert is issued, the announcement can be heard on all ARTCC, FSS, and airport terminal frequencies. The announcement will instruct airborne pilots to contact the continuous HIWAS frequency in their area. The pilot can then switch frequencies (or use the "both" feature of the audio panel) and hear the recorded message. HIWAS is not yet a nationwide service. In areas where HIWAS has been installed, the local FSS and ARTCCs will stop broadcasting alert messages at time intervals around the clock and rely on the HIWAS system. In your preflight briefing, you should ask if the area along your route of flight has HIWAS service.

If you are monitoring a frequency and an alert is broadcast, your next step is to talk with someone. With the exception of an FSS phone call, all the services discussed thus far involve a pilot listening to a recording or a computer-generated voice. But to get the best information, you will have to ask questions that are unique to your situation. If hazardous weather is in your area or along your route of flight, you will have the classic decision. You must decide whether or not to continue the flight as planned, stop at an interim airport, or turn around and go back to where you came from. Federal Aviation Regulation part 91.5 speaks to the required pilot action in the event that something causes you to consider changing plans: "For an IFR flight, or for a flight not in the vicinity of an airport . . . [the pilot must familiarize himself with] alternatives available if the planned flight cannot be completed." If while in flight you hear a weather alert or actually see bad weather ahead, you need information immediately to help you make your decision.

The best thing to do is to talk to someone who has access to real-time information. If the situation concerns precipitation and/or thunderstorms, you want to talk to someone who is watching a radar screen. Your first attempt at communicating should be to a Flight Service Station.

The easiest way to contact a Flight Service Station is on a "discrete" frequency. A discrete frequency means that you dial in the correct numbers and broadcast, then in return the person at the FSS talks back to you on that same frequency. A control tower is another example of a discrete frequency. These frequencies can be found on the top on a thick-lined FSS information block (FIG. 4-2) on a sectional chart. If an FSS and a VOR are co-located (FIG. 4-3), then the entire VOR information block is outlined with a thick line. The frequencies of the FSS are located outside the block on the top thick line. The discrete frequencies are those without the letter *R* beside them. Every Flight Service Station has 122.2 and 121.5 as standard frequencies. So even if you could not find the information block, you could try to contact an FSS on 122.2. The emergency frequency is 121.5, and all FSSs listen in on that channel as well.

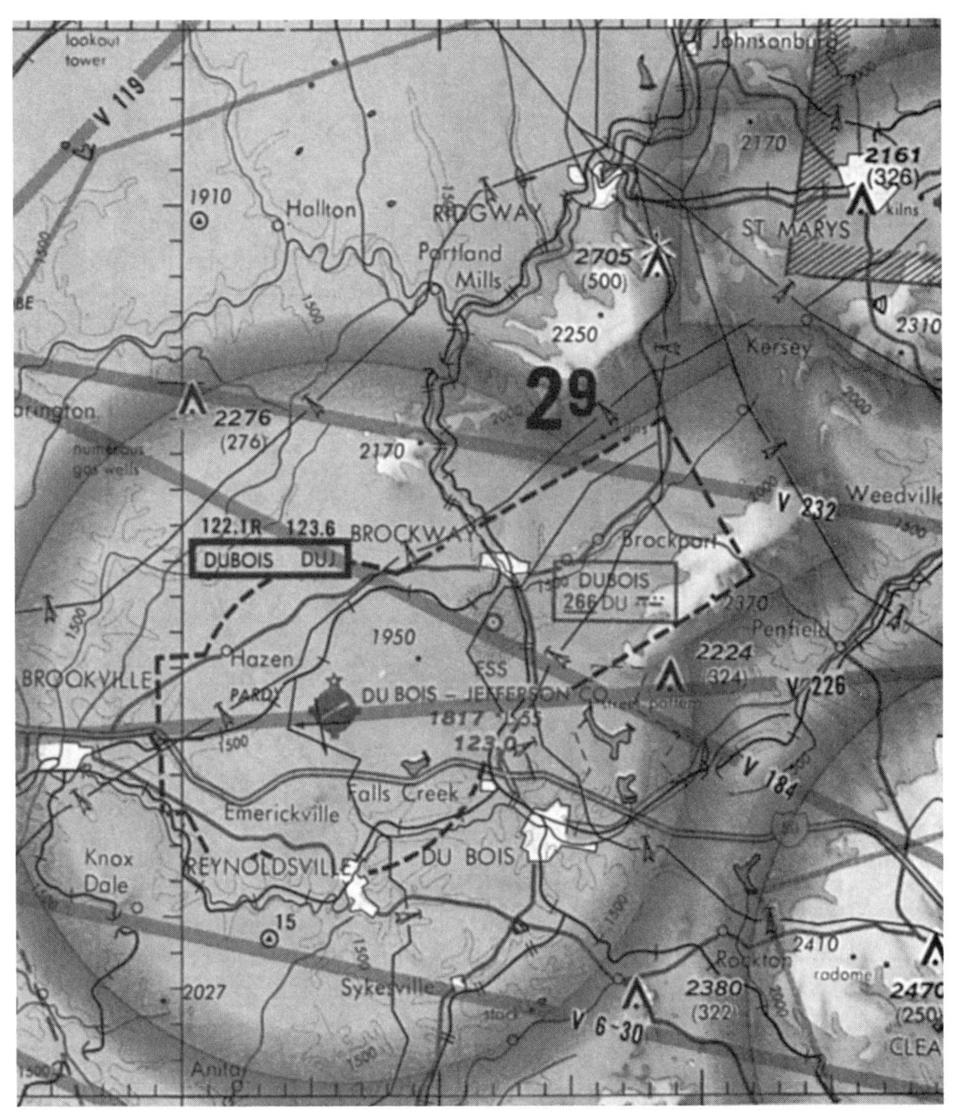

Fig. 4-2. *The thick line box depicts a Flight Service Station on the airport. Here the Dubois FSS is shown located at the Dubois-Jefferson County Airport.*

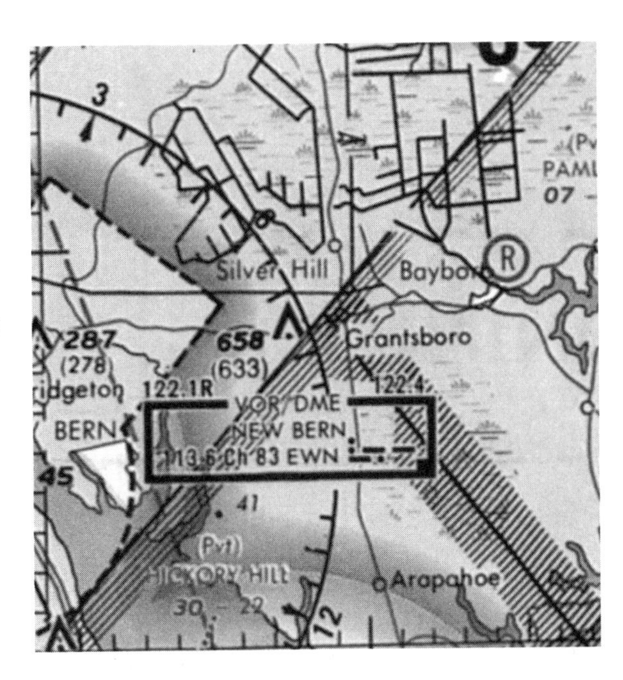

Fig. 4-3. *Where an FSS and a VOR are co-located, the VOR information block will be a thick line box.*

When you speak to the FSS with the discrete frequency tuned in, you can address them with the term *Radio* followed by the name of the FSS. The briefer will reply back to you on the same frequency. Now you can get the valuable information on which to base your decision.

What if, due to the line-of-sight limitations of the VHF radio, you are unable to contact the briefer on the discrete frequency? The answer is certainly not to give up trying to get a personal briefing. You must now fall back to plan B. The FSS system anticipated situations where you would be out of range and designed ways in which the long arm of the FSS could be extended.

The range of the FSS and therefore your ability to receive information in flight is extended at certain VOR stations. When a VOR is capable of providing a communications link from your position to the FSS, the VOR information block on the sectional chart will indicate a "parent" station. Under the VOR block is a bracket. Inside the bracket is the name of the Flight Service Station that monitors that VOR.

Figure 4-4 shows the top of the box, and a frequency is shown with the letter *R* beside it. The *R* stands for receive. In other words, the FSS can receive your transmission if you talk on the frequency indicated. When you do this, your transmission does not have to travel a long distance to the location of the FSS but only to the nearby VOR. Your voice is then relayed by a "land line" to the FSS. The land line is not subjected to line-of-sight limitations and the message gets through. When the briefer responds to your request, he will talk back to you on the navigational frequency of the VOR. Again his voice travels the land line to the VOR and then through the air to your airplane. You must remember two things when using this link: Mention to the briefer

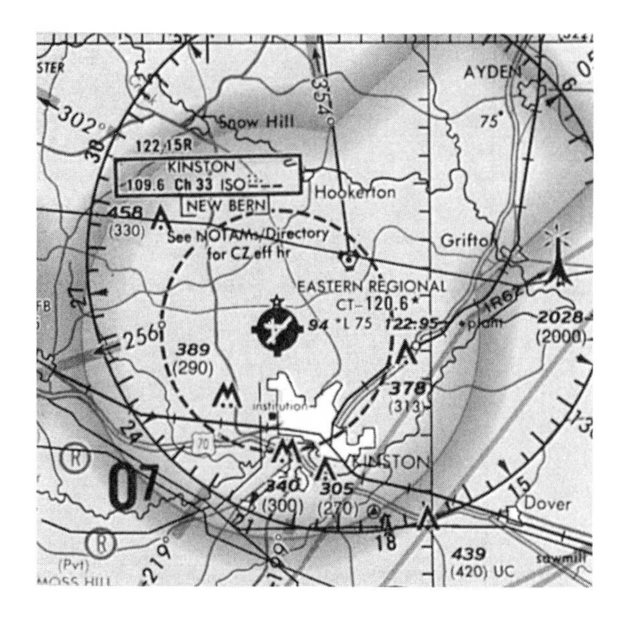

Fig. 4-4. *The "bracket" below the VOR information block contains the name of the distant FSS that monitors this VOR. The radios are set to transmit on 122.15 and receive on the VOR's frequency of 109.6.*

on which VOR you would like him to respond to you and turn up the volume on the navigation side of your radio. Now you talk on one frequency, and the briefer talks back on the VOR. The valuable communication has now been established over a longer distance.

What if the VOR is out of service or there is no VOR in range that provides the link? You must develop another plan. Fall back to plan C. Many Flight Service Stations in addition to monitoring VORs will monitor Remote Communications Outlets (RCOs). The RCO is another radio/land line combination, but it is a discrete frequency and has no navigational function. The RCO is illustrated on sectional charts by a thick blue box with location of the RCO antenna and the letters *RCO*. Figure 4-5 shows an RCO box. The RCO frequency is on the top and the parent station is in the bracket below. When you call an RCO frequency, your voice is transmitted through the air to the RCO antenna. Then your voice takes the land line the rest of the way to the FSS. The briefer returns the favor using the land line for the first part of the trip back to the RCO site and then back through the air to your radio. The actual "through the air" part of the transmission can be up to 50 nautical miles, depending on the line of sight. As the Flight Service Stations consolidate, there will be even more reliance on VOR and RCO communication links.

The Air Route Traffic Control Centers use RCOs as well. The Center controller may be controlling traffic in an area that is hundreds of miles from the actual location of the center. Just like the FSS, the controller cannot communicate using line-of-sight transmissions across those miles to the place where his radar screen has coverage, so he uses an RCO that is located somewhere under the radar coverage.

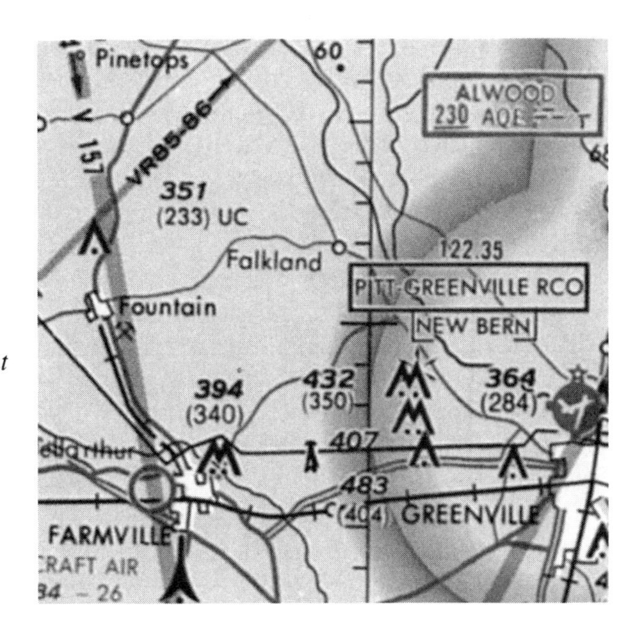

Fig. 4-5. *The Remote Communications Outlet (RCO) extends the reach of the Flight Service Station.*

With the direct communication possibilities to a Flight Service Station, together with VOR and RCO relays, the network of coverage is almost nationwide. If you are approximately 3,000 feet AGL or higher, you should be able to use some method to reach weather information. Someday all these communications will be delivered via satellite, and all the present communication links will no longer be necessary. Then, rather than using land lines to carry voices over mountains and around the curvature of the Earth, we will be able to transmit and receive through an orbiting relay station.

If for some reason plans A, B, and C fail to reach a Flight Service Station, then call the en route specialist: The En route Flight Advisory Service (EFAS). EFAS goes by another name as well: Flight Watch. The Flight Watch briefer is an expert in en route weather; therefore, you should not try to open or close a flight plan on this frequency. The Flight Watch information is no longer shown on sectional charts because now the service is standard nationwide.

Any time you are flying over the United States at 5,000 feet AGL or higher, you can reach Flight Watch. For flights below 18,000 feet MSL, Flight Watch has a universal frequency: 122.0. If you are not sure which Flight Watch station you are closest to, just call on 122.0 and say "Flight Watch" and your aircraft number. Basically the area in which a Flight Watch station has jurisdiction is the same as the ARTCC areas. The Flight Watch specialist is located at an FSS but can communicate by way of RCO over a wide area of responsibility. Flight Watch is usually operated from 6 AM until 10 PM every day. The Washington Flight Watch station is at the FSS in Leesburg, Virginia. The Leesburg facility has RCOs that cover the area approximately the same as that covered by the Washington ARTCC (FIG. 4-6). Complete diagrams of Flight Watch stations and their coverage areas are shown in the Airport/Facility Directory.

The Flight Watch specialist is the "teller" at the bank of Pilot Reports (PIREPs). PIREPs are firsthand pilot report information because more often than not that specialist is the person who took the pilot report in the first place. The Flight Watch specialist will often solicit a PIREP from you when you call for information.

When you talk to Flight Watch, you are talking to someone who is looking at all the weather information possible. If you see bad weather ahead on your route of flight, call Flight Watch because the person at the other end is already looking at that bad weather on radar. The Flight Watch specialist is in the best position and has the best information to give you decision-making data. How wide is the bad weather pattern? Which way is it moving? Can I go around the weather safely? If I can go around, which direction is best? When you get the answers to these questions, it will be easier to make important weather-related decisions. Will you turn around, stop at an airport nearby and wait out the weather, or continue on? The decision is best made with all the facts.

Another aid that a Flight Service Station can give to pilots in the air is the Hazardous Area Reporting Service. In today's automated system, this service is old fashioned but it still serves its purpose. Not all decisions will involve dangerous weather; some will involve potentially dangerous terrain. If you decide to fly across a dangerous area, this FSS service can be important. When VFR routes cross large bodies of water,

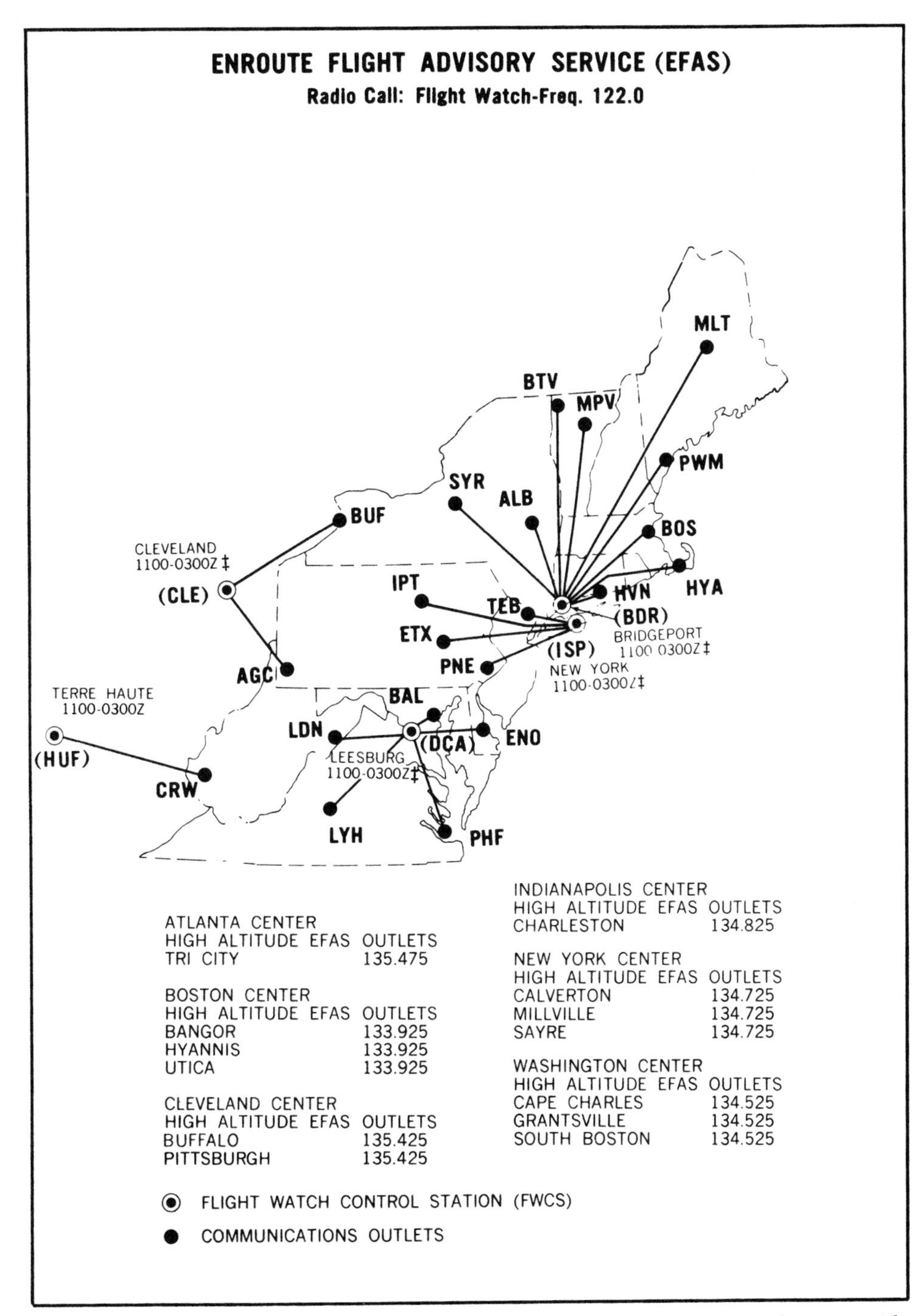

Fig. 4-6. *En route Flight Advisory Service or Flight Watch can be reached over a wide area by using remote communication outlets.*

swamps, and mountain ranges, the area may have the Hazardous Area Reporting Service already in place. The pilot requests the service from a Flight Service Station by radio and gives the following information: type and color of aircraft, route and altitude of flight, number of persons on board, true airspeed, and time over water. Then while the flight through the hazardous area progresses, the pilot calls and reports in to the FSS every 10 minutes. When the area has been successfully crossed, the pilot calls to cancel the service. If during the crossing no radio contact is made between pilot and FSS for longer than 15 minutes, then search and rescue procedures are initiated. The term "Flight Following" is used today to request radar services from a terminal facility or an ARTCC. The term "Flight Following" was originated by the Hazardous Area Reporting Service. The more up-to-date term would be a request for "VFR Advisories." There are six Hazardous Area Reporting Services established in the Eastern United States (FIG. 4-7).

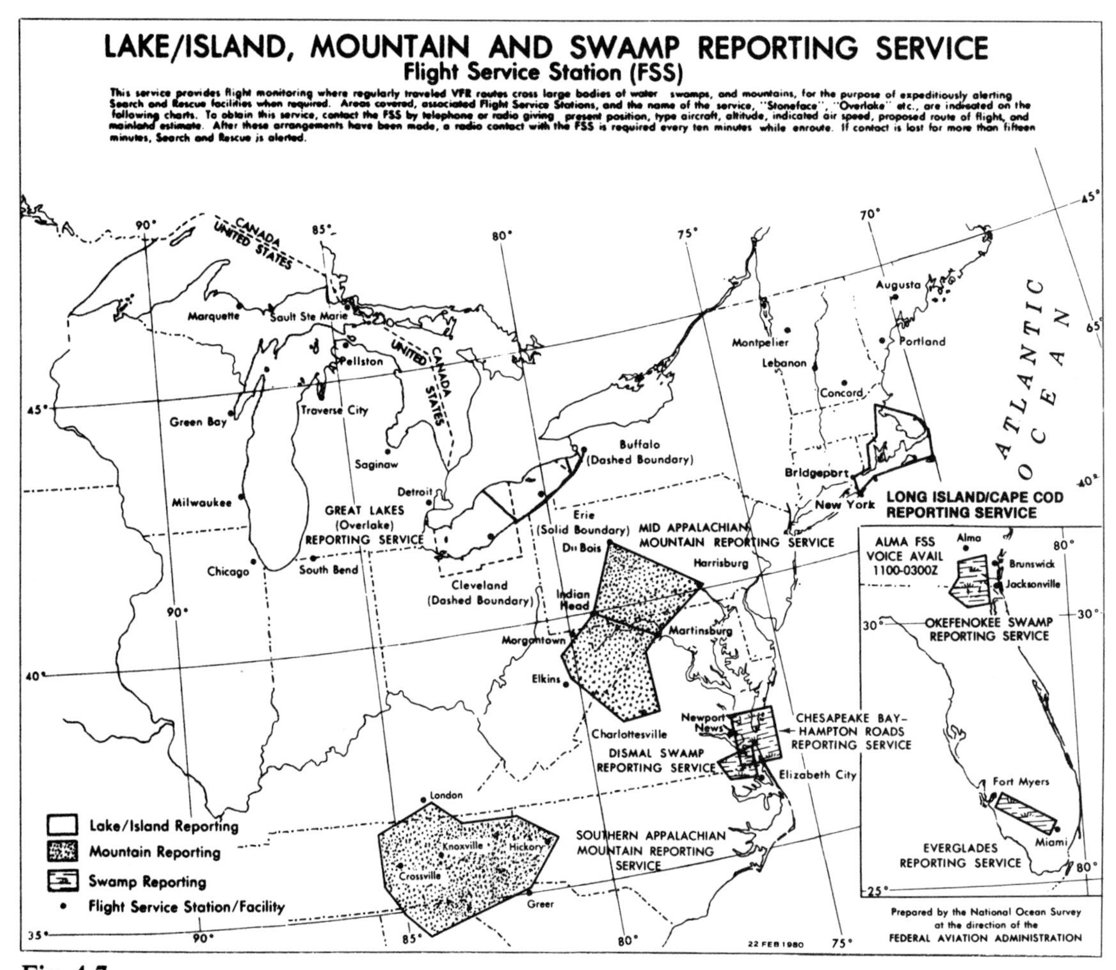

Fig. 4-7

Very few light airplanes have onboard weather radar, but this equipment can provide extremely important information to the pilot. Onboard radar should really be considered "inside" information, but it is covered here to present radar service in general. Radar is not really a word; it is an acronym for Radio Detection And Ranging. A radio signal sent out from an antenna will travel out forever unless some object gets in its way. When a collision takes place between a radio wave and an object, the signal is bounced back. This bounce is called a radar return or an echo. The echo is displayed on a radar screen as a "blip." The distance the echo is from the antenna is determined by how long it takes the radio signal to travel out and then return. It does not take long because radio waves travel at the speed of light: 186,000 miles per second!

The object has to be large enough to cause a return. Clouds are not seen on radar screens, because the microscopic water droplets that make up clouds are too small to cause an echo. The weather radar screen can be completely clear, yet the area might be 200 feet overcast with one half mile visibility. Radar does not see turbulence either; remember, PIREPs are the only source of this information. Larger raindrops can be detected by radar. The larger the drop or the more intense the rain shower, the more intense the echoes will be shown.

If a radar antenna is on your airplane, you will have the best possible source of precipitation information. Essentially you have cut out the middle man and are continuously making your own observations. The radar becomes your probe to what lies ahead. Some radar scopes show only an area of shading where echoes exist; others depict intensity levels with color-coding. Either way you have better information with it than without it. If while inflight the radar begins to show precipitation ahead, you can circumnavigate the shower with precision. If while in IFR conditions the precipitation closes in around you, the radar can help you find the "path of least resistance" out of the weather. In VFR conditions you can make a choice to turn around before getting too close to the poor visibility, turbulence, or icing conditions.

A storm scope is the next best thing to radar. The storm scope is not a radar; it only detects and estimates the range of static discharges. A static discharge can be lightning or the friction (static electricity) caused by wind shears present in thunderstorms. The storm scope depicts these areas as dots on the screen. Your job is to steer clear of the dots. The boundary of the precipitation is not readily defined on a storm scope as it is with radar, so it would be easier to get too close. A storm scope is a cheaper alternative to radar, and the old saying "you get what you pay for" applies.

But the fact remains, very few of us will have these tools with us when we really need them. For those of us without radars and storm scopes, we must feel our way with the help of others. Having radar is like walking through a dark cave waving a stick out in front of you for protection. Having no radar but using someone else to help you over the radio is like walking through the cave with your hands outstretched, hoping to touch something in the way before you get hurt. Talking to nobody about bad weather ahead is like walking through the cave with your arms tied behind your back: you will soon run into problems!

Without onboard radar, how do we receive radar information? All radar systems are not the same. Some radar systems are designed specifically to look for rain, and others specialize in looking for airplanes. The National Weather Service (NWS) radar systems are water-watchers; in other words, they specialize in finding precipitation and determining intensities. The NWS maintains a weather radar network that covers nearly all the United States east of the Rocky Mountains. West of the Rockies, ARTCC radars are used to complete the network.

Now, except for some areas that hide behind mountainous terrain, radar coverage is complete to the 48 mainland states. The briefers at Automated Flight Service Stations (AFSS) can look at any radar site in real-time by using the Radar Remote Weather Display System (RRWDS). This allows personnel on the ground to view the precipitation and watch its movement. If you are in the air and talk to a briefer at an AFSS, you are talking to someone who is looking at the big picture. That person can easily describe to you over the radio the area affected by the echoes, their intensity, and what direction they are going. This is not as good as seeing the radar with your own eyes, but it is information that is reliable for decision making.

The person who answers a call on 122.0 to Flight Watch is also sitting in front of a National Weather Service radar display. The specialist cannot see you on the screen, but if you know your position and tell the specialist where you are, that person can tell you what is taking place around you. A line of echoes can block out a wide area of coverage beyond the first returns, but the RRWDS allows the specialist to look at radar returns from the "otherside" by calling up a different radar site. This feature is even better than onboard radar to some degree because the only view you get from an onboard system is what is right in front of your nose (and side to side in some systems). In flight you cannot look at the weather area from all angles to figure out the best course of action. On-board radar used together with the NWS radar information from Flight Watch or an FSS is the absolute best way to go. But if you cannot see it with your own eyes and equipment, at least let someone talk you through.

Air traffic controllers have radar systems that specialize in looking for airplanes. The type of radar system that the controller has will have some influence on how much weather information he can give you. The earliest radars were very helpful against the Germans in World War II, but they were hard to use in controlling air traffic. They were better than nothing, but they were tedious. All returns were shown on the screen as a "blip." If you looked away from the screen full of blips for even a moment, the blips would have moved and you could not then be sure which blip was which. This obsolete system, Primary Radar, can still be used in an emergency.

When the Air Traffic Control Radar Beacon System (ATCRBS) is used, the system is referred to as Secondary Radar. Secondary Radar uses the information inputs from the transponder in the airplane to more easily identify individual airplanes and keep them identified. Today computers are combined with radar to provide a screen of information for the controller to handle. The ARTS III system combines Primary, Secondary, and Alphanumeric data on one screen. Alphanumerics are the numbers and letters that the computer attaches to a radar return. The numbers are coded to tell the controller information about the type of aircraft the blip represents, the aircraft's speed, and if equipped with a Mode-C transponder, the altitude of the aircraft. The codes will move around following the blip wherever it goes on the screen.

ARTS III has the ability to see precipitation echoes on a Primary Radar basis. Figure 4-8 is an illustration of the ARTS III screen. The controller may not want to see the echoes at times and can change the sensitivity on the system to erase the return.

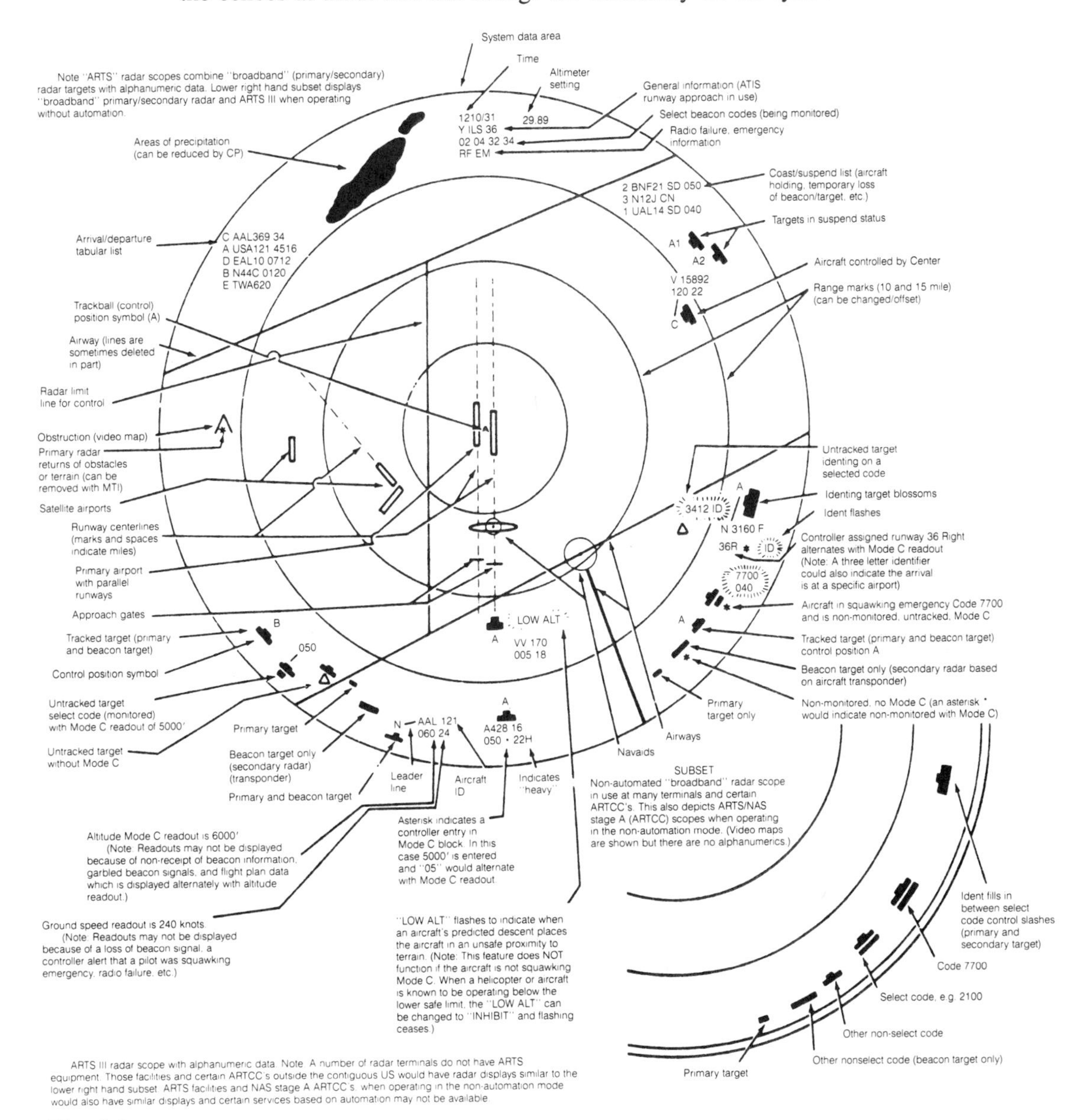

ARTS III radar scope with alphanumeric data. Note: A number of radar terminals do not have ARTS equipment. Those facilities and certain ARTCC's outside the contiguous US would have radar displays similar to the lower right hand subset. ARTS facilities and NAS stage A ARTCC's when operating in the non-automation mode would also have similar displays and certain services based on automation may not be available.

Fig. 4-8

When knowing where the precipitation is becomes important, the Primary Radar can be switched back and the echoes will "paint" the screen. When a pilot asks, "What are you painting?" it has nothing to do with fine art. The pilot is asking for help or at least current information so he will not need help later. With this system the outline of the precipitation can be determined and the information passed on to the pilot. Radar information from ARTS is not as accurate as that from a NWS outlet.

The controller's first responsibility is to keep aircraft apart. There will be times when this priority keeps him so busy that there is no time to give weather advisories. The controller is not obligated to keep you out of precipitation. Any request for weather information must come from the pilot. Then the controller will help you on a workload-permitting basis. This does not offer much comfort when you are being bounced around in moderate to severe turbulence. You feel your situation demands prompt information from the controller. Upon request for assistance you may hear the controller say, ". . . stand by." At this point your anxiety will skyrocket. The solution is to plan ahead. Start asking for information early so you will not place yourself at the "mercy" of a busy controller.

If the controller does give you information about a course of action to take with regards to precipitation echoes, it comes in the form of advice only. A famous lawsuit was brought against the Federal Aviation Administration several years ago involving this situation. A pilot asked for help in penetrating a line of thunderstorms. The controller looked at his screen and pointed out to the pilot the direction where it looked like the rain band was the narrowest. The pilot followed the directions, but after entering the area he lost control the airplane and crashed. The pilot's family sued the FAA under the contention that he had been given dangerous instructions to follow. The FAA successfully defended the case because what a controller tells a pilot about weather avoidance is merely a suggestion. The pilot always has the final say in where the airplane goes.

The ARTS III system has not been around for long, but it is already being replaced by a more advanced system: National Airspace System (NAS) Stage A. The NAS Stage A system has a round radar screen, but the display is not a radar picture at all. All the letters, numbers, and airplane targets are just representations that come from the mind of a computer. There is one major drawback to this system. Since there are no primary targets on the screen and since precipitation echoes are a primary return, the exact outline of echoes are not on the screen at all. Instead a representation of the area is displayed only if the controller desires. The circuit inside the computer that will depict the echoes is called the Weather Fixed Map Unit (WFMU). The WFMU has two intensity keys. The WX-1 key will activate a display of rainfall that occurs in an area that receives up to .2 inches of rain per hour. WX-1 depicts radial lines on the screen that represent echoes based on primary radar. The outline of the radial lines is the representation of the return area. The WX-2 key will indicate rainfall with an intensity greater than .2 inches per hour. Where this level of intensity occurs, the letter "H" will appear on the screen (FIG. 4-9). The "H" stands for Heavy precipitation, but it could stand for Hellacious just as easily.

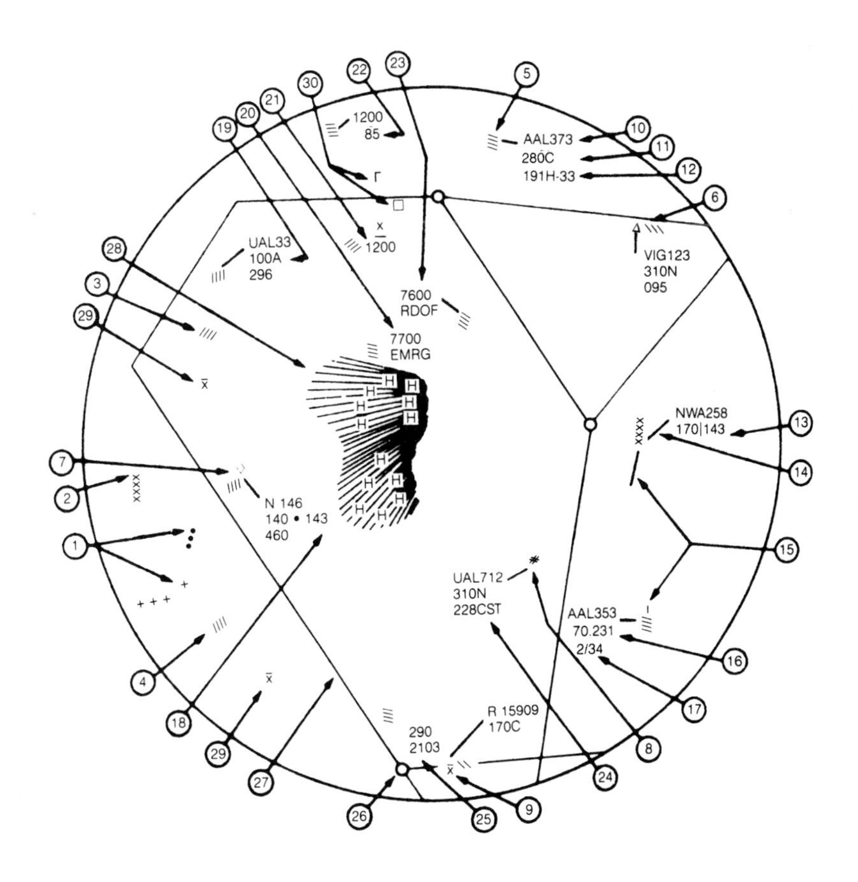

Target symbols

1 Uncorrelated primary radar target + •
2 *Correlated primary radar target x
3 Uncorrelated beacon target /
4 Correlated beacon target \
5 Identing beacon target ≡
(*Correlated means the association of radar data with the computer projected track of an identified aircraft)

Position symbols

6 Free track (No flight plan tracking) Δ
7 Flat track (flight plan tracking)
8 Coast (Beacon target lost) #
9 Present position hold x

Data block information

10 *Aircraft identification
11 *Assigned altitude FL280, mode C altitude same or within ±200′ of asgnd altitude
12 *Computer ID #191, handoff is to Sector 33 (0-33 would mean handoff accepted) (*Nr's 10, 11, 12 constitute a "full data block")
13 Assigned altitude 17,000′, aircraft is climbing, mode C readout was 14,300 when last beacon interrogation was received
14 Leader line connecting target symbol and data block
15 Track velocity and direction vector line (projected ahead of target)
16 Assigned altitude 7000, aircraft is descending, last mode C readout (or last reported altitude was 100′ above FL230
17 Transponder code shows in full data block only when different than assigned code
18 Aircraft is 300′ above assigned altitude
19 Reported altitude (No mode C readout) same as assigned. An "N" would indicate no reported altitude)
20 Transponder set on emergency code 7700 (EMRG flashes to attract attention)
21 Transponder code 1200 (VFR) with no mode C
22 Code 1200 (VFR) with mode C and last altitude readout
23 Transponder set on radio failure code 7600, (RDOF flashes)
24 Computer ID #228, CST indicates target is in coast status
25 Assigned altitude FL290, transponder code (These two items constitute a "limited data block")

Other symbols

26 Navigational aid
27 Airway or jet route
28 Outline of weather returns based on primary radar (See Chapter 4, ARTCC radar weather display. H's represent areas of high density precipitation which might be thunderstorms. Radial lines indicate lower density precipitation)
29 Obstruction
30 Airports Major: □ , Small: Γ

NAS stage A controllers view plan display. This figure illustrates the controller's radar scope (PVD) when operating in the full automation (RDP) mode, which is normally 20 hours per day. (Note: When not in automation mode, the display is similar to the broadband mode shown in the ARTS III radar scope figure. Certain ARTCC's outside the contiguous U.S. also operate in "broadband" mode.)

Fig. 4-9

Even with the WX-2 key activated, the controller will have a hard time pinpointing the exact location of a particular thunderstorm cell. In the past, the controller could help you "pick" your way through the weather; now the controller can only give you an estimate of weather position. I asked an ARTCC controller about this paradox recently. He replied, "You get a little; you give a little." The new system may be a great thing to the controllers and therefore indirectly a great thing for the pilots, but it has its limitations. The NAS Stage A can identify your airplane's exact location in the airspace. The NWS weather radar can identify the exact location of precipitation echoes in the airspace. Only the pilot can put the two together by communicating with both controllers and briefers.

When it comes to bad weather, the decision to proceed to a planned destination or to land short can only be made safely after the pilot gathers all available information. There is plenty of information out there to help you if you know where to look.

5
Navigation Decisions

EVEN IF YOU FLY AROUND THE TRAFFIC PATTERN ON A SATURDAY afternoon, there are decisions to be made; but when you leave the area of the airport, the possible problems and therefore the decisions required multiply. One of the greatest milestones in learning to fly is the first solo cross-country flight. On this flight the pilot learns what it is to be alone. The first solo cross-country is unlike the first solo. The first solo flight is not accompanied by a feeling of isolation because the traffic pattern is familiar, almost like a tether, and the instructor is watching every move. But to leave the security of the home airport and travel out beyond the practice area to another airport in what seems like another world is high stakes.

Flying gives you many legitimate feelings of accomplishment. The day you get your license, for instance, is a day right up their on your list with getting married or becoming a parent. Likewise, the first time you fly off to a distant airport, away from the flight instructor's view and the comfort of a friendly runway and return, is triumphant! A pilot alone but successful and proud.

The first fact that a pilot understands when he's flying cross-country is that unlike navigating in a car, in an airplane you have no road signs and you cannot pull over to the side and look at the map. Whether you get lost or stay on course will be totally determined by how well you plan and fly. As for road signs, they are not written on a billboard (with the exception of water towers), but there are plenty of signs: rivers, highways, bridges, towns. A pilot must learn to read the Earth. A pilot must correlate the patchwork of the ground into understandable information that is used to navigate.

Inside the gray of an IFR flight the pilot must use the radios like a stethoscope, probing what cannot be seen to determine a position. Then the pilot must make timely decisions to arrive at the destination.

Navigation decisions begin on the ground. There are two considerations here: 1) can the airplane handle the requirements of a proposed flight? and 2) can the pilot handle the requirements of a proposed flight?

THE AIRPLANE

Every flight requires that the pilot know a lot of details about the performance of the airplane used. Performance is simply how well the airplane delivers on the promise of flight. How long will it take to get the airplane in the air and over the power lines? How quickly can it climb over a mountain ridge? How high can the airplane cruise? How fast will the airplane go? All of these questions are asking about performance, and performance is affected several ways. First the airplane is affected by the status of the atmosphere in which the airplane must perform. If the air is thick, the airplane will do well. If the air is thin, performance will suffer and the airplane will not do the things that it has done before.

The viscosity of the air is itself determined by three factors: temperature, altitude, and humidity. Hot temperatures, high altitudes, and high relative humidity are all bad for performance. In the first two cases, the density of the air molecules is reduced and therefore the air becomes thinner. In the case of humidity, the number of molecules may not be reduced but the weight of the existing molecules is less. A molecule of water vapor (not liquid water) is lighter than the average dry air molecule. When the molecules are sparse or lightweight, the propeller will have less to grasp, the engine will have less to compress, and the wings will have less with which to produce lift. Every performance chart begins with some consideration of this molecule status called density altitude. Therefore, the starting point for navigation decisions is density altitude and the fundamental question: Will it fly? Once you are convinced that enough lift can be produced to get off the ground, then ask whether the airplane, once it is in the air, will be able to climb fast enough to clear any obstructions in the way. After determining the airplane's ability to safely climb away from the airport ask if the airplane will then be able to climb high enough to sail over any terrain that lies between here and the destination. If the answer to any of these questions is no, then the pilot's decision becomes very easy: Cancel the flight.

The pilot has no control over density altitude, but he can control the time of takeoff. You will have better performance in the morning when the air has not yet had a chance to heat up under the sun. There will be instances when a flight can only be made in the morning. The altitude an airplane can achieve will be lowered as the air is heated. Clearing a mountain range may be no problem before 10 o'clock in the morning, but impossible at 3 o'clock in the afternoon. Plan ahead. Give your airplane every chance to do its job by using good performance judgment.

The equipment onboard the airplane has an influence on where you can fly. After the midair collision over Cerritos, California, to prevent a similar accident, the Federal Aviation Administration changed many laws. The law that has hit closest to home as a result of the Cerritos accident is the Mode C requirement. If your transponder has Altitude Encoding (Mode C), then your altitude is displayed by alphanumerics on the controller's radar screen. Controllers want to look at an entire screen of identified targets complete with altitude information. This allows them to separate traffic more safely and quickly. If a controller sees two targets approaching each other and one or both airplanes do not have a Mode C readout, then the controller cannot be sure that they are at different altitudes. The controller will turn one of the airplanes to avoid the targets from touching on the screen. But if the airplanes have Mode C, then controllers can see that even though the targets might cross on the screen there is plenty of vertical separation and no threat of a collision. This allows the controller to mentally move ahead to solve other problems. This does not relieve the pilot of the responsibility to look for other traffic and avoid collisions when in VFR conditions. The controller has no legal responsibility to keep VFR airplane targets from colliding on the radar screen. The controller might give a traffic advisory if there is time to do so; otherwise, pilots are on their own to look outside and avoid collisions.

The FAA has decided that where traffic congestion is the greatest, and therefore traffic separation is the biggest problem, altitude readouts will be mandatory. Mode C has been a requirement at the nation's busiest airports for many years, but one of the by-products of Cerritos is the 30 nautical-mile Mode C ring. The shape of a Terminal Control Area resembles an up-side-down wedding cake, and in the past you could fly under the extensions of the TCA to a smaller airport without having Mode C. On the radar screen controllers would see targets both with and without altitude readouts. For a target without altitude reporting, the controller would just hope that the airplane was below the TCA altitudes.

Today the TCA's shape has not been changed, but the 30-mile Mode C ring has changed where Mode C is required. The 30 nautical-mile ring is a cylinder shape, not a wedding cake. Anywhere inside the ring from the ground to Earth's orbit is where Mode C is required. This eliminates the possibility of sneaking under the TCA without the proper equipment. Even if you avoid being actually inside the TCA by staying low and under the lateral limits, you are still required to have Mode C so the controllers will not have to hope anymore. The controllers see only altitude reporting traffic. The pilots are no longer trusted to keep the proper altitudes.

Since December 1990, the same Mode C requirements have applied to all Airport Radar Service Areas (ARSAs). Before all the new Mode C laws came out, there were only about two dozen airports that you could not fly to without Mode C. In the case of these airports, there was always a way to go to those cities anyway by flying underneath the TCA and landing at smaller airports. Now with ARSAs joining the list, there are over 150 airports that require Mode C. This list is growing all the time. If your airplane does not have Mode C, your airspace is shrinking. You will be faced with increasing numbers of navigation decisions that involve detours around Mode C mandatory airspace.

The altitude a flight requires will cause the pilot to be faced with decisions. These decisions will include not only an evaluation of how high the airplane can climb versus the height of the terrain, but what equipment you must take along. If you plan to fly at altitudes above 12,500 feet MSL for longer than 30 minutes, the FARs say that you should go on supplemental oxygen. Planning a trip that requires that altitude would also require taking along a supplemental oxygen system. For flights above 14,000 feet MSL, the pilot and required crew members need oxygen for all portions of the flight at that altitude. Then for flights above 15,000 feet MSL, all occupants are required to be supplied with oxygen. Notice that the passengers, who are not decision makers, are not required to use oxygen, but it must be available to them above 15,000 feet MSL. There are many stories about pilots avoiding problems with rowdy passengers by climbing above 14,000 feet MSL. To make the flight a little quieter, the pilot goes on the mask and the passengers fall asleep due to the lack of oxygen. A pilot who was once flying a cargo load of live chickens for a fast food restaurant climbed above 15,000 feet. The pilot went on oxygen, but unfortunately the chickens did not. The restaurant ended up with chickens that were not as fresh as they had hoped.

There are many places in the FARs where you can make a distinction between what is legal and what is smart. In the case of supplemental oxygen, you should use it if you are going to fly for an extended length of time above 10,000 feet MSL during the daytime and above 5,000 feet MSL at night. The eyes see differently at night. The eye, being a biological camera, is sensitive to light and oxygen. Eyes have daytime film and nighttime film. The vision cells used in the dark, nighttime film, require more oxygen to develop the image than do the daytime vision cells. This is why oxygen at lower altitudes is a good idea on night flights. The Federal Aviation Regulations do not change with time of day, however, so this is a personal decision.

The best way to determine your tolerance to oxygen is to visit an altitude chamber. The FAA has established a program where civilian pilots can take a day-long course in physiological training at military bases. There are currently 33 bases that participate in the program (FIG. 5-1). One of the topics covered is hypoxia. To qualify for the training you must have a current FAA Medical Certificate. Usually the military requires that you train in groups of 15 to 20. It would be a great idea to take your Civil Air Patrol group, Aero Club, or just the usual hangar bums to this class. Your group will get a briefing on hypoxia and its effects then be taken to the altitude chamber. Your group will get outfitted with "fighter-type" helmets and oxygen masks (take your camera) and be led into the chamber.

From then on there are no names, just numbers. Each person sits down and plugs into the life-sustaining oxygen supply. Flight surgeons will accompany you in the chamber and throughout the demonstration. Then the chamber operator, who stays outside, starts to suck the air out of the chamber. A limp, tied-off rubber glove is hanging from the ceiling. The glove starts to expand as the pressure around it begins to decrease. The altimeter on the wall eventually reads 15,000 feet. Now it is fun time. Half of the group is instructed through their headsets to take off the oxygen masks.

Aeronautical Center, Oklahoma City, OK	
Andrews AFB, MD	MacDill AFB, FL
Barbers Point NAS, HI	Mather AFB, CA
Brooks AFB, TX	Miramar NAS, CA
Brunswick NAS, ME	NASA-Johnson Space Center, TX
Cecil Field NAS, FL	Norfolk NAS, VA
Cherry Point MCAS, NC	Patuxent River NAS, MD
Columbus AFB, MS	Pease AFB, NH
Corpus Christi NAS, TX	Peterson AFB, CO
Edwards AFB, CA	Point Mugu PMIC, CA
Ellsworth AFB, SD	Reese AFB, TX
El Toro MCAS, CA	Shaw AFB, SC
Fairchild AFB, WA	Shephard AFB, TX
Langley AFB, VA	Vance AFB, OK
Laughlin AFB, TX	Whidbey Island NAS, WA
Lemoore NAS, CA	Williams AFB, AZ
Little Rock AFB, AR	Wright-Patterson AFB, OH

Fig. 5-1. *A list of all the U.S. Government Physiological Training Facilities. Each facility has an Altitude Chamber where trainees experience individual symptoms of oxygen deficiency as well as decompression.*

Each pilot is given a clipboard. The operator tells you to begin writing your name over and over again down the page. Also you are to write down any abnormal sensations your body is feeling. Within four minutes, every member of the group is adversely affected by the altitude. The cigarette smokers are falling apart, turning purple, and gasping within only two minutes. The lesson is clear: The decision to use oxygen must be made before you really need it.

One of the symptoms of hypoxia is euphoria. This means that the part of the brain that controls your judgment and therefore your good decision-making characteristics is affected by the lack of oxygen. The euphoria makes you think that everything could not be better, when in fact nothing could be worse. The lack of oxygen simply destroys the ability to make decisions. An altitude chamber's biggest advantage is to teach pilots what symptoms they will have prior to an irreversible loss of judgment. In my case, I get sweaty palms and cheeks. My face gets hot and my fingers start to tremble. But my symptoms will not be exactly the same as someone else's. Here again, knowledge leads to good decisions. The more you know about how your body reacts to the lack of oxygen, the better decision you will make about using oxygen.

For flights over rough or sparsely populated terrain, a basic first aid kit and a flare gun should be carried onboard. Wear clothes on every flight as if you will be spending the night outside on the land underneath the flight path. Carry flotation gear for flights over water. Always carry a flashlight. Contact lens wearers should have a pair of glasses within reach just in case a lens gets away. Trying to find and replace a contact lens while flying a plane would be a nightmare.

The airplane is required to have anticollision and position lights for flights in the dark. The pilot must remember to turn these lights on when the sun goes down. It is a good idea to turn on lights during the daylight hours to increase the plane's see-ability, but it is the law at night. Except when the airplane is flown for hire, you do not even need a landing light. This is another clear example of what is legal versus what is smart. The landing light should be checked for operation and used even for daytime flights. Lights do burn out, so have a flight instructor go with you some dark evening for some practice lights-out landings.

THE PILOT

The pilot must be equal to the task of flight just as the airplane must be. A pilot should develop a healthy respect for his limitations and establish some personal minimums to assure safety. The personal-minimums idea is simple. The pilot must look himself in the eye with honesty and ask the question: Will the situation that confronts me put me in over my head?

Let this story be the example. A pilot named Mark goes to the airport to practice landings. The wind is blowing directly across the runway at 15 knots. Nowhere in the regulations are there limitations on the strength of the wind and whether or not you can go flying. It is a personal decision. Mark knows that he is weak on cross-wind landings and that attempting touch-and-goes today will stretch his skills. He decides to ask a flight instructor to ride along with him to increase his skill.

At the same time another pilot, Lisa, is finishing her preflight inspection. She has practiced cross-wind landings many times before. She is not overconfident, but she knows this wind will be a challenge her skills can handle. She takes off and flies with complete safety.

Here are two pilots, on the same day, flying similar airplanes. Both are honest about their skill levels. Both know their personal minimums and fly accordingly.

When deciding on a cross-country flight, a pilot must use his personal minimums as his guide. Many years ago when I was a private pilot, I flew my father to Atlanta, Georgia, on a business trip. The thought of flying into that busy airspace scared me to death. I studied the flight for about a week. I decided I should not try this alone, so I asked another pilot to ride along to help with everything. I was not crazy enough to fly a Cherokee 140 to Hartsfield, so I picked a satellite airport: Dekalb Peachtree. From the moment I took off en route to the Atlanta TCA, I knew I was in over my head.

To my amazement, the trip went very well; but I was so relieved when we landed that I forgot all about closing my flight plan. I remembered about two hours later and called the Flight Service Station. I just knew that they had already started a search and that I was in big trouble, but no, the flight plan had already been canceled. The FSS had called the FBO where we had parked and they reported the plane on the ground. It is a bad feeling to stare at an airborne situation and to feel unsure or inadequate.

When planning on a flight, measure the demands of the flight not only against the airplane's capabilities but also against the pilot's capabilities. Before flying at night, or into a busy airport at any time, or into IFR conditions, ask yourself the tough questions and set personal minimums. Then work to expand your personal minimums.

Now if you are a non-instrument-rated private pilot with less than 400 hours flying time, you are required to take an Annual Flight Review. After passing the 400 hour level or after earning your instrument rating, you will only be required to take a Biennial Flight Review. Many people worry about their flight reviews. They remember the ''check ride-itis'' they had for their initial certification. An AFR or BFR should not be something to worry over; it should be a building experience. It is the only time when personal minimums are required by the FARs to be updated.

You should get the most from any flight review. First, it is a no-lose situation. A Certified Flight Instructor cannot fail you on the flight review. He can, however, recommend that you receive additional review before he writes the flight review endorsement in your logbook. In other words, the CFI cannot fail you, but he can elect not to give the BFR endorsement. A good flight instructor will tell you this up front. A flight review has no set length of time or number of flights. The flight review is completed when the CFI determines that you meet the standards of the certificate you hold. The flight review then is a great opportunity to learn and to expand personal minimums.

All flight reviews will contain airspeed control maneuvers, stalls, takeoffs, and landings. But in addition to these areas, talk to the CFI about where your personal minimums fall short of where you think they should be. I have conducted BFRs at night because the pilot requested that he get more night experience. I have conducted BFRs to busy airports because the pilot was not comfortable with the radio work involved. In each case, the pilots knew what they needed and asked to specialize in those areas.

A flight review is the law, but it is the responsibility of a pilot to measure what the law requires against what is a smart thing to do. Do not wait until it is required by law to expand your minimums. Attack weak areas early before you are thrust into a situation where a tough decision will be required.

The more decisions that are made on the ground, where takeoffs are optional, the less crucial decisions are required in the air. Make the decision to go only after all factors have been considered: density altitude, length of flight, time of day, weather en route, equipment on board the plane, pilot capabilities, and pilot readiness for the flight. If every question of preparedness is answered with a yes, then head for the sky.

The navigation decisions then become more complicated. After takeoff all decisions must be made while you are flying the airplane. The airplane takes up quite a lot of your conscious effort, leaving little extra room to reason out problems. While in flight, navigation decisions never stop; however, they are no longer your top priority. Flying the airplane and watching for traffic is number one. Anything that you do from the little office of a cockpit must be done efficiently and accurately.

Make a good plan, then fly the plan. A navigation log (FIG. 5-2) is your first line of defense against getting lost. Use it. There are several good navigation log formats on the market. Decide which one you like the best and use it over and over. This way you will know exactly where everything on the log is without fumbling in flight. Navigation logs are divided into two parts. The first part is the predicted information. This includes predicted ground speed, time en route, and fuel consumption. The second part, which is filled in during flight, includes the actual ground speed and the actual time en route. The two parts are not segregated on the log; they are mixed in together. Many pilots do not use the actual information that presents itself on a cross-country flight, but it is easy to do and can help you stay out of trouble.

Check points	VOR ident freq	Course	Altitude	Wind dir vel temp	CAS / TAS	TC −L+R WCA

TH +W−E var	MH +/− dev	CH	Dist leg rem	GS est act	Time eta	Off ete ata	GPH / Fuel

Fig. 5-2. *Use a navigation log to organize all the pertinent information.*

The checkpoints that are used to make up the route of flight are very important. Good, readily identifiable landmarks should be chosen, then used. One of your first goals on a cross-country flight is to determine how accurate the wind information is that you received in your preflight briefing. Remember, the winds aloft forecast on which you base your wind correction angles is just an educated guess. When you are actually flying, you deal with real information, not predictions. Timing the legs between the checkpoints is the key to understanding exactly what the wind is doing to you. Estimate your time to the next checkpoint based on your estimate of the ground speed and the distance to the checkpoint. Convert the time en route to time of arrival (in other words, what you think your watch will say as you pass over the checkpoint). If the checkpoint is crossed right at the predicted time, then your weather report of predicted wind velocity and directions and your ability to pilot the plane to meet your plan has been accurate. It's even better if the checkpoint is right under the airplane like it is supposed to be because that confirms that your estimate of wind correction angle was accurate. When this happens, you can be confident that the calculations to the next checkpoint and beyond to the destination will be reliable.

Determine the actual ground speed anytime the airplane does not cross a checkpoint at the predicted time. Use a standard flight computer for this quick and easy calculation. Keep track of how long the leg between checkpoints actually took. The mileage between checkpoints should already be on the navigation log. With the time and distance determined, figuring out actual ground speed is easy. If the distance between two checkpoints is measured to be 19 nautical miles, and if the distance took 12 minutes to fly, the actual ground speed was 95 knots. Rotate the wheel of the flight computer so that 19 nautical miles on the outside scale aligns with 12 minutes on the inside scale. Then look at the "pyramid" index marker. It is lined up with 95 knots (FIG. 5-3).

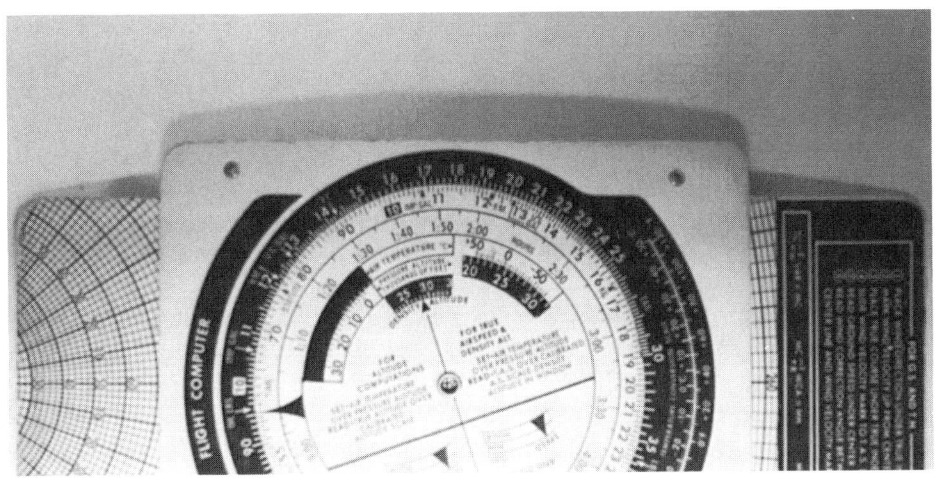

Fig. 5-3. *Actual ground speed can be obtained while inflight if distance and time is known. This computer has been aligned so that 12 minutes is across from 19 miles. The result is a ground speed of 95 knots, indicated at the "pyramid."*

Knowing the actual ground speed is very important. If you have predicted a ground speed of 120 knots based on weather information available on the ground, information that is wrong, you must learn this fact. If the fuel consumption was determined based on a speed of 120 knots, you run the risk of fuel starvation when you find yourself actually traveling at 95 knots. The airplane will need to be in the air longer to reach the destination, and of course the longer the engine is running, the more fuel it will burn. A decision needs to be made. Even though the pilot does everything right in preparing for the flight, the predictions don't always hold true. The pilot who becomes aware that the flight is taking place slower will have the best opportunity to take the appropriate action. Knowledge leads to good decisions. The smart pilot determines early that a flight that may have taken only 20 gallons of fuel yesterday will require 24 today. The plane may only hold 23 gallons. With knowledge the decision is easy: Stop for more fuel.

The very first time I set out on a solo cross-country I got lost. The weather was perfect: no clouds and only a slight breeze. I took off armed with a perfectly organized navigation log and turned toward the Tennessee River. I arrived at my first stop on time, drank a Coke, and took off again. I was flying this time to a VOR station, then I would turn north and head for home. After making the turn I slowly drifted off course, but I had no idea what was happening. The slight breeze that was predicted for that afternoon was now a cross wind on my last leg home. I crossed Interstate 40 and thought I was home free. The problem was that Interstate 40 is 3,000 miles long, and I was not sure exactly where I had crossed it. I was actually 10 miles to the east of my intended course, and when the time ran out and I was supposed to be over my familiar airport, I was not. I had flown the last leg without total awareness of my situation. I had become a spectator. I had many lessons to learn.

If the wind's velocity or direction are unlike that predicted in the preflight briefing, the plane can easily slide off course to one side or the other. Having good checkpoints is the best way to prevent this from happening. If the airplane passes a checkpoint on the right, but the checkpoint was supposed to be on the left, a light should go off in your head. This means one of two things has happened. First, you could have been holding the wrong heading. Your plan is correct but your flying is sloppy. Or second, it is quite possible that the Directional Gyro has precessed and that the reading is no longer in agreement with the Magnetic Compass. In this case carefully reset the DG, making sure the knob used to make the adjustment does not get stuck against the panel. Then correct the airplane's heading and continue the flight.

If the heading has been flown correctly and the DG is set correctly, the only answer for the checkpoint not being in the correct location is the wind. The wind is either not from the direction predicted or the wind correction angle used does not match what is needed. To determine how this unknown wind will affect the remainder of the flight, it is important to find out what the wind is actually doing. With the "wind face" of the flight computer, perform a missing wind calculation. It is a good idea to practice these problems with hypothetical data on the ground so that while you are in the air this procedure will not take you away from flying the airplane.

The actual wind can be determined by working a typical wind face problem "backwards." To arrive at the answer you first must know the actual ground speed, true airspeed, wind correction angle, and magnetic course. The true airspeed and magnetic course are part of the navigation log, so the pilot should have these numbers available. Actual ground speed is determined by knowing time and distance, as discussed earlier. The wind correction angle is a little harder to come by. After passing over a checkpoint, look ahead and find an object that lies on the course. The object could be your next checkpoint in some cases, but that is not a requirement. First, point the nose of the airplane at the object. In time the airplane may drift so that a turn is required to keep the nose of the plane pointed at the object. This indicates that a wind correction angle is needed. Now aim the nose of the airplane upwind of the object and determine an angle that will cause the airplane to have a straight ground track toward the object. Once this has been established, determine the angle between the heading the airplane must fly to hold a straight ground track and the magnetic heading. This is the actual wind correction angle.

Using the wind face side of the flight computer, place the Magnetic Course under the true index. Then slide the card so that the ground speed rests underneath the center hole (grommet) of the wind face. Now, holding the wind face so that it does not turn, draw a dot at the intersection of the wind correction angle and the true airspeed. Last, turn the wind face so that the dot just drawn is under the true index. Now the heading that is under the true index is the direction from which the wind is actually coming. The distance between the dot and the center hole measured against the scale is the actual velocity of the wind. With the actual wind known, the remainder of the flight and the remainder of the decisions that have to be made will be made more accurately. Figure 5-4A shows the computer set-up if Magnetic Course is 090 degrees, Wind Correction Angle is 10 degrees to the right, True Airspeed is 110 knots, and ground speed is 100 knots. Figure 5-4B reveals the missing wind to be 155 degrees at 11 knots.

If a pilot ever tells you that he has never been lost in an airplane, he is lying. All pilots at one time or another lose track of their exact location and have to find themselves again. A former student of mine who now flies for a major airline company was flying from San Francisco to Cincinnati in a Boeing 767 when all the automated sys-

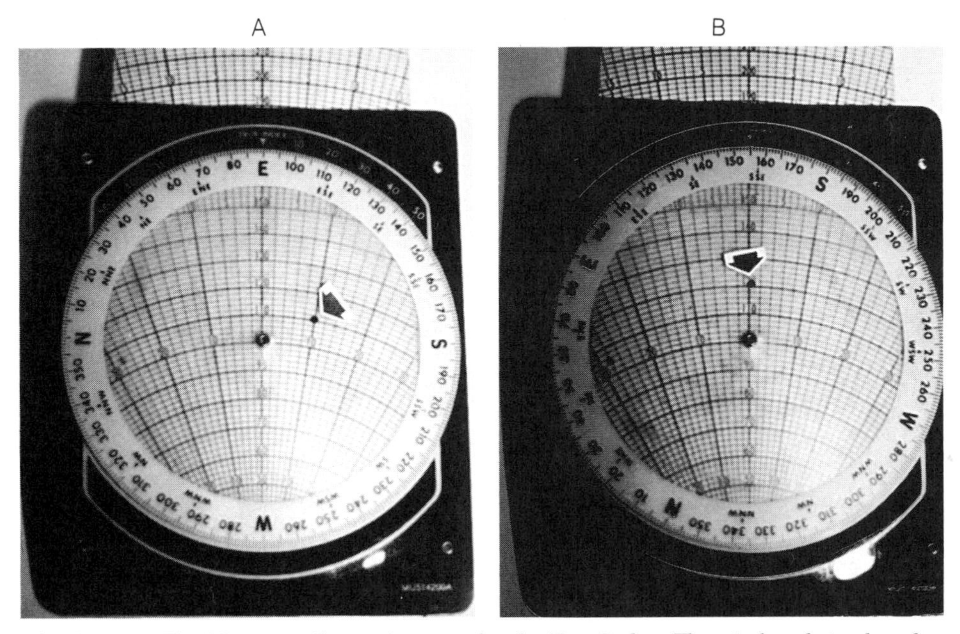

Fig. 5-4. *(A) The Magnetic Course is set under the True Index. The wind scale is placed so that the center (grommet) is over the ground speed. The arrow indicates the intersection of Wind Correction Angle and True Airspeed. (B) The Wind Face of the computer is now rotated so that the dot previously placed on the intersection comes to rest directly under the True Index. The dot now reveals the missing wind. The velocity of the wind is the difference between the dot and the center hole. The wind direction is read under the True Index.*

tems went out. It was the middle of the night, and for several minutes they flew east aimlessly until they could get oriented using antique VORs. Even airline pilots get lost—momentarily.

The key is to stay lost only a very short time. Although I got lost on my first solo cross-country, I finally made it home. My instructor gave me a C− for navigation but an A+ for lost procedures. The fact is that getting lost is not unusual, so the ability to get un-lost is very important.

Obviously, the best thing is not to get disoriented in the first place, but if it does happen go to work on solving the problem immediately. Look for warning signs that things are not working out correctly. If your first checkpoint passed by on the right, but it was supposed to be on the left, make a correction. Do not let the signs pass you by unnoticed.

Once the fact that you are lost sinks in, go to work on fixing the problem. Most times the pilot can find the solution without outside help, but do not wait too long to admit you are lost. The accident reports are filled with fuel starvation accidents involving lost pilots who would not or could not ask for help. One such report concerns a student pilot making his second solo cross-country in a Cessna 152 who got lost on his first leg. He eventually located himself and landed at his proposed destination. He had used up more fuel than planned on the first leg, due to the fact that he had wandered around for a while. At the destination airport he did not put any fuel in the airplane but decided to fly back home.

On the return trip the engine sputtered and stopped. The student successfully landed in a field. (This took place in Texas where there are plenty of good landing sites!) He asked a farmer if he could get a ride to the nearest airport and return with more fuel. The pilot bought 10 gallons that he carried back to the plane in the farmer's gas can. He fueled the plane and took off again. Soon thereafter the student determined that he was lost again. This time he admitted his problem on the emergency frequency of 121.5 MHz. The control tower at Dallas' Love Field heard the call and began vectoring the pilot to the Addison, Texas, airport. But 10 gallons was not enough. He ran out of fuel for the second time in one day. This time the plane flipped upside-down in a wet pasture. The student was not hurt, but later his instructor probably was.

Being lost not only adds stress to the pilot but can be very dangerous. Without knowing the exact location of the airplane, a pilot cannot know if the airspace he is in is safe for flight. A pilot could easily wander into a restricted area. Restricted areas might contain missile launchings or artillery firing. A disoriented pilot once flew over the Space Shuttle during the final countdown. To prevent a Cessna from becoming a Spacecraft hood ornament, the launch computers had to be recycled at great expense. Also, there is the danger of inadvertently flying into high density areas without a clearance or proper equipment. One of the contributing factors that led to the midair collision of the DC 9 and the Piper in the Los Angeles TCA in 1986 was an airplane that was not involved in the accident. The pilot of a Grumman Tiger wandered into the

Los Angeles TCA. When radio contact and radar identification was made, the controller informed the Grumman pilot that he was in the middle of the TCA and suggested that, "In the future you look at your TCA chart. You just had an aircraft pass right off your left above and at five thousand feet and we run a lot of jets through there right at thirty-five hundred." While this conversation was taking place, the two other planes collided and disappeared from the radar screen. This is not to say that if the controller had not been talking to the intruder he would have given traffic advisories that would have prevented the collision. But the controller was distracted by a pilot who was lost or did not know the rules or both.

When you are lost, first try to reestablish position with a VOR cross-check. To do this successfully, the pilot must know how the VORs work. It also helps to have a chart, a hard surface to write on, and three hands. Before the flight, notice what VOR stations will be near your intended flight path. Write down VOR frequencies and ask for NOTAMs about VOR operation in the preflight briefing. Then in flight, tune in a VOR station and identify it with recognition of the morse code identifier. Then center the CDI needle with a FROM indication showing in the window. Be patient with the needle. When a pilot is lost, it is easy to get anxious. The pilot must solve the problem while there is still gas in the tanks, and the swinging gas gauge indicators do not help the nervousness. The CDI will take several seconds to center, so if the pilot whips the OBS knob around hoping for some helpful information, the CDI cannot catch up and the needle will swing past the center like a windshield wiper. Many students have done this and then proclaimed the thing inoperative. Banging on the glass (except in cases of a stuck needle) does not help. While you are lost, your actions must be cool and calculated.

When the needle does center with a FROM indication, the instrument is giving information about which line (radial) from the VOR station the plane is located on (FIG. 5-5). Here is where a properly prepared cockpit pays dividends. Draw a line on the chart that starts at the VOR station symbol and extends through the proper radial on the compass rose. Then extend the line on past the compass. The airplane is on this line; the question now is where along the line.

Of course, the plane has to be flown during these navigation maneuvers. To keep the airplane straight and level while performing the cross-check takes practice, and you have to be able to handle the VOR without confusion. Pilots can get even more disoriented while they twirl the dials of a VOR in an attempt to cross-check when in fact they do not know how it is done.

To determine the location on the first line, a second VOR station is tuned in and identified. The steps outlined previously are repeated. Center the needle with a FROM indication and read the OBS setting. Draw another line from the second VOR through the compass rose at the OBS setting. Where the two lines cross is the location of the airplane.

What if the lines do not cross? This problem will definitely send you farther toward panic. The two VORs that are chosen may not have a very good angle with

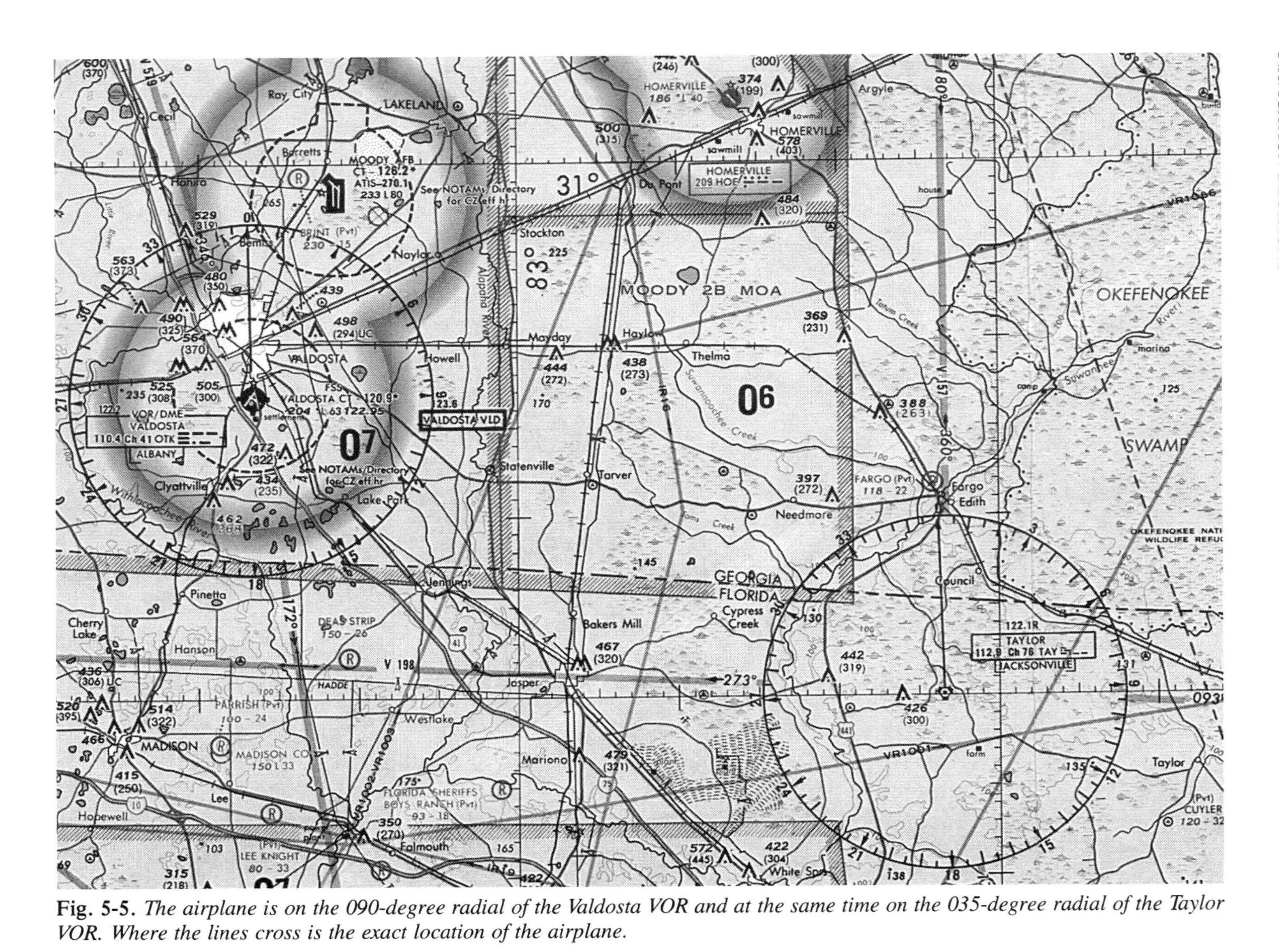

Fig. 5-5. *The airplane is on the 090-degree radial of the Valdosta VOR and at the same time on the 035-degree radial of the Taylor VOR. Where the lines cross is the exact location of the airplane.*

each other. The best cross-check information will result when the lines cross at a 90-degree angle. If the VOR angles are much greater or less than 90 degrees, small errors will be magnified. If the airplane's location is directly between the two VORs, then the lines might not cross or they might completely overlap. If this happens, choose a third VOR with a better angle to cross-check. This might require the pilot to climb so more stations can be received.

Another problem is using a TO indication instead of a FROM indication. In theory, it really does not matter, but in application, it is easy to get mixed up. If a TO indication is used, then the line must be drawn from the reciprocal radial. A reciprocal may be found easily without math problems by looking at the opposite side of the VOR from the OBS setting. Or use the ADF card to determine the opposite direction. Using a FROM indication eliminates this step altogether and prevents the possibility of forgetting a reciprocal is needed. If the pilot forgets to draw the line at the reciprocal and draws it the other way, he will enter the twilight zone. Additional confusion will result when proper decision making is as lost as the pilot.

After the position has been established with a VOR cross-check, look outside for landmarks that will confirm your VOR location. The skill to identify a symbol on the chart and then recognize the same landmark on the ground is extremely important. Using landmarks and radio navigation aids in cooperation is the key to getting found again.

Once the location has been established, more decisions need to be made. Can the flight be resumed as planned? What heading should now be flown? Will additional fuel be required to reach the destination? These inflight decisions will determine the next move.

If all incockpit efforts fail to locate the airplane's position, ask for help. Before leaving the ground on any cross-country flight, find out the radio frequency of any facility that has radar services along the flight path. While flying VFR and talking to nobody, the pilot can feel very isolated. But in fact, the airplane is probably crossing someone's radar screen. If you are lost, that person can get you un-lost. The problem is talking to that person. If the proper frequency is part of the preflight planning, the problem dissolves. Calling the emergency frequency might not always get the fastest help. All towers and FSSs monitor the 121.5 MHz emergency frequency, but not all these facilities have the necessary radar to help solve the problem. If a pilot talks to a VFR tower controller on 121.5 MHz, the controller can only tell the pilot what frequency to call to get radar assistance. Communicating through this extra set of frequencies and transmissions takes up valuable time.

Once talking to someone who is watching the radar screen, the pilot will be asked to squawk a transponder code or make a turn for radar identification. Once identified, vectors will be assigned to get the pilot back on course or to an alternate airport. This assistance, although vital to the pilot, is still on a time-share basis for the controller. The lost pilot will have to share communication with all other pilots on that frequency, remembering that IFR traffic gets first shot at the controller's attention. If the situation becomes critical in the lost pilot's mind, that pilot should not hesitate to declare an emergency. After this declaration, the controller will be at the pilot's service, especially if the pilot includes the phrase "minimum fuel" in the sentence.

If the pilot contacts a radar controller and the airplane's actual position is not on that controller's screen, the controller will help find out which screen the airplane is on and therefore which frequency the pilot should call. But radar is not the only form of outside assistance. Some facilities, Flight Service Stations most often, have Direction Finder (DF) equipment. DF equipment allows the operator to determine from which direction a transmission is coming. It does not give range information, only direction. Using a combination of DF equipment and VOR radials, a DF Steer can establish a position. Without VOR radials, it can be used to vector a pilot back to the location of the DF equipment. A pilot once called an FSS and asked for a "practice DF Steer." The FSS briefer was busy and replied that there was nobody available to give a "practice DF." The pilot then said, "Well, can I get a real one then?" The pilot was lost, but he was afraid to admit it to the world. Remember, getting lost is not a problem: Staying lost is.

Determine in the preflight planning if any facilities along the route have DF services. If you need a DF Steer or just want a practice one, call the facility and ask for one. The controller or briefer will ask for a "count." The pilot should key the mike and say, "This is Cessna 1234A, 5, 4, 3, 2, 1, 2, 3, 4, 5." This lengthy transmission will allow enough time for the briefer to look at the direction indicated on the DF equipment. Even instrument approaches can be done using DF equipment.

While inflight, a crossroads decision about diverting away from the original plan may evolve. Before leaving the ground, the pilot is required by regulations to review "alternates available if the planned flight cannot be completed." Think ahead and identify possible alternate airports that lie along your course. In this way, a diversion to a midcourse airport will not be an unknown. The term "diversion to an alternate" is mentioned in the Practical Test Standards. It means a situation has come up that the pilot recognizes as trip threatening. Then the pilot shifts to "plan B," and makes an unplanned landing at a different airport than originally proposed. This change in plans might be forced due to weather. A new heading will be required unless an airport lies directly on the course. Once the decision is made, begin flying in the general direction of the diversion airport, and then while en route worry about using a plotter to determine an exact heading.

Any pilot that becomes lost and then found again should consider a diversion to an airport that is short of the intended destination. While a pilot is lost, many variables will change: fuel, weather, pilot readiness to go on. It is always easier to reason out a problem while on the ground. Getting lost raises the stress level in pilots. A pilot's stress tolerance can be exceeded to a point where the remainder of the flight would demand more than the pilot has to give. Being lost drains a pilot. After a stress-related precautionary landing, the pilot can relax and evaluate the situation much better. A student pilot should call his flight instructor to inform him of ANY diversion from the original plan.

I once greeted a pilot at the airport terminal's front door, who had just calmly strolled in from his airplane. He did not say much but went right to the phone booth. He did not make a call but merely looked at the phone book and then returned to his airplane. It is better to discover your location on the ground, even if you must look at the name on a phone book, than to run out of gas figuring it out in flight.

6
The Mystery of Airspace

EVEN THE NAME, AIRSPACE, IS MYSTERIOUS. USUALLY AIR AND SPACE ARE separate. Airplanes fly in the air. Spacecraft fly in space. Most pilots do not even like to talk about airspace. It is so restricting, and flying is supposed to be so free: The two don't match. Something inside pilots naturally repels the study of airspace.

Airspace is usually taught as a mass of statistics consisting of boundaries and altitudes and pilot requirements. Pilots get avalanched by all the facts and figures, and the original reason for airspace is lost. We are reduced to rote memorization of MSL or AGL, Statute or Nautical, True or Magnetic, Heading or Course. No wonder we hate it. Then, if a pilot gets it down, the FAA will change the rules. That is when we really hate it.

If a doctor takes an x-ray of a broken arm, he does it to evaluate the arm, not to see if the x-ray machine works. The x-ray machine is just a tool to get a result. Likewise, airspace rules are just tools to get a result. If the doctor does not know how to operate the x-ray machine, then the final result cannot be achieved. If the pilot does not know the airspace rules, the final result cannot be achieved either. The final result for the pilot is collision avoidance. That is the underlying reason for the pile of numbers, rules, codes, the alphabet soup of airspace types (TCA, ATA, ARSA, TRSA, etc.), and all the hours spent trying to understand airspace. The rules give us the best chance of keeping one aircraft from running into another.

Nearly all collisions take place in VFR conditions. Regardless of whether a pilot flies on an IFR flight plan, a VFR flight plan, or no flight plan, the pilot must look out the window when in Visual Meteorological Conditions (VMC). The regulations place the responsibility squarely on the pilot: "Vigilance shall be maintained by each person operating an aircraft so as to see and avoid other aircraft." Vigilance is a power-packed word. The regulations are pretty hard to read because the language is so legalistic and bland. But here is an exception. The word "vigilance" conjures up the image of a sentinel standing watch, never falling asleep on guard. The pilot, ever vigilant, is on guard against flight path intrusion. This idea is tough to bring to reality when the pilot's job is also cluttered by charts, radio transmissions, instruments, and passengers. Even if all the pilot did was look outside, there are large chunks of air that are blocked from view by the aircraft itself. But the burden must lie somewhere. It lies not with the controllers but with the pilots.

As stated previously, the controllers are under no obligation to prevent aircraft targets on the radar screen from intersecting. If the targets are on an IFR flight plan, the chances are better that the pilot will get a traffic advisory, but traffic advisories are given on a time-share basis. When a controller is working with traffic on a VFR day, and out of the corner of his eye he sees two targets nearing each other on another part of the screen, he just has to think to himself, "They will probably miss each other, but it is their problem, not mine." Do not get the idea that controllers are callous to this situation: They are not. But controllers can only do so much. What is done is prioritized. VFR traffic advisories are on the priority list, but they are not at the top of the list.

So, see and avoid is the way of flying. Simply put: The pilot must first see other aircraft and then do whatever is necessary not to hit other aircraft. No matter how high-tech the system has become, this simple fact remains: If a pilot wants to avoid a midair collision, he must not run over anybody or be run over. Nobody else can be counted upon to help the pilot accomplish this job, and nobody else will ultimately be responsible for the job. This applies to small airplanes, airliners, military aircraft, everybody.

The challenge now becomes seeing the traffic and avoiding situations where traffic cannot be seen. A pilot's eyesight is extremely valuable to him. But good eyesight alone will not guarantee vigilance. A pilot may have 20/20 uncorrected vision but not know how to use his eyes properly. Airspace rules are written to give the pilot the best chance to see traffic, but the pilot must finish the job. The pilot must spot the danger.

During flight, the pilot must divide his attention between what is outside and what is inside. Use a personal "time-share" arrangement with your eyes. Do not spend long periods of time on any one item. Follow a pattern similar to this:

1. Look outside to the left and rear.
2. Look at the flight instruments.
3. Look outside down the left wing.
4. Look at the flight instruments, or make a notation on the nav log.
5. Look outside over the instrument panel out the front.
6. Look at the engine instrument, or check a chart position.

7. Look outside down the right wing.
8. Look at the flight instrument, or change a frequency.
9. Look outside to the right rear.
10. Start over again with number one and repeat.

The more proficient the pilot is in working the radios, using charts and nav logs, and identifying problems on the instrument panel, the more time is left over for looking outside. When the pilot looks outside, he or she should not "sweep" the sky, but rather look in one direction long enough for the eyes to focus. The eyes do not focus while they are in motion. If a pilot looks up momentarily from the problem of navigation and swings his head from side to side in the name of collision avoidance, nothing has been accomplished. Even 20/20 eyesight will not help if the eyes are not allowed to work. When the eyes are directed outside, they will focus on the first thing in the field of vision. If the first thing is a bug on the windshield, the eyes will focus on the bug and temporarily miss what is on the other side of the bug, namely another airplane.

The IFR hood is used in training VFR pilots. The reason is NOT to have a VFR pilot prepared to fly into the clouds, even though many student pilots believe it to be true. The reason is to train the eyes to move quickly from one position to another, all the while picking up information. If that skill is learned, then it may be transferred. The eyes are more ready to move inside and outside in order to pick up information, and collision possibilities are reduced.

The proper use of the eyes is just part of the story. The rest is airspace rules. The goal of the airspace rules is to give the pilot the best opportunity to see and avoid air traffic. Here is where a study of airspace, aeronautical charts, and regulations all entwine. Most well-prepared pilots can easily recite the basic VFR minimums but have a hard time putting them into practice, much less understanding their real purpose.

THE CONTROLLED VERSUS UNCONTROLLED AIRSPACE MISUNDERSTANDING

Essentially, controlled airspace exists wherever IFR traffic can be present. There are some exceptions to this statement, which will be covered later. Whenever both VFR and IFR traffic coexist in the same airspace, there is the possibility of conflict. The conflict may be resolved if pilots see each other in enough time to avoid a collision. The basic distance from clouds in "controlled" airspace above 1,200 feet AGL below 10,000 feet MSL is "500 feet below; 1,000 feet above; 2,000 feet horizontal" (FIG. 6-1).

Many pilots believe that these distances are provided so that VFR pilots do not inadvertently find themselves inside clouds. They have been told horror stories about VFR pilots losing aircraft control within seconds after entering clouds, and they feel these distance rules are in place so they will stay away from the danger. The separation limits

VFR visibility and distance from clouds				
Altitude	Uncontrolled airspace		Controlled airspace	
	Flight visibility	Distance from clouds	**Flight visibility	**Distance from clouds
1200′ or less above the surface, regardless of MSL altitude	*1 statute mile	Clear of clouds	3 statute miles	500′ below 1000′ above 2000′ horizontal
More than 1200′ above the surface, but less than 10,000 MSL	1 statute mile	500′ below 1000′ above 2000′ horizontal	3 statute miles	500′ below 1000′ above 2000′ horizontal
More than 1200′ above the surface and at or above 10,000 MSL	5 statute miles	1000′ below 1000′ above 1 statute mile horizontal	5 statute miles	1000′ below 1000′ above 1 statute mile horizontal
	*Helicopters may operate with less than 1 mile		**Control zone ceiling not less than 1000′	

Fig. 6-1. *The Basic VFR minimums as prescribed by FAR 91.155.*

are thought to be merely exaggerated safety factors that can be ignored by the competent pilot. The danger of spatial disorientation of VFR pilots in IFR conditions is certainly real, but that is not why the cloud distance rule exists.

Refer to FIG. 6-2. In situation 1 of this figure, two airplanes are approaching head-on. The regulations say, "When aircraft are approaching head-on or nearly so, each pilot shall alter course to the right." This works great if the pilots see each other.

Assume that the distance between aircraft A and aircraft B of situation 1 in FIG. 6-2 is three statute miles. Three statute miles is the basic VFR visibility minimum in controlled airspace below 10,000 feet MSL. The FAA is telling the pilot with this rule that if two airplanes are within one and one half miles of a collision (three miles apart but converging at the same speed), that there is plenty of time to see and avoid. These are very bare safety minimums. The closure rate of two Cessnas would be approximately 200 knots. This means that collision will occur in 45 seconds. A Piper with a speed of 100 knots and a Lear jet with a speed of 250 knots (the speed limit below 10,000 feet MSL) would have a closure rate of 350 knots. If the pilots in this situation were flying with only three miles visibility, the time to recognize the problem and take evasive action would be just 26 seconds. The 26 seconds would start when the airplanes were first visible to each other, at three miles apart. But the pilots probably will not see the other's plane exactly when it comes into view. The time interval between when the other plane is visible and when it is actually seen will reduce the reaction time. If either pilot is scanning as quickly as once around every 15 seconds, then the time interval for evasive maneuvers could only be approximately 11 seconds. If the pilots were scanning once around as often as 30 seconds, they could collide without ever seeing each other. Most pilot scans take longer than 30 seconds. The

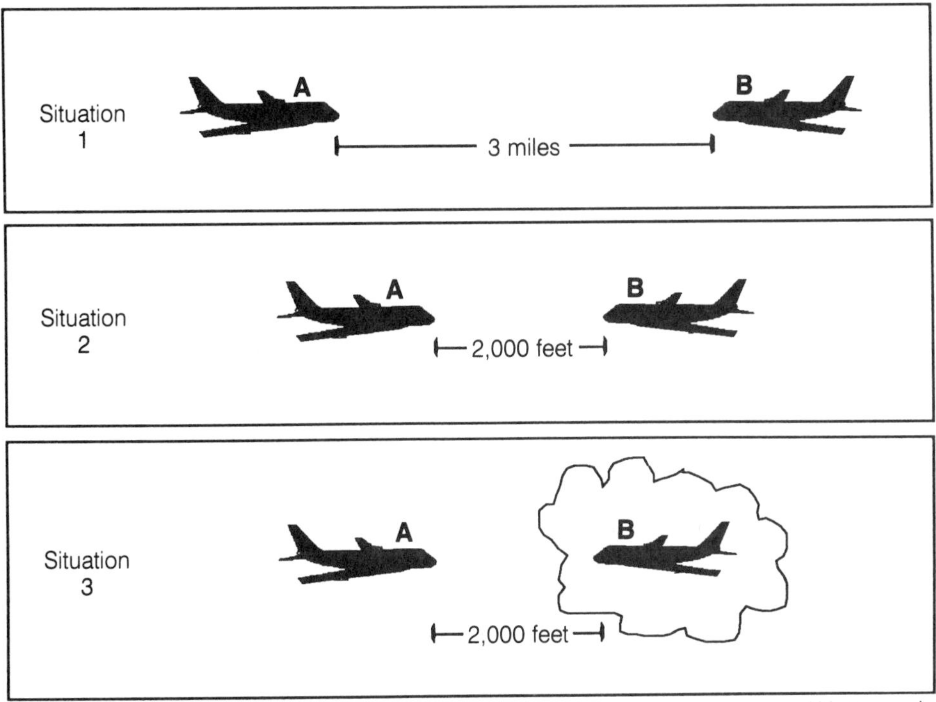

Fig. 6-2

FAA thinks this situation is O.K. Pilots get lulled to complacency by thinking that everything that is legal is also safe. This is certainly not the case.

Now look at situation 2 of FIG. 6-2. These planes are not head-on, but they are on a collision course with each other. Their actual distance apart is 2,000 feet or less than one half statute mile. If at this distance the pilots first saw each other there would be virtually no time to miss each other. It was discovered by autopsy that the pilot of the Piper in the midair collision over Cerritos, California, experienced a heart attack prior to impact. The conclusion is that the man looked up to see a windshield full of DC-9 seconds prior to collision, but with no time to avoid the other plane, had a heart attack in fear. This is chilling, to say the least. Nobody would purposely place himself so close to another airplane that there is no time to avoid a collision. But in situation 2, an unavoidable collision is about to occur.

In situation 3 of FIG. 6-2, all factors are the same as in situation 2 except one. One of the airplanes is on an IFR flight plan at an assigned altitude. While on this clearance, the pilot will hold altitude and fly through whatever clouds stand in the way. The other pilot is on a VFR flight plan or no flight plan. Airplane B is inside a cloud and doing what he is told. Airplane A has ventured to within 2,000 feet horizontally of the cloud. The airplanes are on a collision course but not necessarily head-on. Within one second, airplane B will pop out of the side of the cloud. Fifteen seconds after that, with a closure rate as slow as 150 knots, there will be impact. The closer that airplane A gets to the cloud, the less time will exist to get out of the way. A pilot who flies just clear of clouds will have absolutely no time to avoid traffic. Forget about the dangers of VFR pilots flying in the clouds. The real danger is that the clouds can be filled with moving metal! I would much rather fly long distances while solidly embedded in IFR conditions than fly popping in and out of the clouds on a VFR day.

Any time a VFR airplane flies in controlled airspace below 10,000 feet MSL these rules must be followed—and not because there is a risk of being caught. The question always comes up, "Who is going to know if I fly closer than 2,000 feet? Is there a police plane behind the cloud waiting to give me a ticket?" No, the FAA cannot enforce this one. But there is a death penalty.

If you fly above 10,000 feet MSL, you enter an area of no speed limits short of the speed of sound. In order to provide legal (but maybe not safe) time intervals at these altitudes, the VFR minimums expand to 5 miles visibility and 1,000 feet below; 1,000 feet above; 1 mile horizontal. One mile separation between a head-on Cessna with a speed of 100 and a Boeing 727 going 400 knots allows 6 seconds to first see then avoid. The FAA feels this is O.K. Here is where you must adopt personal minimums that are more stringent than FAA rules, if you feel that 6 seconds is not enough time.

If you fly in uncontrolled airspace below 1,200 feet AGL (700 feet AGL in some places), then you are allowed to reduce the VFR minimums. In these locations, just one mile visibility is required and pilots can fly as close to clouds as they wish as long as they do not actually enter the clouds. The reason this is allowed is that there is less chance for IFR traffic to pop out of the clouds with little or no time to miss each other. The chances of collision are reduced but not completely eliminated. There is a loophole in the regulations that allows IFR flights in uncontrolled airspace without a clearance. FAR 91.173 says, "No person may operate an aircraft in controlled airspace under IFR unless they have filed an IFR flight plan and received an appropriate clearance." Nothing is said about a flight plan and clearance in uncontrolled airspace. This is a clear case of a situation where what is safe and what is legal are miles apart. While flying legal VFR in uncontrolled airspace with one mile visibility and clear of clouds, you could run into a legal IFR flight coming out of those clouds.

There is another, more common danger at airports with non-precision approaches such as VORs and NDBs. Very often the Minimum Descent Altitude (MDA) of a non-precision approach passes the IFR pilot from controlled to uncontrolled airspace. This allows for an IFR pilot to pop out of the MDA while at the same time a VFR pilot flying with one mile visibility and clear of clouds can be skirting the cloud bases in the traffic pattern. Both pilots are flying their airplanes in accordance with the FARs, but both are in jeopardy.

What decisions must be made about airspace when the visibility goes below three miles? The best decision for VFR pilots is to stay on the ground. There may be a legal way to fly, but this may start a bad decision chain. If flight is attempted, the pilot must at all times be aware of the boundary between controlled and uncontrolled airspace. On a Biennial Flight Review, I once asked a man to get his chart out and point out some uncontrolled airspace. He said he could not do that because he only had a Charlotte Sectional with him. I asked why that would be a problem and he said, "Because there is no uncontrolled airspace east of the Mississippi River." We had a long talk about airspace.

The truth is that uncontrolled airspace is just about everywhere, but especially down low. That makes sense because controlled airspace is used to protect the IFR pilot, and IFR pilots in the clouds cannot fly low because they cannot see obstructions while flying in Instrument Meteorological Conditions (IMC). Most of us live in uncontrolled airspace. My house is not within a Control Zone (discussed later) and my house is above the ground but not taller than 1,200 feet, so I live in uncontrolled airspace.

To determine where controlled airspace is, and is not, look at a sectional chart. The sectional chart has blue and magenta colors surrounding many airports. These are referred to as transition areas (FIG. 6-3). Anywhere on the chart where the plane's position is surrounded by the reddish, magenta-colored shading, the controlled airspace begins at 700 feet above the ground. Outside the magenta shading will be blue shading. Everywhere outside the magenta, or beyond the blue, the controlled airspace begins at 1,200 feet above the surface and travels up to outer space.

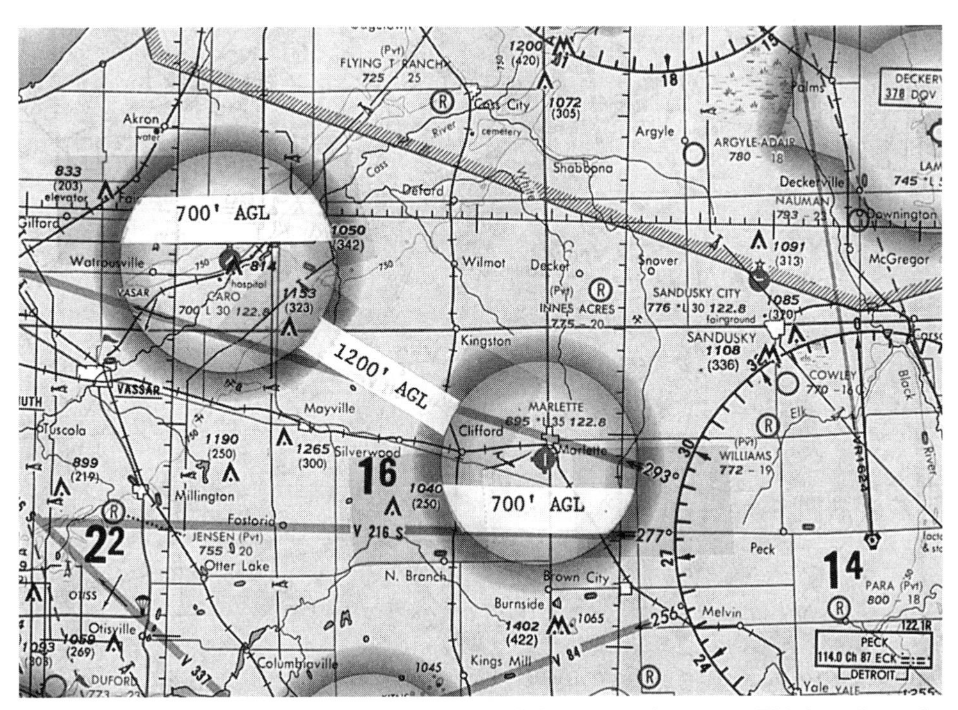

Fig. 6-3. *Inside the magenta circle the controlled airspace begins at 700 feet above the surface. Anywhere outside the circle and between the blue shading the controlled airspace does not begin until 1,200 feet above the ground. All airspace below these AGL altitudes is uncontrolled.*

It would be easier to picture this if the entire chart were either shaded with blue or magenta, but the chart designers feel this would clutter the chart, making other information harder to see. So pilots must fill in the missing shaded areas with imagination. Viewed this way, the entire United States would have a blue blanket covered over it. The blanket would exactly mirror the terrain. When the elevation of the ground went down closer to sea level, the blanket would go down as well. When the land rose up away from sea level, the blanket would rise up. When the land had rolling hills and ripples, the blanket would have an identical shape. However, at no time would the blue blanket be closer to the actual surface than 1,200 feet. All air above the blanket would be controlled, the domain of IFR protected flights. All air below the blanket would be uncontrolled.

At various places, there would be holes cut out in the blanket. The holes would mainly be above airports and would have magenta fabric in them that would always remain 700 feet above the ground. As the pilot looked out across the top of the blue blanket, there would appear to be many wells where controlled airspace (and all its rules of visibility and cloud separation) would be allowed to get a little closer to the surface. An uneven surface with holes all around, it might resemble a putting green. The bottom of the holes would not extend to the surface, but would rise and fall with the terrain and always be 700 feet above the terrain.

A pilot on an IFR clearance, popping in and out of the clouds above the blue blanket, can safely descend into the magenta, passing in and out of clouds without fear of collision from VFR traffic. This gives the IFR pilot the best opportunity to get underneath the clouds and into the clear in order to avoid traffic and make a landing. This allows the IFR pilot to "transition" from IMC to VMC with reduced collision fears: hence the name Transition Area.

In some places, the blue blanket with the magenta wells would have another hole cut out. This hole would lie inside the first hole. This hole would cut all the way to the ground and in doing so the controlled airspace (and all its rules of visibility and cloud separation) would drain down to the surface. This deeper hole that goes to the ground is called a Control Zone (FIG. 6-4).

Not all airports that have Control Zones have precision approaches, but many do. The purpose of precision approaches is to allow an IFR pilot to use an Instrument Landing System (ILS) approach to the airport while in controlled airspace. An ILS approach can bring a pilot down to within 200 feet of the ground. If the airplane pops out with only 200 feet between the wheels and the ground, there is no room remaining for collision avoidance with a VFR pilot using the clear of clouds rule. So a Control Zone's first reason for being is to accommodate ILS approach traffic. The second reason is to protect IFR pilots on non-precision approaches from entering uncontrolled airspace prior to reaching the MDA and hopefully clear conditions. The transition from blue shaded area to magenta shaded area to Control Zone (indicated on a chart by dashed blue lines) offers the IFR pilot a staircase to fly down to a landing.

The Control Zone is said to be in effect sometimes and not in effect other times. This is a source of confusion. The Control Zone plays its role for traffic separation

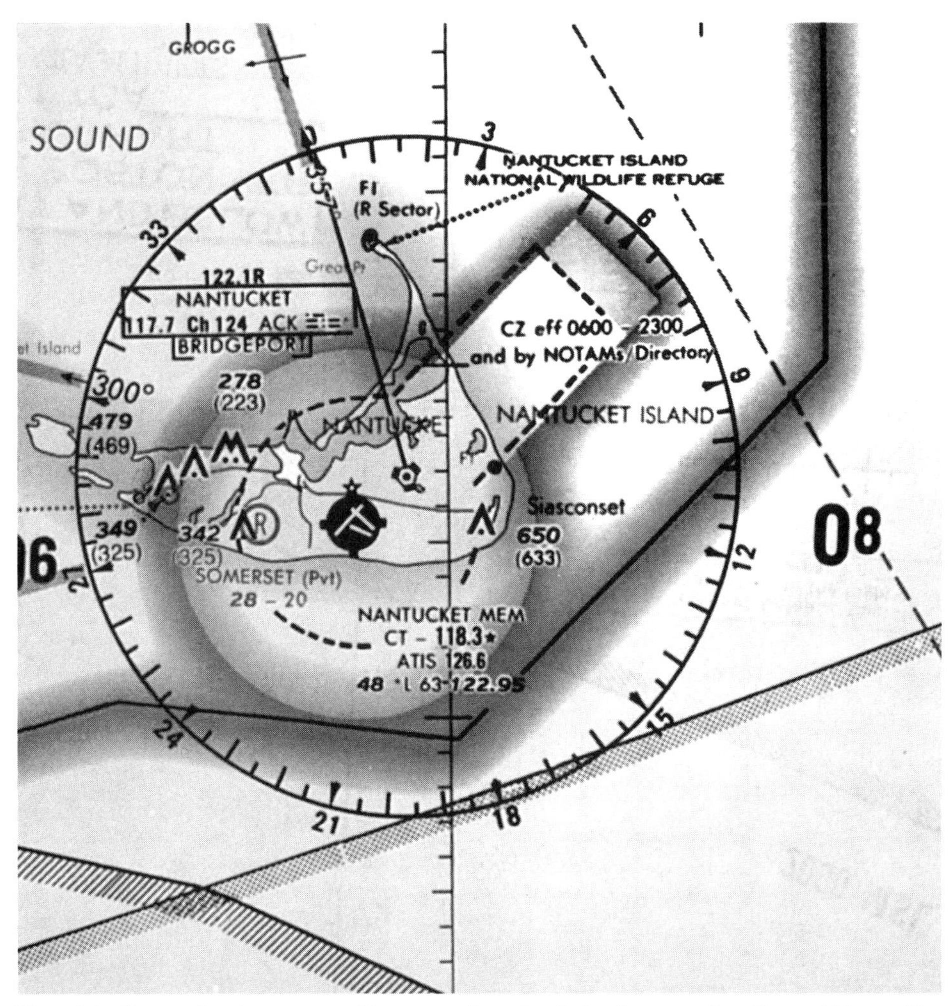

Fig. 6-4. *Nantucket has a transition area in a keyhole shape and a Control Zone. The controlled airspace steps down from 1,200 AGL in the blue, to 700 AGL in the magenta, to the surface in the Control Zone.*

during times when the visibility goes below three miles and/or the cloud ceiling is less than 1,000 feet AGL. Then the reasons stated earlier for IFR approach protection are required. But a Control Zone does not go into effect until an FAA-qualified weather observer is in position at the airport within the Control Zone. When the weather observer arrives, the base of controlled airspace actually moves. If the airport is under a transition area, the floor of controlled airspace is 700 AGL. When the weather observer arrives, the Control Zone goes into effect and controlled airspace lowers to the surface. When the observer goes home, the airspace jumps back up to 700 AGL.

The weather observer makes the decision whether or not IFR conditions exist within the Control Zone. If the observer determines that the visibility is less than three miles and the ceiling is less than 1,000 feet, he can declare the Control Zone to be IFR. If the Control Zone is IFR, and since basic VFR minimums require at least three miles visibility, the Control Zone becomes off limits to all but arriving and departing IFR traffic.

If the visibility is less than three miles, then the only place you may fly VFR is in uncontrolled airspace below 10,000 feet MSL or within 1,200 feet of the ground regardless of MSL altitude. If the visibility is only 2 miles, you must stay below the blue blanket. You can sneak into an airport that lies in uncontrolled airspace, but if the airport has the magenta shading around it you must descend to within 700 feet of the ground while in that area. If you do this, stay away from any instrument final approach segments. You can find these in a NOS or Jeppesen approach chart book. But if the visibility is only 2 miles (or anything less than three but more than one), a Control Zone becomes a barrier. You cannot fly under a Control Zone like you can a transition area, because the Control Zone touches the ground. The transition area only comes as close as 700 feet AGL. The only vehicles operating under a Control Zone must be digging an underground tunnel!

Under these circumstances, the Control Zone barrier must be avoided. The pilot must not enter the Control Zone for fear of an IFR/VFR collision. The pilot can fly around the zone but nowhere can he fly through the Control Zone. If the Control Zone contains the destination airport, a pilot cannot get in without a Special VFR Clearance.

A Special VFR may even be the savior to a really dangerous problem. If a pilot began a flight with better than basic VFR minimums but during the flight the weather got progressively worse, diversion to an airport may be the safest thing to do. If the nearest airport also has a Control Zone, then a Special VFR Clearance must be received before entering the zone. IFR approaches may still be in progress to the airport when the weather observer has gone home for the day, but the need for IFR/VFR separation remains. The Special VFR clearance must be issued by someone who knows if that airport will be having any IFR arrivals or departures during your proposed penetration to the airport. That person will be a controller. The controller might be at a non-radar tower, but most often he will be sitting behind a radar screen handling traffic. A Flight Service Station can get a Special VFR for a pilot, but they must first give a call to the controller, and the pilot gets the message third-hand.

When a Special VFR Clearance is issued, it is done only at the request of the pilot. The controller cannot say, "How about taking a Special?" If the controller does this and the pilot then has a problem, the controller is on the hook for baiting you into something you might not have been prepared to handle. I heard a clever controller once say to a stranded VFR pilot, "The field is IFR due to ceilings, but another VFR pilot just landed with a Special VFR." This was the closest legal way for him to remind the pilot that asking for and receiving a Special VFR Clearance was the only way to get home.

A Special VFR Clearance is issued only when a collision hazard does not exist. How will the controller know this, even without radar? Because Special VFR Clearances are only issued one at a time and when there are no IFR arrivals or departures. The pilot cannot hit anybody else because there is nobody else there to hit. This holds true unless another VFR pilot violates the Control Zone. When the clearance is issued, the pilot is on his own to cross the Control Zone boundary and find the airport.

A Special VFR Clearance can be used to depart a Control Zone when the conditions are IFR. This would allow a pilot to do touch-and-goes in the traffic pattern with less than three but more than one mile visibility. It would also allow a pilot who is headed for uncontrolled airspace to escape the Control Zone to an area where less than three miles but more than one mile visibility is allowed for VFR. A Special VFR Clearance is not issued between sunset and sunrise unless the pilot has a current instrument rating and the airplane is equipped to fly IFR.

Some busy airports never issue Special VFR Clearances. Airports that are very busy will have many airplanes in the Control Zone at one time. But a Special VFR requires that only a single airplane be in the zone at a time. At many large airports, there is never a time 24 hours a day, 7 days a week, 52 weeks a year, when the Control Zone is empty. Since the zone is never empty and since its being empty is a requirement for Special VFR, a Special VFR Clearance is never a possibility. These airports indicate this fact by using blue *T*'s (FIG. 6-5) rather than a dashed blue line to mark the boundary of the Control Zone.

When you begin comparing controlled versus uncontrolled, some confusion exists between controlled airports and controlled airspace. A controlled airport exists wherever an operating control tower is present. It is possible for an uncontrolled airport (no control tower) to be in controlled airspace if the airport has a Control Zone. The weather observer that is required for a Control Zone to be in effect does not have to be an FAA employee. Many airline companies will have an employee trained as a weather observer so that they can control the times when the Control Zone becomes effective.

While in flight with visibility below three miles, it is vital that pilots stay outside controlled airspace in all its forms. Here again, the sectional chart provides the information about the horizontal and vertical boundaries of controlled airspace.

The chart has clues to help pilots view it not as a flat piece of paper but as a three-dimensional Earth and sky. The colors of the chart depict the elevation of the Earth, not what the Earth looks like from above. Living and learning to fly in the lush southeastern United States, I started off believing that charts for that area were green because the Earth looks mostly green from above. By looking at the Denver Sectional Chart, which is mostly brown, I thought that the jagged Rocky Mountains did not have any green plants growing on them and that the chart was brown because only brown dirt was exposed to the pilot's view. The chart's color has nothing to do with vegetation or the lack of it, only how high the ground is above sea level. This is the first key in determining where controlled airspace ends and uncontrolled airspace begins.

How high is the ground? This question requires the pilot to think in three dimensions, to think like a pilot. I asked the question, "How high is the ground where you live?" once to a two-dimensionally oriented non-pilot. He answered by saying, "It is

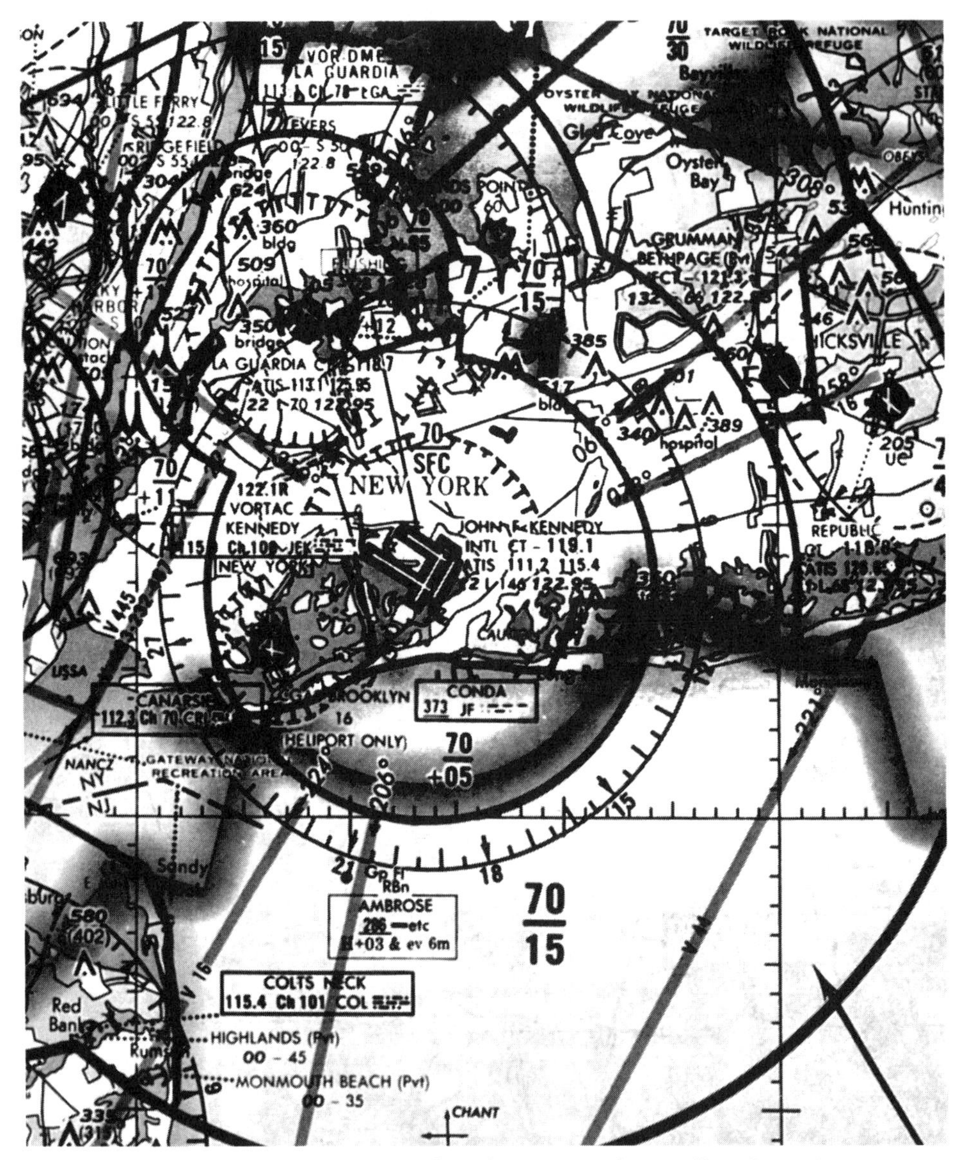

Fig. 6-5. *The John F. Kennedy and La Guardia airports do not allow Special VFR traffic. This is indicated by the* T*'s around the Control Zone boundaries.*

mostly flat except in the back, where there is a little rise." This person had no conception of elevation above sea level and gave the correct answer based on his perception. But pilots must know how high the ground is to determine where controlled airspace exists.

Knowing that controlled airspace begins at 700 AGL (in the magenta shading) or at 1,200 feet AGL (beyond the blue shading) is not enough for actual application. The altimeter in the airplane reads the distance between the airplane and sea level, not between the airplane and the ground. Yes, radar altimeters are available that read the distance between airplane and ground, but finding this equipment in light airplanes is rare. Since the controlled airspace boundary is formed at an AGL altitude and the altimeters used are based on MSL altitudes, a conversion must be made. The ground elevation in feet above Mean Sea Level must be known. Then the appropriate Above Ground Level distance to the base of the controlled airspace can be added. If the field elevation of an airport is 547 feet and the airport is surrounded by magenta shading on the chart, the altimeter will read 1,247 when the airplane enters controlled airspace. This number is arrived at by adding 547, which is the MSL altitude of the ground, to the 700 feet above 547 MSL where the controlled airspace begins. 547 plus 700 equals 1,247. Any time I fly above this airport and the visibility is less than three miles, my properly set altimeter must read less than 1,247. Under 1,247 puts the airplane in uncontrolled airspace where only one mile visibility is required.

When an airplane takes off and makes one circuit of the traffic pattern on a VFR day, the pilot, using a one-thousand-foot-AGL traffic pattern, will climb out of uncontrolled airspace somewhere on cross wind. Then the pilot will fly the downwind in controlled airspace, but somewhere on base leg he will descend back into uncontrolled airspace. When the visibility is less than three miles, the pilot cannot legally do a normal one-thousand-foot-AGL traffic pattern.

When flying away from the airport, the vertical boundary line is just as important. The ground, however, might not be level, and the boundary will rise and fall with the terrain accordingly. The chart gives ground elevation information in various ways. The terrain contour lines offer help. When the elevation rises above a one-thousand-foot interval, the color on the chart changes. The color changes are bounded by light gray contour lines. Actual terrain elevations are indicated when there is a rapid rise in the ground. A dot with an elevation number will be shown on the chart to depict this peak. The highest elevation on a sectional chart is given with Latitude and Longitude coordinates on the flap on the chart. The actual location of the highest chart elevation is shown on the chart in bold numbers.

Even the symbols for towers are clues to airspace. Look at FIGS. 6-6A and B. Figure 6-6A is the symbol for an obstruction less than 1,000 feet AGL. The tower lies within an area of magenta shading. Figure 6-6B is a side view of the same tower. The figure depicts both the relationship of sea level and ground level to the top of the tower. A pilot is flying VFR and passes over this tower. It is a hot summer day and the high humidity has produced thick haze. In fact, there is only two miles visibility. Just as the airplane passes over the tower the airplane's altimeter reads 1,600 feet. Is this pilot flying legally under VFR conditions? Yes!

The top of the tower is shown to be 1,245 feet MSL. But how high is the ground? The chart also shows that the top of the tower is 304 feet AGL. If the top is 1,245 MSL and at the same time the top is at 304 AGL, subtracting the two numbers yields the height of the ground: 941 feet MSL. Since controlled airspace starts at 700 feet AGL and goes up from there, and since the ground is 941 feet MSL to begin with, the MSL

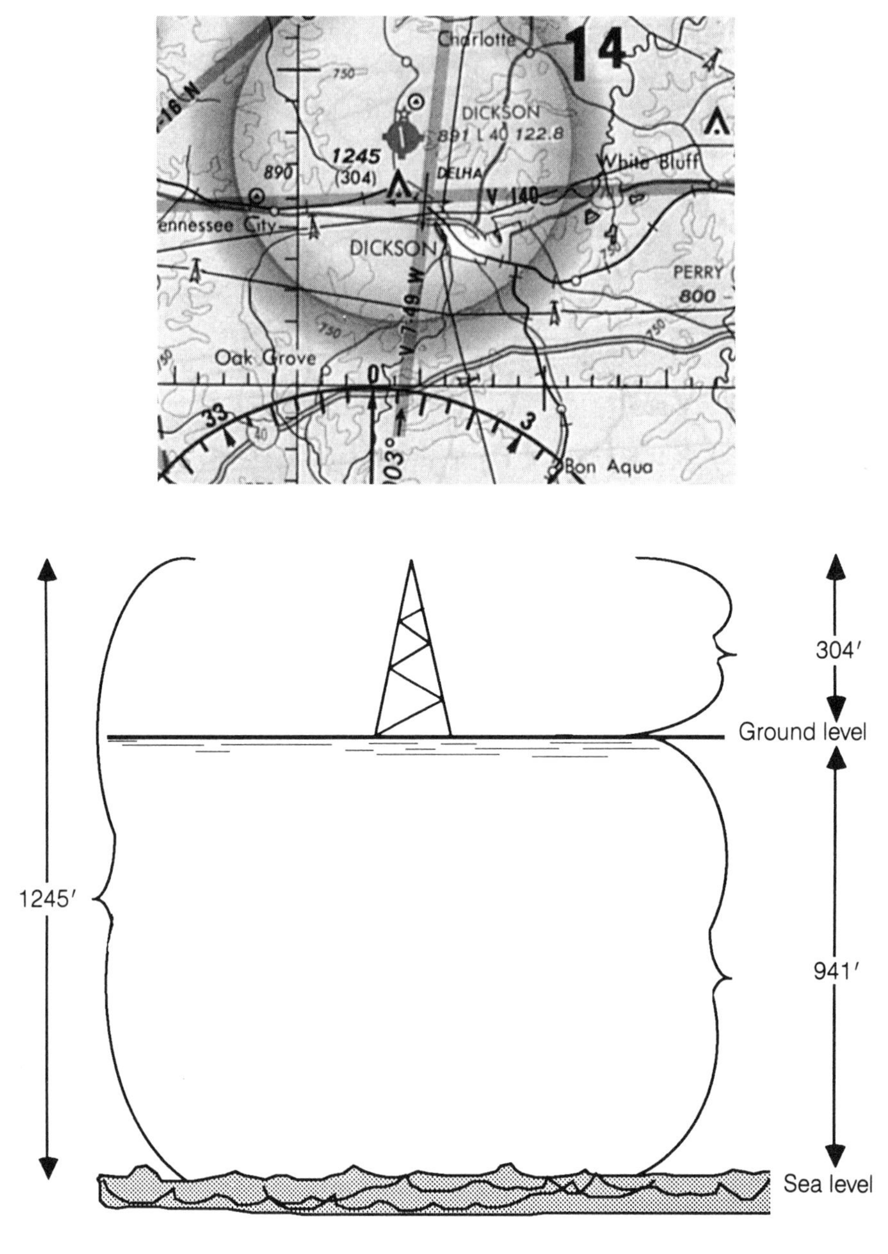

Fig. 6-6 *(A) The top of the tower just south of the Dickson Airport is 1,245 feet MSL. The top of the tower is also 304 AGL. With these altitudes known, ground elevation can be calculated and therefore the base of the controlled airspace can be calculated. (B) The tower south of the Dickson Airport seen from the side. Even though Dickson is hundreds of miles from the sea, the position of sea level is indicated as a reference.*

altitude that the controlled airspace starts is (941 + 700) 1,641 feet MSL. In this case, 700 AGL is the same altitude as 1,641 MSL. The airplane is flying at 1,600 feet MSL or 41 feet lower than the base of controlled airspace. Being below controlled airspace means that at this altitude the pilot is required to have only one mile visibility. Here the pilot has two miles visibility, so he is perfectly legal. Is the pilot safe flying around low with such bad visibility? Probably not, but the question here was, "Is the pilot legal?" The value in understanding this three-dimensional idea is not so pilots can go out and scud run legally, but to understand the boundaries and purpose for the VFR weather minimums: collision avoidance.

AIR TRAFFIC CONTROL

All other airspace types are just variations on the basic collision avoidance idea. The least stringent of all airspace types is called an Aeronautical Advisory Station. This is a fancy name for unicom and is not really an airspace type at all. The use of unicom is completely optional, and there are no boundaries for its use (FIG. 6-7). It is

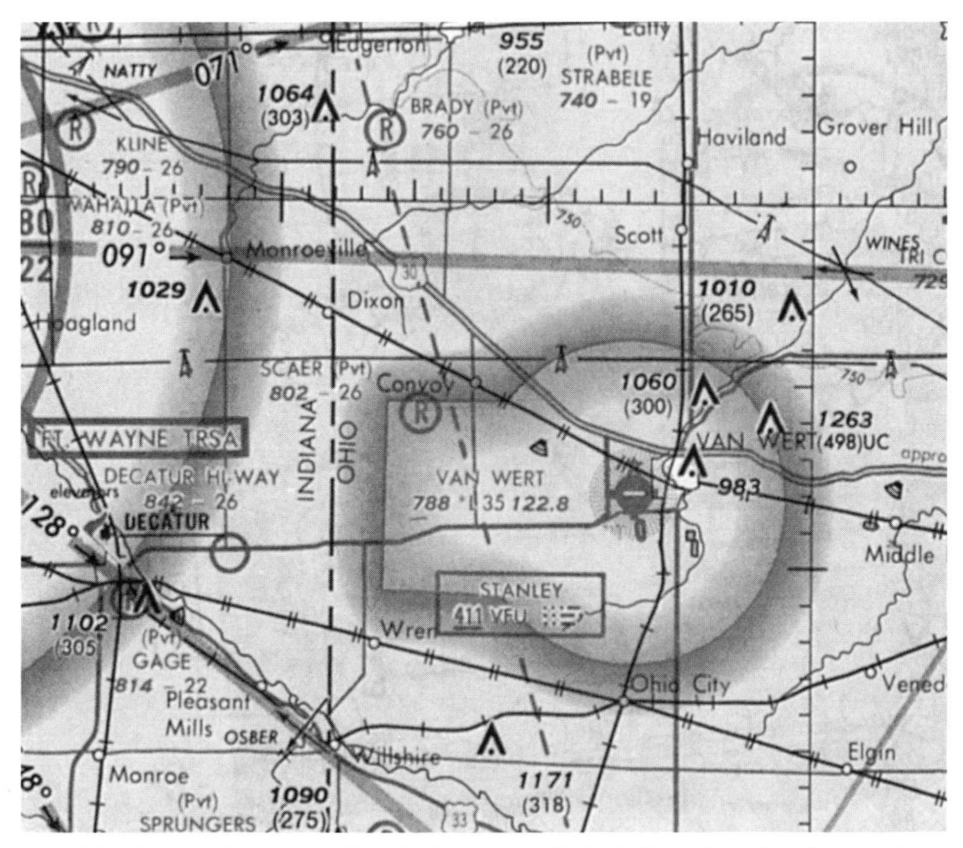

Fig. 6-7. *The Van Wert Airport lists the frequency of 122.8. This alerts the inbound pilot to the fact that a unicom station exists at the airport.*

recommended that a pilot monitor the proper unicom frequency from 10 miles out when flying inbound to an airport with unicom. In the air near an uncontrolled airport that lists a unicom frequency as its Common Traffic Advisory Frequency (CTAF), see and avoid rules are the only defense against collision. The pilots in the area must work together by announcing their positions and intentions continuously. In this way, pilots are also controllers. The pilots determine the flow of traffic and the sequence of airplanes to the runway. The unicom is a party-line frequency. Anyone on the ground talking over the unicom can only give information such as wind direction and favored runway. The person talking from the ground on unicom is never a controller.

Strict adherence to a traffic pattern is essential to safety. The traffic pattern has a certain course and altitude. Pilots who have trained at airports with control towers often do not see the importance of the proper traffic pattern and entry. The Airman's Information Manual (AIM) recommends that all turns in the traffic pattern be to the left unless otherwise indicated on a segmented circle. The AIM also recommends all entries be made at a midfield position of the downwind leg and all exits be made straight out or at a 45-degree angle to the cross wind leg. By following these guidelines, pilots know best where to look for traffic and the sky is narrowed down.

When no unicom frequency is listed, pilots should still talk on the radio. In this case, all the communications between pilots will take place on multicom (FIG. 6-8). The job of controlling the flow of traffic is still the pilot's job, but in the case of multicom use nobody is on the ground to give runway and wind information. Multicom is 122.90 MHz, but verify this in a current AIM because it has changed over the years.

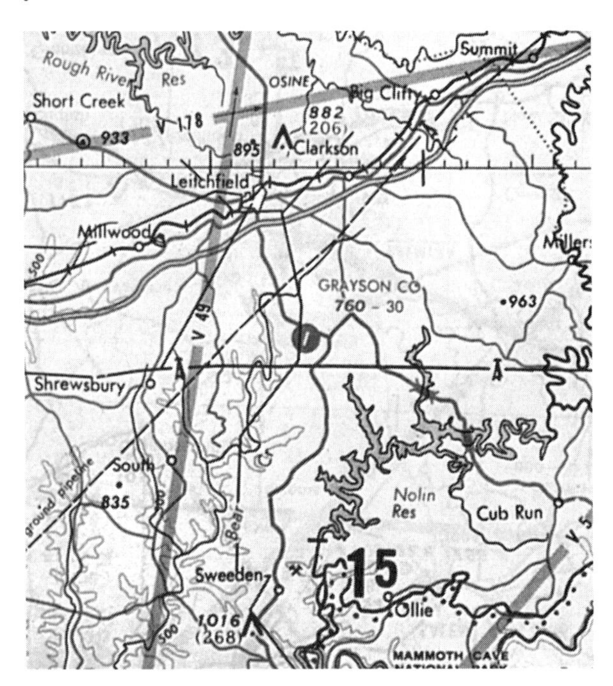

Fig. 6-8. *The Grayson County Airport lists no radio frequency. This means pilots should talk to each other on the multicom frequency.*

When a Flight Service Station is in operation at an airport, the area around that airport becomes an Airport Advisory Area (FIG. 6-9). The name ADVISORY is important in understanding just what service is provided. A Flight Service Station gives advice to pilots in the area. The people who give this advice ensure that the information received will be more reliable than information obtained over unicom. The FSS personnel do not control traffic. They do not issue landing and takeoff clearances.

It is recommended that pilots flying into an Airport Advisory Area call the proper frequency at least 10 miles out. When the radio transmission is made, address the FSS with the term *Radio*. By calling "Watertown Radio" you are addressing the Flight Service Station in Watertown. A pilot should also give information about his position in relation to the airport. The FSS personnel will then relay the information about the pilot's approach to other pilots in the area. This information will narrow down the sky so that pilots know where to look for traffic.

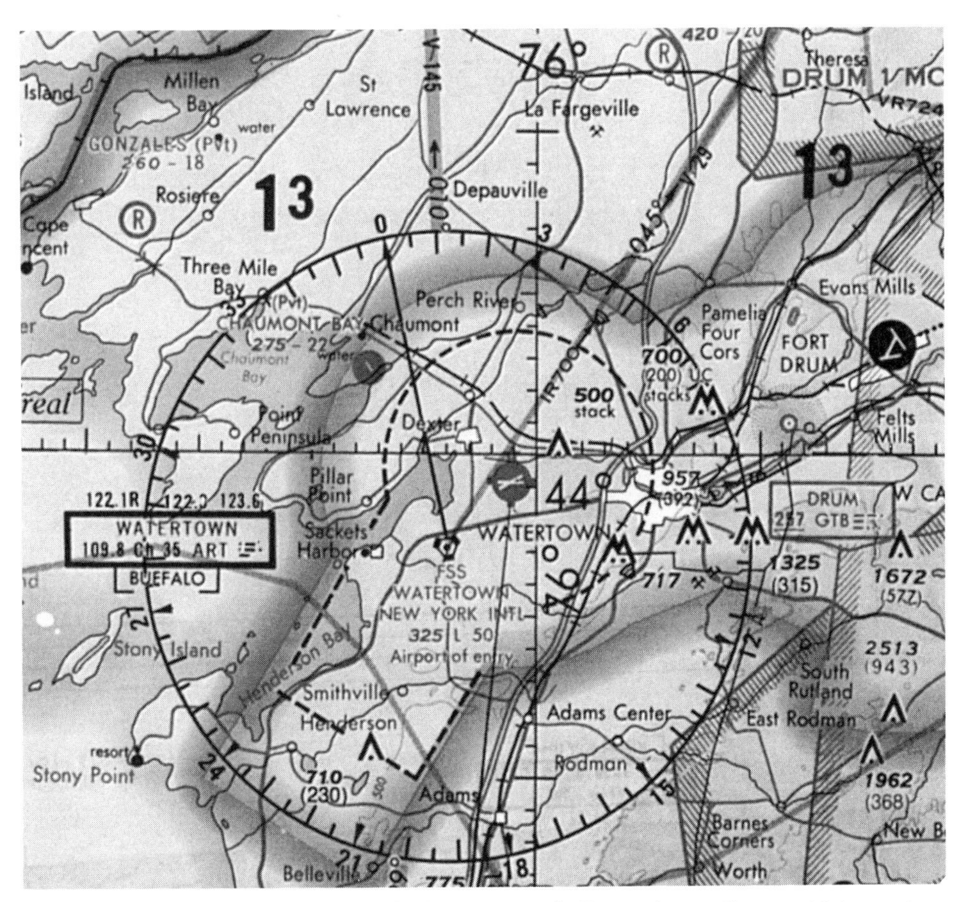

Fig. 6-9. *The Watertown, New York, International Airport is an Airport Advisory Area because a Flight Service Station is on the field. There is no Control Tower at Watertown, but a Control Zone and Transition Area are present.*

While operation in an Airport Advisory Area, or when using unicom or multicom, remember that communication over the proper CTAF is optional. Pilots who do not use the radio, tune in the wrong frequency, or fly with no radios may still be flying in the area. Constant vigilance must be maintained for unannounced traffic in these areas.

Many Flight Service Stations do not operate 24 hours per day. In these locations, the airport could be an Airport Advisory Area when the FSS is open but then becomes an Aeronautical Advisory Station (unicom) when the FSS is closed. The time of day would determine which frequency to use and what services to expect. As the FSS system goes automated and the smaller outlying stations close, there will be fewer Airport Advisory Areas and more unicom stations in the future.

Wherever an operating control tower exists, there is also present an Airport Traffic Area (ATA). There is no symbol that marks the boundary of an ATA on sectional charts (FIG. 6-10). The only way a pilot can know if an ATA is present is by determin-

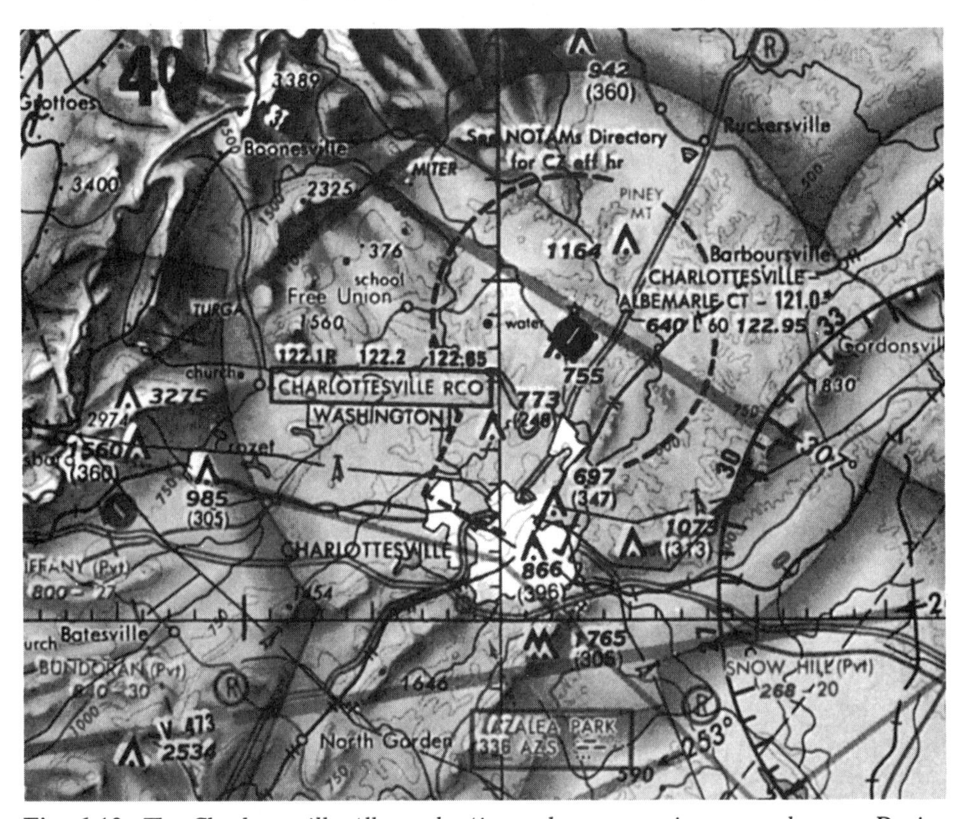

Fig. 6-10. *The Charlottesville-Albemarle Airport has a part-time control tower. During the tower's operation, an Airport Traffic Area exists but is not depicted on the chart. The pilot knows the ATA is present because the airport's symbol is blue and the letters* CT *appear in the airport information. While the tower is open, an overlap exists between ATA and Control Zone.*

ing the color of the airport symbol. The blue airport symbol means a control tower is located on the field. Then the pilot must determine if the control tower is in operation at the time of arrival. The control tower has complete jurisdiction inside an ATA. The ATA will begin at the surface and go up to but not include 3,000 feet above the airport surface. The horizontal boundary is a ring five statute miles from the center of the airport. The ATA is a short cylinder shape.

Any traffic that wishes to operate in the ATA must first ask the operating control tower for permission. A pilot may enter the ATA by one of two ways: from the ground or from the air. Permission to enter the ATA from the ground is given in the form of a takeoff clearance. When an airplane is cleared for takeoff, the controller has only issued that clearance after analyzing the air traffic situation at hand. The pilot never gives up the see-and-avoid rule, but in this case the control tower is acting as an informed pair of eyes for traffic.

To enter the ATA from the air, the pilot must radio the control tower and ask for permission to enter the ATA prior to the time that entry actually occurs. This must be done even if the pilot does not intend to land in the ATA. Even flights that just pass through must have clearance. The pilot should tell the tower controller inside an ATA the airplane's position relative to the airport and his intentions. "Kinston Tower, this is Piper 1234B, 8 miles north, inbound for landing." This is a request for ATA entry. A pilot should never report four miles north, because four miles is at least one mile inside the ATA. Approval must be given before a pilot gets that close. When the visibility is worse than five miles, pilots must make this request to the tower before they can see the airport. This requires the pilot to be aware of position even in the surrounding area so accurate position reports can be made. After the tower controller receives a request to enter the ATA, he will give traffic pattern instructions. "Piper 1234B, enter on a two-mile right base for runway 23." By making this statement, the controller has cleared the Piper to cross the ATA boundary and find his way to a two-mile base leg.

Many control towers are considered VFR towers. Even though these towers routinely handle IFR clearances and traffic, they are not equipped with radar. Without radar, the controllers cannot verify an airplane's position. The controllers must take the pilot's word for it. The controllers also cannot give the pilot vectors or headings to get to the airport. Pilots are on their own to find the traffic pattern. Once the pilot has arrived at the assigned position (two-mile right base to runway 23), he should announce that position and await the next instruction. The tower controller may clear the plane to land or to "continue." Continue means the pilot should continue making the traffic pattern from his assigned entry point until clearance to land has been received.

Making a right base traffic pattern entry inside an ATA is perfectly all right if that is what the tower controller assigned. Making a right base traffic pattern entry at an uncontrolled airport can be quite dangerous. The difference in the two situations is clear: The tower controller has knowledge of air traffic that the pilot does not have. With this knowledge he can assign a pilot to a safe, non-standard entry. At an uncontrolled field, there is nobody else around to add to the pilot's knowledge of traffic. In that case, it is safer to do what is expected, which is to enter downwind at a 45-degree angle.

There is a situation where ATA entry can take place without prior approval. If an airplane's radios fail, the pilot should enter the ATA and join the traffic pattern. The control tower should see the airplane and give light gun signals for clearance. Choose the ATA in which to do this wisely. Extremely busy ATAs are not well equipped for surprises. An airplane suddenly appearing on downwind could certainly disrupt the existing traffic flow. If radios fail, consider the decision to land at an uncontrolled airport first. Get the radios fixed there or telephone ahead to the control tower and work out entry arrangements.

When flying cross-country flights, look on the sectional for the blue airport symbols. If a flight is planned in the vicinity of an ATA, plan to fly over it (above 3,000 feet AGL), or around it, or through it with permission. "Grand Strand Tower, this is Bonanza 1234C, 10 miles south, request transition through the ATA at 2,500 feet." This pilot is asking to pass through. The tower controller will usually say, "Bonanza 1234C, transition approved, report when cleared the ATA."

When leaving an ATA, it is good practice to call back to the tower and tell the controller. "Jonesville Tower, Cessna 1234D has cleared the ATA to the east." This transmission will allow the controller to stop including this pilot in his collision-avoidance plans. When control towers are used in conjunction with radar departure control, the distance the pilot travels before being released is farther. Determine in preflight planning if the ATAs the flight will cross are radar-equipped or only VFR towers. Radar-equipped towers require a much earlier call up to approach control. The Airport/Facility Directory has this information.

Much confusion begins to set in when these various types of airspace overlap (FIG. 6-11). There are airports where a part-time control tower coexists with a 24-hour FSS. In this case, an Airport Traffic Area exists during hours when the tower is in operation but downgrades to an Airport Advisory Area when the tower closes and the FSS is open. Then, if the FSS is closed, the airport might downgrade one more time to an Aeronautical Advisory Station. One airport could be all three types, but never at the same time. Add to this that the airport could be at the bottom of a Control Zone, and there is more overlap. When the control tower is in operation, a short cylinder-shaped ATA (from surface to 2,999 feet above the surface) will lie within a tall cylinder-shaped Control Zone (up to 14,500 feet MSL).

When radar is introduced to airspace rules, the boundaries are extended. The least stringent form of radar airspace is the Terminal Radar Service Area (TRSA). Mode C transponders are not required inside a TRSA, and radio communication with controllers is optional. At the heart of a TRSA is an ATA. Since communication is required for entry to the ATA, it is good practice to communicate with the approach controllers of a TRSA so aircraft can be blended into the flow of traffic. Legally, a pilot could enter the TRSA and talk to nobody until just outside the ATA, then talk to the tower controller and by-pass approach control. In practice, however, a pilot using

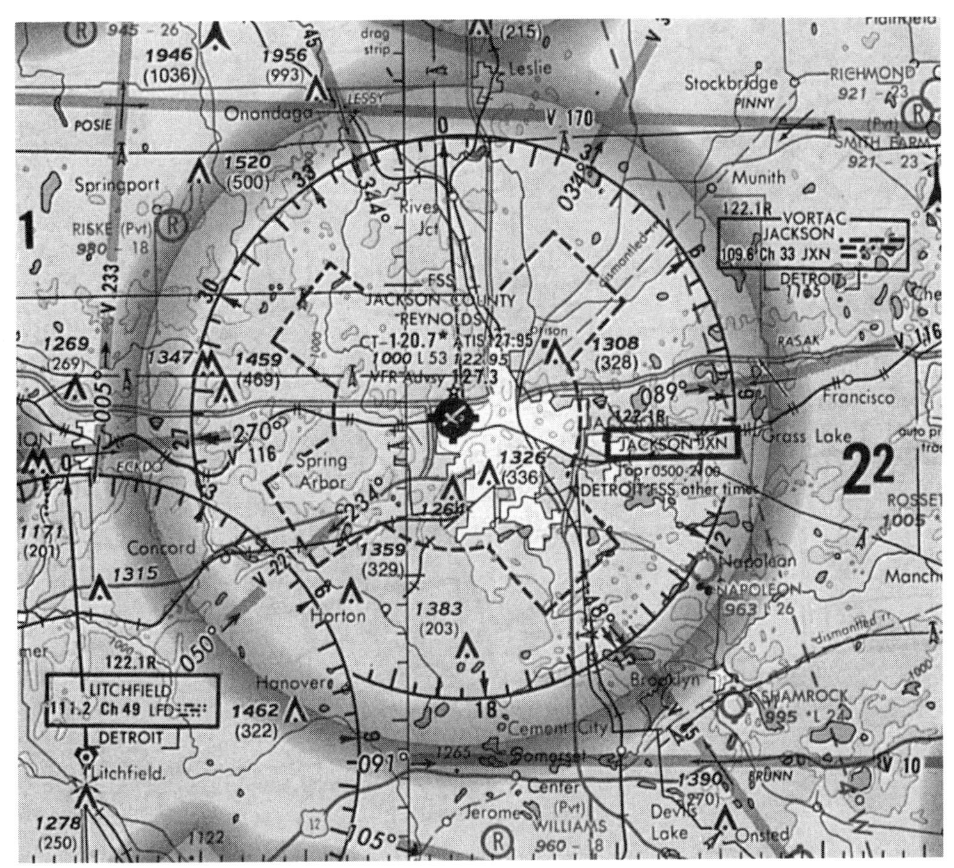

Fig. 6-11. *The Jackson County-Reynolds Airport has overlapping airspace. When the control tower is in operation, an Airport Traffic Area lies within a Control Zone. When the tower is closed and the FSS is open, it becomes an Airport Advisory Area within a Control Zone. When the tower and FSS are closed, it becomes an Aeronautical Advisory Station (unicom).*

this procedure will be in the air longer since the tower controller will place the pilot in the back of the line. The pilot may even have to go back out to the rim of the TRSA to get properly sequenced to the airport. To avoid this, call early and call approach control first.

The FAA began tightening the hold on air traffic when the Airport Radar Service Area (ARSA) was invented (FIG. 6-12). Many TRSAs have been changed over to ARSAs in recent years. An ARSA is an upgrade in air traffic control from a TRSA. The biggest difference is that pilots are required to communicate with approach control prior to entry into any portion of the ARSA. If the airplane has no radios, an ARSA is off-limits except with prior approval.

When ARSAs were first introduced, a jousting match began between general aviation pilots and the FAA. Pilot groups feared that the outside rim of an ARSA would

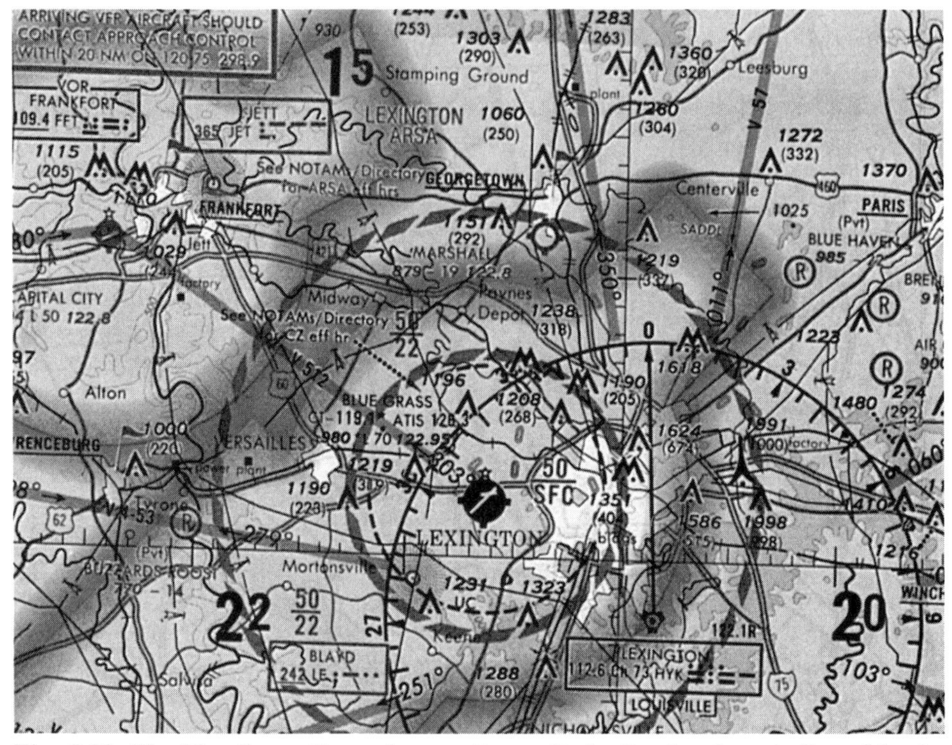

Fig. 6-12. *The Blue Grass Airport has an Airport Radar Service Area, indicated by the dashed concentric circles.*

become a very hazardous area. Since communication is required to operate in the ARSA and since IFR traffic is a controller's first priority, VFR pilots believed there might be a time when a controller would deny VFR aircraft entry to the ARSA. If the controller became saturated with other traffic, he could essentially close down the ARSA to any new traffic. This would leave the VFR pilot to wander around on the rim of the ARSA hoping for an entry slot. If several VFR airplanes were "holding" on the rim, a collision could occur.

This seemed like an outright attempt to limit VFR airspace, and the fight began. The pilot groups then read the fine print in the ARSA rules and determined they had discovered a loophole. The rule says, "No person may operate an aircraft in an ARSA unless two-way communication is established with Air Traffic Control prior to entering the ARSA." The phrase "communication is established" is a weaker statement than "must receive permission" would have been. The pilot groups then argued that if a VFR pilot called the approach control of an ARSA and was told to "stand by" that two-way communication had been established and entry to the ARSA was approved. The controllers know this ploy now, and if the ARSA is indeed saturated to the point where no more VFR traffic can be allowed to enter, the controller will tell the pilot on initial call up to "remain clear of the ARSA." If the ARSA is not saturated and VFR arrivals are being accepted, but the controller is temporarily unable to talk to the arriving VFR pilot, he will say "stand by." The pilot should then continue toward the ARSA, even enter the ARSA, and the controller will continue communications as soon as other problems are resolved.

The ARSA has three rings to know about (FIG. 6-13). Only two of the three rings appear on the chart. The Inner Circle is cylinder-shaped with the base sitting on the ground. The top of the cylinder is at 4,000 feet AGL. The cylinder is five miles in radius or ten miles across, and the primary airport lies in the center. The Outer Circle does not touch the ground. This space is doughnut shaped and fits down around the inner cylinder. The bottom of the doughnut remains 1,200 feet above the terrain that it overlies. The top of the Outer Circle is 4,000 feet above the airport. The Outer Circle has a 10-mile radius. Both the Inner and Outer Circles are depicted on the chart with MSL altitudes showing the ARSA base and top. The Outer Area is not on the chart. This area is a larger ring with a radius of 20 miles or 40 miles across. This is an "establish communications" area. It is recommended that initial calls to approach control be made in this area. Hopefully, contact will be made and entry approved to the ARSA before the airplane reaches the Outer Circle.

Once the pilot is inside the ARSA, the controllers may give him vectors to the traffic pattern, but they are not required to do so. Again, the services a controller provides to VFR traffic are limited to a time-share basis. If no vectors are given, the

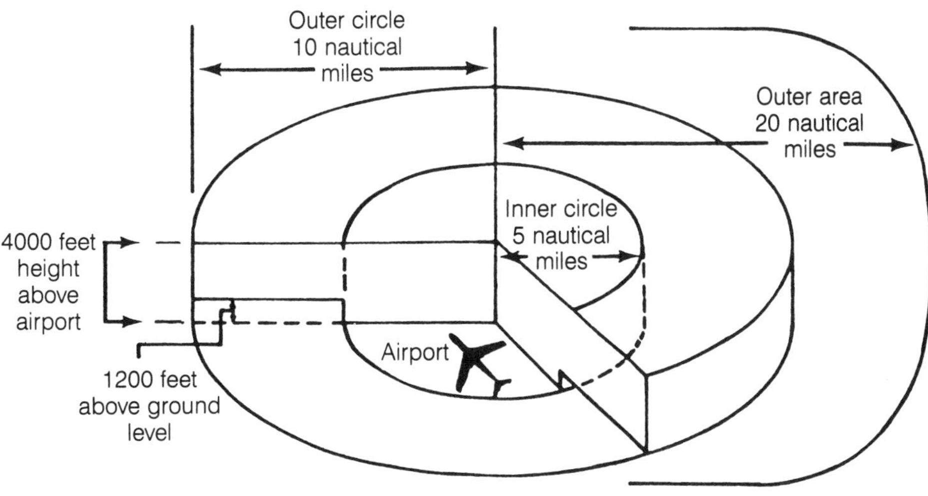

Services upon establishing two-way radio communication and radar contact:
Sequencing arrivals
IFR/IFR standard separation
IFR/VFR traffic advisories and conflict resolution
VFR/VFR traffic advisories

Note: The normal radius of the outer area will be 20nm, with some site specific variations.

IFR: Instrument Flight Rules
VFR: Visual Flight Rules

Fig. 6-13. *Airport Radar Service Area (ARSA).*

ARSA becomes essentially a big Airport Traffic Area. The pilot will find his way to the assigned entry to a traffic pattern, all the while responsible to see and avoid other traffic.

After December 30, 1990, transponders with altitude reporting equipment (Mode C) became required inside all ARSAs. Mode C was made mandatory above 10,000 feet MSL on July 1, 1989. The upper limit of an ARSA is 4,000 feet AGL and, depending on the elevation of the ARSA airport, there could be as much as a six-thousand-foot gap between the upper limit of the ARSA and 10,000 feet MSL.

Pilots can fly over the ARSA and not be subjected to the ARSA's communication rules. But when the ARSA transponder altitude reporting rule came into effect, the airspace above an ARSA also went Mode C. In order to allow the controllers at an ARSA's radar facility to see only altitude reporting targets, the gap has been filled in. If a pilot flies over an ARSA, the airplane must have Mode C equipment, regardless of altitude. This is a three-way rule. Mode C is required in an ARSA, over an ARSA, and above 10,000 feet MSL. Without altitude reporting, an ARSA is a restricted area.

Where an ARSA exists, chances are great that hidden within the ARSA are an Airport Traffic Area and a Control Zone. All three airspace types have a common base. Each extends out from the center of the airport horizontally for five statute miles. The Airport Traffic Area is the smallest. The ATA's cylinder shape climbs off the ground to 2,999 feet AGL. The Inner Circle of the ARSA climbs up to 4,000 feet AGL, and the Control Zone goes up to 14,500 feet MSL. Three airspace types overlapping at the same airport, each with different dimensions, purposes, and rules.

TERMINAL CONTROL AREA (TCA)

The next, and final, upgrade is the Terminal Control Area (TCA) (see FIG. 6-14). There are no more "group" ratings. In the past, a Group I TCA was the most stringent airspace in the world, followed by a Group II designation. Now TCAs are considered equal, with one exception. The original Group I TCAs still prohibit student pilots from landing at the primary airport. The TCAs where student pilots are still not allowed are:

Atlanta—Hartsfield
Boston—Logan
Chicago—O'Hare
Dallas—DFW International
Los Angeles—LAX International
Miami—Miami International
Newark—Newark International
New York—Kennedy
New York—LaGuardia
San Francisco—SFO International
Washington, DC—National
Andrews Air Force Base

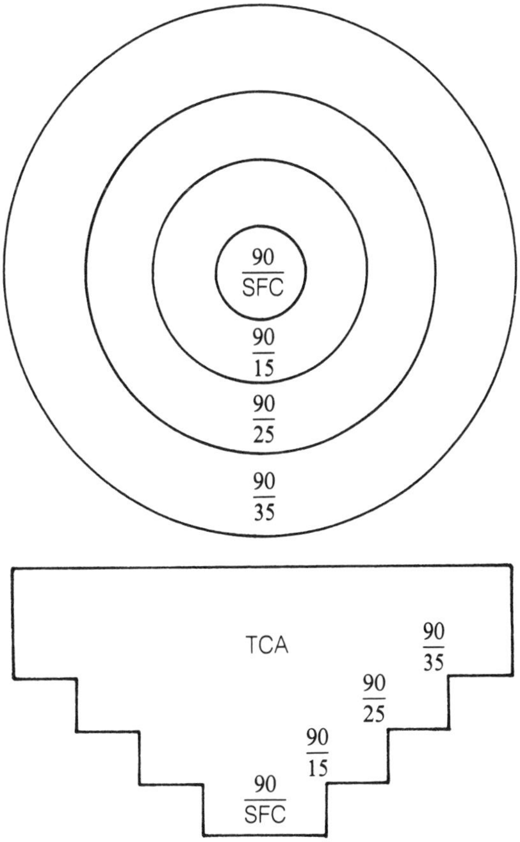

Fig. 6-14. *A Terminal Control Area (TCA) overhead view and side view. The upper limit is 9,000 MSL. The Area between 9,000 feet MSL and 10,000 feet MSL is not inside the TCA, but a Mode C transponder is still required. All airspace above 10,000 feet MSL requires Mode C.*

All other TCA primary airports can be flown to and landed at by student pilots as long as the student carries an endorsement from a Certified Flight Instructor saying the student is competent to make the flight. Actually, the CFI must provide two endorsements: one to land at the TCA primary airport and another to fly in the TCA airspace.

After the student pilot rule, all TCAs are alike. The airplane must be equipped with an operating VOR or TACAN. The pilot must be able to communicate with Air Traffic Control on a two-way radio that can tune in all the necessary frequencies used in the TCA. The airplane must have an operating transponder with altitude reporting capability (Mode C).

The biggest difference, aside from equipment, between a TCA and all other forms of airspace previously discussed is approval. The controllers must issue the pilot "appropriate authorization" prior to entering the TCA airspace. This means the controller must say the words, "You are cleared into the TCA." There is no room for the "establish communications" loophole. *Clearance* is a term usually reserved for IFR flying, but here is a situation where VFR pilots require a clearance. If a pilot is about to enter the airspace of a TCA and has not yet heard the words, "You are cleared into the TCA," the pilot should ask, "Am I cleared to enter the TCA?" and get a positive response. The pilot should leave no room for doubt.

The TCA is a huge mixture of airspace types. The TCA alone will have cut-outs, corridors, and arrival gates. The TCA is small at the bottom and gradually expands with altitude. The center ring of the TCA goes down to the surface, but outside rings do not. This means that airspace types can lie underneath the outside rings of a TCA. There could be transition areas, Airport Traffic Areas, Airport Advisory Areas, and Aeronautical Advisory Stations. The inner circle of the TCA will contain an Airport Traffic Area and probably a No-Special VFR Control Zone. All of this is contained in the 30-mile Mode C cylinder. What a mess! Each overlapping part has individual rules and requirements that the pilot must remember.

POSITIVE CONTROL AREA (PCA)

When pilots fly to altitudes above 18,000 feet MSL, they enter the Positive Control Area (PCA). From 18,000 feet MSL to 60,000 feet MSL, the PCA is a region of fewer rules and faster speeds, like the autobahn in Germany. All traffic in the PCA is conducted under Instrument Flight Rules, regardless of the weather. All pilots flying in the PCA must be instrument-rated, and flying instrument-equipped airplanes. Since pilots must maintain a watch on an assigned frequency, they must have two-way radios. All flights above 10,000 feet must have Mode C, so the PCA requires altitude reporting as well. Airplanes in the region are so fast that receiving a local altimeter setting becomes impractical. Altimeter settings are to be updated every 100 miles. By the time a pilot determines what altimeter setting to use, it is almost time to find another one. To eliminate this problem, all flights when passing through 18,000 feet MSL change their barometric pressure setting to 29.92 inches of Mercury. This allows for better aircraft separation because everyone is using the same reference plane. When 29.92" Hg is reset in the altimeter, the altitude reading becomes a Flight Level. Flight Levels are abbreviated by dropping the last two zeros of the altitude. 60,000 feet then becomes Flight Level 600 or just FL 600. In the PCA and above FL 290, altitudes are assigned at 4,000-foot intervals for even greater aircraft separation.

SPECIAL-USE AIRSPACE

Some airspace has been allocated to the military for training purposes. These areas range from very dangerous to civilian traffic to harmless. The danger might change from day to day or be based on time of day. Consider a scale from one to 10 where 10 is "no trespassing" and one is "come on in, but watch out."

Prohibited Areas are a 10. Civilian flights are always prohibited in Prohibited Areas. The most conspicuous Prohibited Area is the Mall in Washington D.C. Within this area lies the United States Capitol, the White House, and the Monuments. The National Air and Space Museum ironically is within a no-flying zone. There is a moving Prohibited Area around the President and Vice President at all times, wherever they go. Even former presidents have Prohibited Areas over their residences. Figure 6-15 depicts the airspace over Plains, Georgia. There are circular Prohibited Areas across the American midwest, each covering an Intercontinental Ballistic Missile silo.

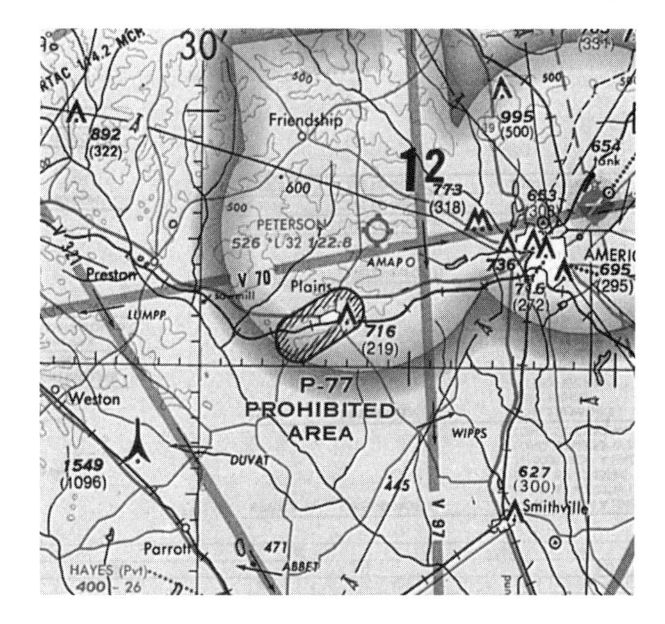

Fig. 6-15. *The Prohibited Area over Plains, Georgia.*

Temporary Prohibited Areas can be formed by NOTAMs whenever the FAA Administrator decides to do so. Temporary Prohibited Areas are formed during Space Shuttle launches and recoveries. A Prohibited Area was thrown up around the area where the top secret Stealth fighter crashed.

Restricted Areas are a 9. Most of the time, flying a civilian airplane into a "hot" Restricted Area is life threatening. The military is lobbing artillery shells through the air, or firing at drones, or dropping bombs. The reason these areas are classified as Restricted rather than Prohibited is that there are times when these areas go "cold." Cold means inactive. Hot means stay out.

On the lower tab of sectional charts a white strip can be found. That strip contains information concerning all Special-Use Airspace on that chart. A Restricted Area's time of operation will be indicated here. Some Restricted Areas are hot all the time; others have a schedule of operation. Before flying into any Restricted Area, radio the controlling agency to determine the status of the area. Do not even trust NOTAMs. The time of the NOTAM may change without notification. If an IFR flight plan is filed with a route of flight through a Restricted Area and the plan is approved as filed, then no further clearance will be required. The Air Traffic Control computer will have verified that the Restricted Area is cold and that you are cleared to pass through.

Warning Areas are a 9. The danger to civilian aircraft in a Warning Area is identical to the dangers inside a Restricted Area. So why do they go by separate names? It is a matter of airspace ownership. Warning Areas are over international waters that begin beyond the three-mile offshore limit. Airspace over international water is considered international airspace. The United States cannot fully restrict international airspace because it is not ours to restrict. Instead, the military merely warns pilots to stay away.

Alert Areas are a 5. These areas contain a high level of military flying activity; no bombing or firing, just lots of fast moving aircraft. Civilian pilots do not need special authorization to fly within an Alert Area, but extreme caution is urged.

Military Operations Areas (MOAs) are a 5. Civilian flight schools usually set up unofficial practice areas for students to perfect flight maneuvers. MOAs are official military training or practice areas. Alert Areas are usually situated around military bases, while MOAs are out in uncongested areas. Civilian pilots are encouraged to use caution when flying within an MOA, but special clearance is not required. Many MOAs do not reach down to the ground. An MOA can be a block of airspace that starts at a predetermined MSL altitude. Check the tab at the bottom of the sectional chart for MOA dimensions.

Military Training Routes (MTRs) are a 4. Thin gray lines on a sectional chart indicate preset military routes. The routes are identified by either a VR or IR designation. These routes can be flown under IFR conditions where the IR designation exists or under VFR conditions. These routes are for high speed, low altitude practice runs. Military jets pay no attention to civilian speed limits, so it is not uncommon for these aircraft to do better than 400 knots at treetop level. Some military wings are good about calling the local FSS and announcing the use of a particular route. Some wings are not. The information from the FSS about hot or cold MTRs can be totally unreliable. The best idea is to avoid the area altogether. The rating here was a 4. This was lower than MOAs and Alert Areas because pilots should be able to narrow down the location of this traffic by observing the path the gray lines take. The gray lines are a misconception as well. They look very thin on the chart, but the jets can spread out on either side of the lines for several miles. Another clue: If you see one military jet, look for another one quickly. They usually travel in pairs.

AIRSPACE SIMPLIFICATION

Airspace Simplification sounds like a contradiction in terms. During the 1980s, the FAA studied the current system and proposed rule changes and airspace reclassifications. The driving idea behind the changes is good. Taking a look at airspace, pilots see many situations where airspace types and rules overlap into a confusing mess. The simplification idea would consolidate airspace types. The basic rules would be the same but combined. The plan would assign a single letter to each type instead of a name. The proposal looks like this (FIG. 6-16):

Former name	*Airspace Class Letter*
Positive Control Area (PCA)	Class A
Terminal Control Area (TCA)	Class B

Airport Radar Service Area (ARSA)	Class C
Airport Traffic Area (ATA)	Class D
All other Controlled Airspace	Class E
Uncontrolled Airspace	Class G
International Airspace	Class F

Note: The Continental Control Area is abolished

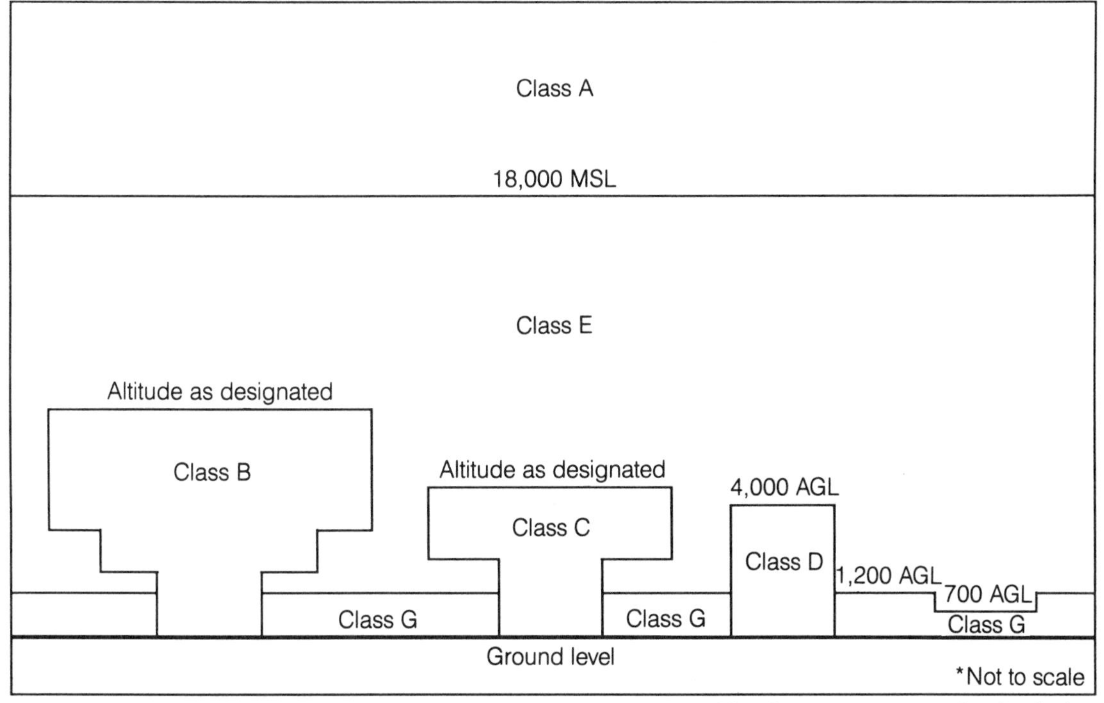

Fig. 6-16. *The FAA's proposed Airspace Simplification system would reduce airspace overlap by designating only seven classes of airspace.*

Class A Airspace is the same as the Positive Control Area, with no changes except the name. Operations and limitations: IFR traffic only; two-way radio communications required. Services provided: IFR aircraft separation and traffic advisories.

Class B Airspace combines the TCA and Airport Traffic Area. Operations and limitations: IFR and VFR flights allowed; transponder with altitude reporting required; two-way radio communications required; private pilot certificate or better required; student pilots only with instructor endorsement; ATC clearance to enter required; VFR flights must have 3 miles visibility and remain clear of clouds. This VFR minimum is a change. The FAA believes that to fly near but not into clouds will be all right due to the fact that all flights will be Mode C monitored and on a clearance. Services provided: Aircraft separation and safety advisories.

Class C Airspace combines the ARSA and Airport Traffic Area overlap. Operations and limitations: IFR, VFR, and Special VFR flights allowed; transponder with altitude reporting required; two-way communications required; standard VFR minimums (distance from clouds 2,000 feet horizontal, 1,000 feet above, 500 feet below) and three miles visibility. Services provided: Aircraft separation; conflict resolution between IFR and VFR traffic; safety advisories; traffic advisories.

Class D Airspace expands Airport Traffic Areas' horizontal boundary to five nautical miles rather than five statute miles (5 nautical miles = 5.75 statute miles). Airport Traffic Areas would also have raised vertical boundaries to 4,000 feet AGL. This would equal the height of Class C Airspace (formerly ARSA). Operations and limitations: IFR, VFR, and Special VFR flights allowed; two-way radio communications required; basic VFR weather minimums. There is no Mode C transponder requirement. Services provided: Aircraft separation, safety advisories, and traffic advisories when workload permits.

Class E Airspace. All airspace in this classification was formerly designated as controlled airspace (all airspace above the blue blanket). Operations and limitations: IFR and VFR flights allowed; basic VFR weather minimums; no required radio communications; no requirement for Mode C Transponders. Services provided: Aircraft separation and traffic advisories when workload permits.

Class G Airspace. All airspace in the classification was formerly designated uncontrolled airspace (all airspace below the blue blanket). Operations and limitations: IFR and VFR flights allowed; VFR weather minimums during daylight—one mile visibility and clear of clouds, at night—three miles visibility and 2,000 horizontal, 1,000 above, and 500 feet below clouds except within one half mile of an airport, where it remains one mile and clear of clouds. Services provided: Limited safety and traffic advisories.

Notice that the proposal eliminates Control Zones but that Special VFR clearances, which are a function of Control Zones, remain in Class C and D Airspace. Also, the Continental Control Zone is gone. This is great because nobody ever figured out what it was really for anyway.

THE FUTURE

The next big improvement in collision avoidance is Mode S. Mode S is the Transponder Collision Avoidance System (TCAS). TCAS is already in operation experimentally on some airliners. Under the current system using Mode C, information is given to a person on the ground. If that person sees a conflict of air traffic, the controller will issue an advisory. Then the pilot tries to solve the problem. The advantage of TCAS is that the middle-man is cut out of the loop. The pilot is the person who is ultimately in danger of a collision, not the controller. Why should information vital to the pilot leave his hands only to be sent back by someone who is not actually responsible, and only if that person has time to send a message? Provide the information to the cockpit first, and prevent delays and miscommunications.

With the Mode C system, an interrogator on the ground sweeps the skies and asks a transponder in the air for a code and an altitude. The transponder replies. With Mode S, an interrogator onboard an airplane sweeps the skies asking for a reply. If a transponder onboard another airplane receives the interrogation, it will reply. Air to Air. The original transponder alerts the pilot of traffic without delay.

Technology moves so quickly that greater levels of Mode S service are developed before the previous level is implemented. The debate now is whether to move ahead installing current hardware or to wait until even more sophisticated hardware is developed.

Currently, there are three levels in various stages of completion, from experimental to already for sale. Level one is a basic system. A Mode S interrogator asks blindly if any other transponders are near. If the interrogator receives a reply, a cockpit alert is sounded. The pilot now knows there is traffic in the area and begins to look in an attempt to spot the target. The pilot does not know which way to look, just that there is something to look for. Many military aircraft already have this level of TCAS on board. This makes the "transponder-on" rule even more important. The rule requires pilots who have a transponder to turn it on while in flight. The regulations still do not require all aircraft to have transponders, but if one is available it must be used. A transponder in operation will trigger a reply to these military aircraft. The pilots may not know exactly where the traffic is located, but heads are up. Without the transponder on, no attention is drawn outside.

The second level of Mode S interrogates, and can receive a reply, but goes further. This level can isolate the direction from which the reply was generated. The alert then given to the pilot comes with a general direction in which to direct the eye. When an air traffic controller gives a traffic advisory, the pilot has an advantage because he can scan in the direction he knows the traffic exists. Zeroing in on the target with a known direction enhances the possibility of spotting the traffic. The second level of Mode S does this automatically. The pilot starts looking for traffic earlier because the message is delivered sooner.

The third level of TCAS technology does all the jobs of the previous levels but goes beyond. Level three advises the pilot as to what the best course will be during evasive maneuvers. The system will point out the traffic, and if a collision is imminent, the system will evaluate the situation and recommend a way out. Think of all the accidents that would have been prevented by a system like that.

Of course, the cost is prohibitive for use in small airplanes at this time, but I can remember when pocket calculators cost over 150 dollars. Eventually it will happen. It may even be mandated, as Mode C transponders are today. There will be Mode-S-only airspace. That will cause the FAA to rewrite the airspace regulations once again. As long as more than one aircraft invades the skies, pilots must remain vigilant and willing to adapt to the changes.

7
Risk Management

THE COST OF TRAVEL IS RISK. ANY TIME A PERSON BOARDS A TRAIN, drives a car, or flies an airplane, there is some chance that the trip will not turn out as planned. Many aircraft accidents occur because mistakes in judgment were made. When the National Transportation Safety Board investigates an accident, their mission is to determine a "probable cause" for the accident. When the results of individual accidents are compiled, there is one category that stands alone as being the greatest pilot killer. It is not thunderstorms or engine failure; it is *pilot error*. The term *pilot error* is very vague. It can mean so many things and contain hidden factors.

Pilot error is the result of a pilot taking on more risk than he can handle. Each pilot has a different tolerance. An individual's ability to offset the risk is very complex. Balanced against risk is judgment. Judgment itself is a variable that can change from day to day. The chances of acquiring and maintaining judgment, however, do depend on a person's level of experience, knowledge, and skill. A pilot with many years of experience and thousands of hours of flight time may have absolutely no problem landing an airplane with a 10-knot cross wind, but the same wind would be dangerous to a low-time private pilot who has not practiced cross wind technique for over a year. The risk is the same to each pilot, but the more experienced and proficient pilot has more weight to offset the burden of risk. The result is a safer situation for the pilot because his experience cancels out the amount of risk present. The more experienced pilot sees the wind and its direction, then determines that he is equal to the challenge. Risk is evaluated and determined to be within personal limits. Safe risk evaluation is part of safe airmanship (FIG. 7-1).

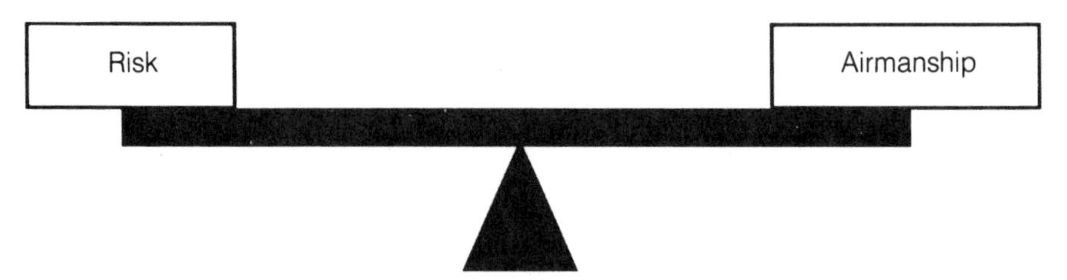

Fig. 7-1. *Airmanship can offset risk. The pilot's job is to evaluate the "weight" of the risk versus the "weight" of airmanship.*

SOURCES OF RISK

Balancing risk is a three-step process. The pilot must 1) identify a risk, 2) measure it against his and the airplane's abilities, and 3) take action with the risk in mind. To complete the first step, a pilot must know something of the sources of risk. Where does risk come from?

There are many sources of risk. To a pilot the categories can be narrowed down to: the weather, the airplane, the pilot.

To evaluate the risk presented to a flight by the weather, the pilot must know the facts pertaining to the weather at the proposed time of the flight. A decision made by a pilot to cancel a flight due to adverse weather is actually an admission that the risk was too great for the situation. A pilot that makes that call shows a good deal of maturity and airmanship.

The airplane has capabilities and limitations. The pilot of a PA-28-181 Archer flew into a mountain ridge near Garberville, California, in 1985. He had taken off from Shelter Cove Airport, which is near sea level, and attempted to outclimb an elevation change of 2,000 feet in two and a half miles. The pilot must not have been aware of the airplane's climb performance. The risk presented to the pilot by the density altitude, the airplane's loading, and the steep rise of the terrain went undetected. The pilot did not balance risk well because he was unaware of the amount of risk. Better decisions are always made from a position of knowledge. Pilots should look for risk factors.

Each pilot has unique capabilities and limitations. Being human, a pilot's capabilities fluctuate. As an airplane's performance changes with its environment, so does the performance of a human change with environment. Stress, fatigue, illness, job pressures, and family pressures all lead to increased risk of pilot error. A pilot's defenses against making mistakes are experience, knowledge, and skill: the very foundations of airmanship. Negative human factors can add up to deteriorate a pilot's ability to offset risk, and mistakes will be more frequent. Good decision making is related to the ability of a pilot to evaluate the level of risk in a situation and act accordingly.

Stress is a silent killer, and it is cumulative. Problems can combine to raise an individual's stress level to a point where risk of accident is greatly increased. Ice can cover an airplane's control surfaces and render a pilot helpless. The ice would be an outside threat. But stress sneaks in behind the lines like an unseen spy. Stress is an inside threat that can render the pilot helpless to make clear decisions.

Life events tend to accumulate and increase the level of stress present in a person. If a person's ability to ingest information is compared with an empty jar's ability to take in water, we can see a parallel. When the jar is empty, it is able to bring in the greatest amount of water. But if the jar is filled halfway up, the space remaining for new water is reduced. If a person comes to the airport with a clear head, empty of confusion and stress, he will function better as a pilot. But if the pilot brings a head full of concerns and problems, there will be less room left to analyze risk and make good decisions. Very few people have their jars empty of stress.

All stress is not due to bad things occurring. Buying a house, becoming a parent, and getting a job promotion are all positive situations that can cause a great deal of stress. Each item adds water to the jar.

Most of us associate stress with negative things that happen. Everyday frustrations add water to the jar. A stack of unpaid bills, a traffic violation, an argument at work all take their toll. Marital problems, children in trouble with the law, bankruptcy, or death of a spouse will really mount up the stress levels, leaving very litle room for much of anything else.

A pilot starts out with all of his capabilities available for use. Stress soaks up some of these capabilities. The accumulation of stress will corrode the pilot's mental abilities, leaving only small amounts available to use in decision making. Decisions made under stress generally yield poor results because they do not balance risk well.

The frequency of accidents is high among people who have experienced a significant number of stressful events in their lives. When looking for risk factors, pilots must look within themselves. Many accident reports determine the probable cause to be pilot error. But what causes the pilot to make the error? It could be a lack of knowledge or experience. It could be that the pilot was not familiar with his airplane. It could be more insidious. The pilot can be his own worst enemy.

STRESS MANAGEMENT

Pilots must train themselves to be risk-factor detectives. The greater knowledge a pilot has of the risk inherent in a situation, the easier it will be to measure and manage. Measuring risk is healthy. It forces the pilot to see where his own limitations are hidden. Evaluating risk is good airmanship. Taking action based on honest risk assessment is good decision making.

8
Weather Decisions for VFR Pilots

THE FAA AND NATIONAL WEATHER SERVICE CAN PROVIDE ACCURATE and current weather information; the aircraft can be completely airworthy; but the decision to fly or not to fly rests solely with the pilot. Many critical decisions may follow, but the first decision to leave the ground starts the chain. Remember, takeoffs are optional.

FINDINGS OF THE NTSB VFR WEATHER-RELATED ACCIDENTS STUDY

Still, pilots make wrong decisions. Even in the information age when weather information is literally at our fingertips, improper judgments are made. Risk is not balanced. The National Transportation Safety Board conducted a special study that involved VFR weather-related accidents. From the files of the NTSB accident reports, 2,026 fatal, weather-related accidents involving general aviation aircraft were considered. These accidents all took place within a 9-year period. The board examined the circumstances surrounding each accident in order to identify any patterns. In the 2,026 accidents, a total of 4,714 people had been killed. These weather-related accidents represented 36.6 percent of all fatal general aviation accidents during the same time period. The accidents took place at approximately the same rate during the time period of the study, even though improvements were made to aircraft, instrumentation, training, training facilities, air traffic control, weather facilities, weather services, and navigational aids.

Comparing the accidents did show some striking similarities. Sixty percent of the fatal accidents took place while the pilots were on pleasure flights. Twenty percent of the accidents occurred during non-commercial business flights. The other 20 percent was spread out over 35 other classifications of flight. Pilots who fly for fun, use an airplane for vacation travel, or use an airplane to travel on business accounted for over 80% of all fatal, weather-related accidents. Dual Flight Instruction constituted only 1.48 percent.

At the conclusion of the study, the NTSB summarized the statistics. Based on the evidence, a pilot profile emerged. The following characteristics describe a pilot who is most likely to have been involved in a general aviation, weather-related, fatal accident:

1. The pilot on the day of the accident received an adequate preflight weather briefing. The most common way to get the briefing was over the telephone. The information that the pilot was given was "substantially correct" 73.68 percent of the time. The actual weather conditions were "considerably worse" than forecast only 5.4 percent of the time.
2. The pilot was making a pleasure flight.
3. The pilot had a private pilot certificate, but did not have an instrument rating.
4. The pilot had accumulated between 100 and 299 hours of flight time.
5. The pilot had flown less than 50 hours within the 90 days preceding the accident.
6. The pilot crashed after flying into IFR conditions during daylight hours.
7. The pilot had received between 1 and 19 hours of simulated instrument time. In other words, the pilot had previously flown under the hood with a flight instructor in the airplane.
8. The pilot had no actual IFR flight time.
9. The pilot did not file a flight plan.
10. The pilot was accompanied by at least one passenger.
11. December had the highest accident rate, followed by November, September, August, and January. February had the fewest accidents.

The summary points to many areas where the pilot came to a point of decision and took a fatal path. The statistics show that pilots do call to get weather information and that the information is essentially correct. Why then do fatal accidents occur? If the weather is going to be marginal and the pilot knows this fact, why is flight attempted? Why do pilots press on in the face of deteriorating weather? Because the wrong decision is made. The decision is made without the most current information or the decision is tainted by the person's stress, motivation to fly, or personality.

The summary determined that crashes most often took place during the daylight hours. This means that the pilot saw a cloud and flew into it anyway. At night, flying into clouds is easier to do because at times they cannot be seen. During the daytime, clouds are visible, so why would pilots dive into them? The summary also shows that these pilots had received some instrument training. This fact could have led the pilots to believe that they would have no problem in the clouds. A very poor decision. Not only did they decide to fly into the clouds rather than turn around, they overestimated their own ability. They were unable to offset risk with skill. Flying simulated instruments using an IFR hood is not the same as flying in the clouds. When under the hood, the subconscious mind knows that there is actually clear air outside the plane. If anything should go wrong, the hood can be taken off. The pilot knows this and anticipation and panic are not present. But in the clouds, the subconscious mind goes to work. The mind knows that there is no escape. If anything goes wrong now, the results are fatal. Panic sets in and spatial disorientation will soon follow.

Only 8 percent of the accidents involved a student pilot; private pilots were much more likely to be involved in an accident. This seems to be a paradox. Why are pilots who are just learning more safe than pilots who should know better? Again it points to decision making. Student pilots do not make their own decisions; they are guided by another, more experienced pilot. When a student pilot prepares to fly a solo cross-country, I always tell him that he must call to get the weather and make his own decision about making the trip. That is what I tell him, but as soon as he is out of sight, I call the FSS myself to see what is going on. I make a decision for the student and see if the student's decision matches my own. This trains him to depend on his decisions, but as a flight instructor I hold veto power.

Private pilots do not have help with their decisions. They can now be pilot in command and have all the responsibility that comes with it. The majority of the accidents took place when the pilot had between 100 and 299 flight hours. This suggests that there is a "baptism by fire" period every pilot goes through. During this time, although their ability to make safe decisions has not yet fully developed, legally they can put themselves into positions where good decisions are required. The pilot examiner with whom I took my private pilot check ride informed me that I had passed by saying, "You now have your license to learn." I had no idea what he was talking about; I thought now that I was a pilot all the learning was behind me. To survive the 100- to 299-hour range, pilots must grow up fast. Will Rogers, the famous humorist, left home when he was 17 because he could not get along with his father. He returned when he was 21. He said after his return, "It was amazing how much my father had learned when I was gone." There was a time when I thought I knew it all; thankfully, I survived a lot of bad decisions until I found out otherwise.

POINTS OF DECISION

Pilots get caught up in events. One decision leads to another, and if a pilot isn't careful he can paint himself into a corner. Identifying the "points of decision" is important. Pilots must be alert to see where decisions must be made. Let's follow a typical VFR pleasure flight and see where the forks in the road exist.

Bob is a private pilot. He and two friends went together and bought a Cherokee 180 last year. The three partners are perfectionists when it comes to maintenance on the airplane. If there is anything wrong, they get it fixed right away. The plane is old but in great condition.

Bob and his wife waited for weeks after the purchase of the plane to find some time when both would be off work. They wanted a quick getaway vacation in the mountains with their two children. They arranged to get a Monday and Tuesday off, figuring a flight to the mountains early Saturday morning would give them just the break they needed. Bob scheduled the airplane and made reservations at their favorite mountain inn for Saturday night through Tuesday morning.

The flight Bob planned out on Friday night would depart his home airport of Franklin County, Georgia, and go to the Andrews-Murphy airport in the North Carolina Smoky Mountains (FIG. 8-1). Bob had taken this same flight on a sparkling day back in October. The view of the fall colors in the mountains had been breath-taking. Now it was May, and Bob hoped to repeat that great experience.

Point of Decision: Bob had worked all week and had no time to keep track of weather systems that might affect the flight. He had been so busy that the weather for the flight was a complete unknown. Toward the end of the week, he once thought that he needed to see a weather outlook for the weekend, but he quickly got caught up in another of the many details that made up his job. Bob was at a crossroads: Get an outlook forecast tonight or wait until tomorrow when there would be more time.

At ten o'clock Bob called the toll-free telephone number of the Anderson Flight Service Station. When the briefer answered the phone Bob said, "Yes sir, this is Piper Cherokee N5957R. I would like an Outlook briefing for a VFR flight tomorrow from Franklin up to Murphy."

"What will be your time off?" the briefer asked.

"I would say around 11 in the morning." Bob and his wife planned to get up a little later than usual. This weekend was for relaxation.

The briefer went to work and returned with the forecast. "There is a low pressure area dominating the weather in Tennesee and Kentucky. Nashville has had ceilings below 1,000 feet for the past six hours. A weak cold front extends from east of the Nashville area down toward Birmingham. That low pressure center is expected to move the whole pattern east. Knoxville is forecasting broken clouds at 3,000 feet for tomorrow morning and then lower clouds all afternoon. Here at Anderson we expect good VFR conditions through about noon tomorrow, but then the weather will reach us, and we are forecasting scattered to broken clouds between 2,000 and 3,000 feet after 2 o'clock in the afternoon. And there is always a chance of a thunderstorm this time of year."

Bob tried to copy down as much of the information as he could. "Thanks. I'll call you in the morning with a flight plan," he said and hung up the phone.

Point of Decision: The forecast indicated that tomorrow afternoon the weather, although predicted to be VFR, would get worse by mid-afternoon. A planned departure at 11 o'clock would place Bob in changing weather conditions as he reached the mountains. Bob was at a crossroads: Plan an earlier flight or keep the plans the same.

Bob went in to tell his wife that they should get an early start in the morning because the weather would not be as good in the afternoon. Bob could only have made this decision based on his knowledge of weather conditions. Bob knew the weather

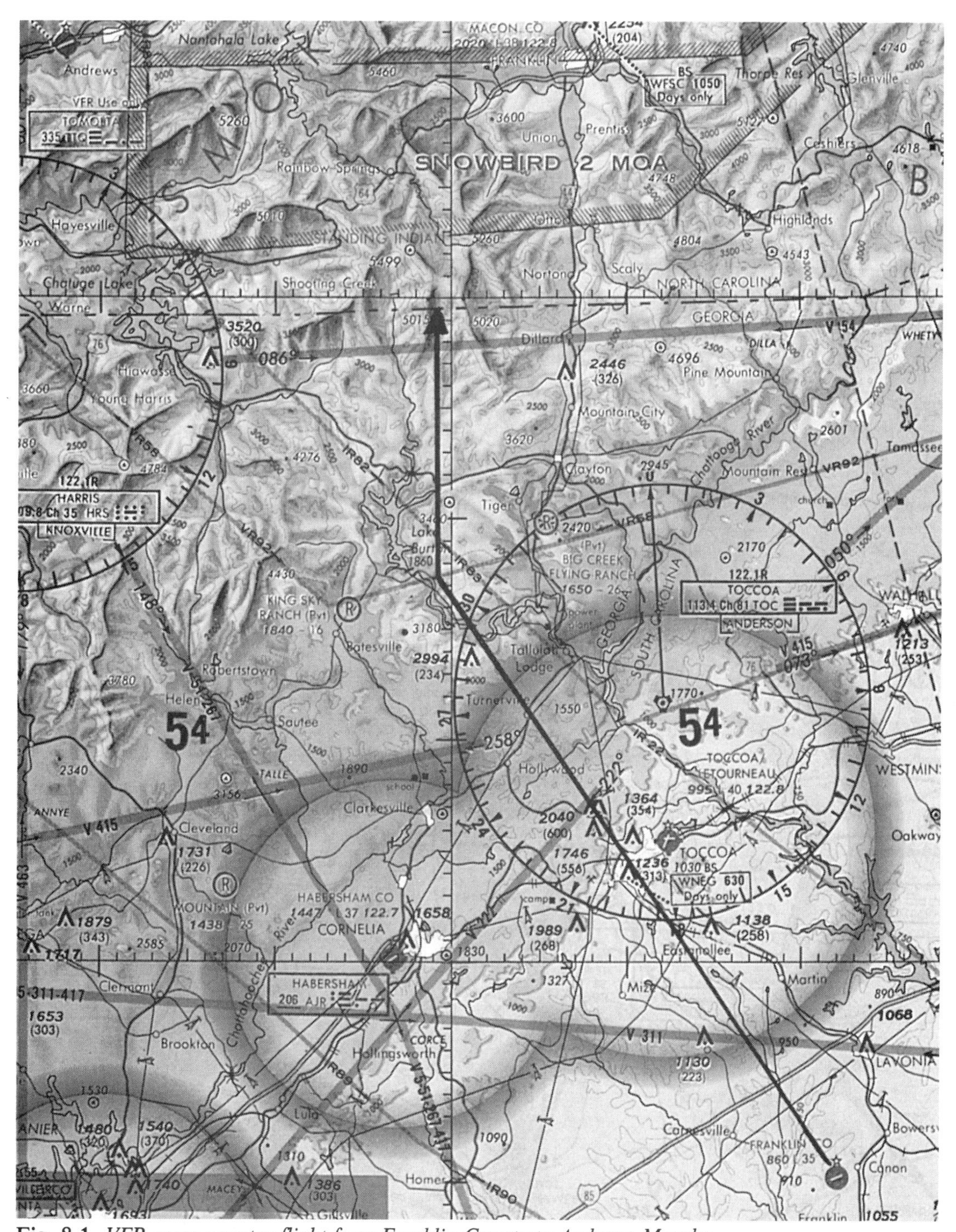

Fig. 8-1. *VFR cross-country flight from Franklin County to Andrews-Murphy.*

conditions because of an earlier decision he made to call and receive an Outlook briefing. One good decision led to another. Bob was forming a good decision chain even the day before the flight.

The next morning the kids were up early and everyone was packing for the trip. Each kid had a large duffle bag full of tape players, books, ball gloves, and baseball cards. Bob planned to take some proposals from work to read over during the weekend, so he had a briefcase full of books. The family's clothes were in three suitcases, and of course Bob and his wife were taking their golf clubs. All these items were being loaded in the car when the phone rang. One of the kids answered and called, "It's for you, Dad."

Bob answered the phone and talked for about five minutes with a look that could kill. "What is it, Bob?" his wife asked when he hung up.

"One of our clients is coming to town earlier than expected next week. On Tuesday instead of Thursday."

"Bob, we aren't going to have to cancel the trip, are we?"

"No, but I have to swing by the office on the way to the airport and prepare a list for the meeting. It won't take very long." Bob finished packing the car and they were off, but not to the airport.

It was 10:30 before Bob and the family left the office for the airport. Bob was worried about the meeting he would miss on Tuesday. He had worked on the project for over a month and nobody in the office knew it quite like he did. They arrived at the airport and pulled the plane from the hangar. The guy who would have to do his part of the presentation was really just a numbers man—no creativity as well. The presentation would just not be the same.

Point of Decision: Due to factors beyond Bob's control, he had arrived at the airport with the world of work on his mind. He would begin a preflight inspection in a moment, but he would be thinking about out-of-town clients, charts, graphs, and incompetent business associates. Bob was at a crossroads: Continue the preflight while preoccupied with something else or take a deep breath, clear his mind, and think only about flying.

"Bob, you can't help what happened. Now don't let it ruin our weekend. We've waited so long for this," his wife said.

"You're right. Have the kids put their stuff in the plane, and I'll call for the weather." Bob thought flying again and headed for the telephone.

"This is Cherokee 5957R at Franklin County. I would like a Standard briefing for a VFR flight from here to Andrews-Murphy departing within the next half hour." Bob prepared his pencil and paper to copy what the briefer would say.

"You want to go VFR?" the briefer asked.

"Yes, sir, that is correct." Bob had not had any time to work on an instrument rating. He and his two partners in the airplane had intended to start studying together for the written test as soon as things eased up at work.

"There is an area of marginal VFR weather just west of the mountains. Knoxville this hour reports a measured ceiling of 1,500 overcast with four miles visibility. Their temperature is 83 and dewpoint 79. East of the mountains things are a little better. Asheville's got 2,000 broken with five miles, and here at Anderson we have 2,500 scattered with seven. Winds aloft for the area are generally coming from the northwest. 290 degrees at 20 knots at 6,000 feet and 310 at 28 knots at 9,000. The forecast calls for lowering ceilings throughout the afternoon, and the outlook for this evening after 7 o'clock is IFR due to ceilings."

Point of Decision: Bob was getting a later start than planned. The weather he learned about last night was moving in. The longer he waits, the worse it will be. Bob was at a crossroads: He must choose between hurrying to get started and canceling the trip altogether.

Bob gathered together his charts and weather notes and headed for the airplane. There was no time for detailed trip planning, and in his haste he never considered filing a flight plan. When he arrived at the airplane, his wife and kids had packed the baggage compartment.

"Is everything all right, Bob?" asked his wife.

"Everything is great. Let's go have some fun."

Point of Decision: All the luggage and the golf clubs were in the aft baggage compartment. Bob had no idea how much all that stuff weighed and no way of finding out. Doing a weight-and-balance calculation on the airplane would use up valuable time, and the exact weights were not known anyway. Bob was at a crossroads: Determine the center of gravity of the airplane or leave things as they were and take off and land a little faster than usual to make up the difference.

"Kids, you're going to have to hold those duffle bags on your laps."

"Ah come on, Dad. There's plenty of room in the back for that stuff," the kids complained.

"You two are going to have to learn that when an adult tells you to do something you just have to do it because there must be a good reason!" Bob yelled.

Bob completed the preflight. At 11:27, he started the engine and they were finally off. The hard-surface runway at Franklin County is 3,500 feet long with trees at both ends. Bob glanced at the outside temperature gauge and read 88 degrees. The wind was almost directly across the runway, but Bob determined that runway 25 was slightly favored.

Point of Decision: Bob faced a takeoff from an average length runway with above-average temperatures. The plane was heavy, but Bob was not sure just how heavy. Bob was at a crossroads: Check the aircraft manual to determine how the present conditions will affect the plane's ability to clear the trees or look both ways and go.

"Franklin County Traffic, N5957L is departing runway 25." Bob announced on multicom. The plane's engine roared to life and away they went. Bob held the airplane on the runway until about five knots faster than normal and pulled it off. The climbout was slower than normal, but the trees were cleared with plenty to spare.

The night before, Bob had planned to fly from Franklin County direct to the Toccoa VOR as the first leg of the trip. But the VOR's location is not on a direct route to Murphy.

Point of Decision: Flying the original plan to the VOR was really out of the way. Tracking directly over the VOR would make it easier to determine position, but time was more important. Bob was at a crossroads: Should he fly direct, making up checkpoints as he goes or turn to the VOR?

Bob spotted Interstate Highway 85 and determined that point-to-point navigation using the landmarks would work fine. He decided to take radials off the VOR as he passed by to the southwest to help determine position.

The flight was going great now. The kids were reading some books that they had balanced on their duffle bags. The clouds were slowly changing from scattered to broken, but there was at least a 2,000-foot separation between Bob's cruising altitude and the cloud bases. Bob spotted the city of Toccoa, Georgia, which is directly on course to Murphy.

Soon the terrain started to rise, and over Lake Burton, Bob observed an area of dark clouds ahead. He could look under the clouds and had no problem seeing the horizon on the other side.

Point of Decision: There was possible adverse weather on the course. The underside of the dark clouds still had good visibility. The building, or Cumulus, stage of thunderstorms does not produce rain at the surface. The Cumulus stage only has updrafts that pull the hot, moist air to great altitudes. If this was the birth of a thunderstorm, it could be very turbulent under the building storm. Also, the mature stage of the storm could be reached by the time the airplane got under the clouds. In that case, they would encounter heavy rain, more turbulence, and reduced visibility. Bob was at a crossroads: Fly under the dark clouds and hope for the best or get more information.

Bob decided to call the Anderson Flight Service Station and ask for a weather update. He tuned in the frequency of 123.6.

"Anderson Radio, this is Cherokee 5957L, over."

The radio was silent. Bob tried again. The radio remained silent. Bob checked to be sure the microphone was plugged in properly and that the audio panel switches were set in the correct location. Bob tried a third time to call Anderson. There was no reply.

Point of Decision: Bob was not able to contact Anderson by using the discrete frequency. Bob was at a crossroads: Give up and determine the weather himself or try another way to contact the FSS.

Bob checked the chart and saw that the Toccoa VOR (FIG. 8-2) has a link with the Anderson FSS. This is indicated by the bracket under the VOR box. Inside the bracket the name Anderson is written. The block shows that the FSS receives when called on using frequency 122:1 and will return the call over the Toccoa VOR. Bob tuned in 122.1 on the communications side of the radio and 113.4 on the navigation side of the radio. He threw the number one navigation radio switch on the audio panel to the speaker position and turned up the volume. The morse code identifier for Toccoa was heard.

"Anderson radio, this is Cherokee 5957L, listening over the Toccoa VOR."

"57L, this is Anderson. Go ahead," the radio responded.

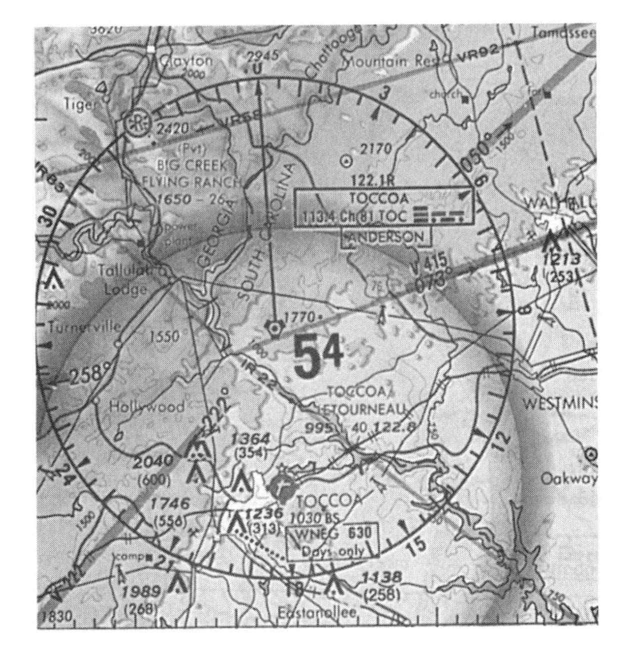

Fig. 8-2. *The Toccoa VOR is monitored by the Anderson FSS. Communication with Anderson is possible by transmitting on 122.1 and receiving on 113.4.*

"Anderson, 57L is on a VFR flight to Murphy and would like to check the radar for the area around the Toccoa VOR and north, over."

The radio fell silent for a moment, then the briefer began, "57L, the Athens, Georgia, radar shows widely scattered precipitation echoes all over the southern Smokey Mountains. There is a moderate return at 25 nautical miles northwest of Toccoa."

Point of Decision: Bob had successfully updated his knowledge of the weather. Precipitation did exist along or near his route of flight. Bob was at a crossroads: Continue on course or divert around the building storm. Bob needed more information if he was going to divert.

"Anderson Radio, 57L, do you have any information about the movement of the echoes at 25 miles northwest of Toccoa?"

"57L, the radar trend indicates movement to the south-southeast at 10 knots. The range-height indicator is out of service at Athens, so no information is available on the precip tops, over."

"57L, roger, we will divert course to the north. Thank you for your help."

Bob turned the airplane so the dark clouds would pass off the left wing. This course would take the flight toward the Snowbird 2 MOA (FIG. 8-3).

Point of Decision: Civilian pilots do not need any special clearance to fly within an MOA. Bob was at a crossroads: Fly on and enter the MOA or find out more about it.

Bob turned his chart and found the position on the top flap (FIG. 8-4) where information about Prohibited Areas, Restricted Areas, and MOAs are listed. Bob read that the Snowbird 2 MOA has a floor of 2,000 feet AGL and a ceiling of 11,000 feet MSL. Bob made a mental note to be extra careful when he got to that area.

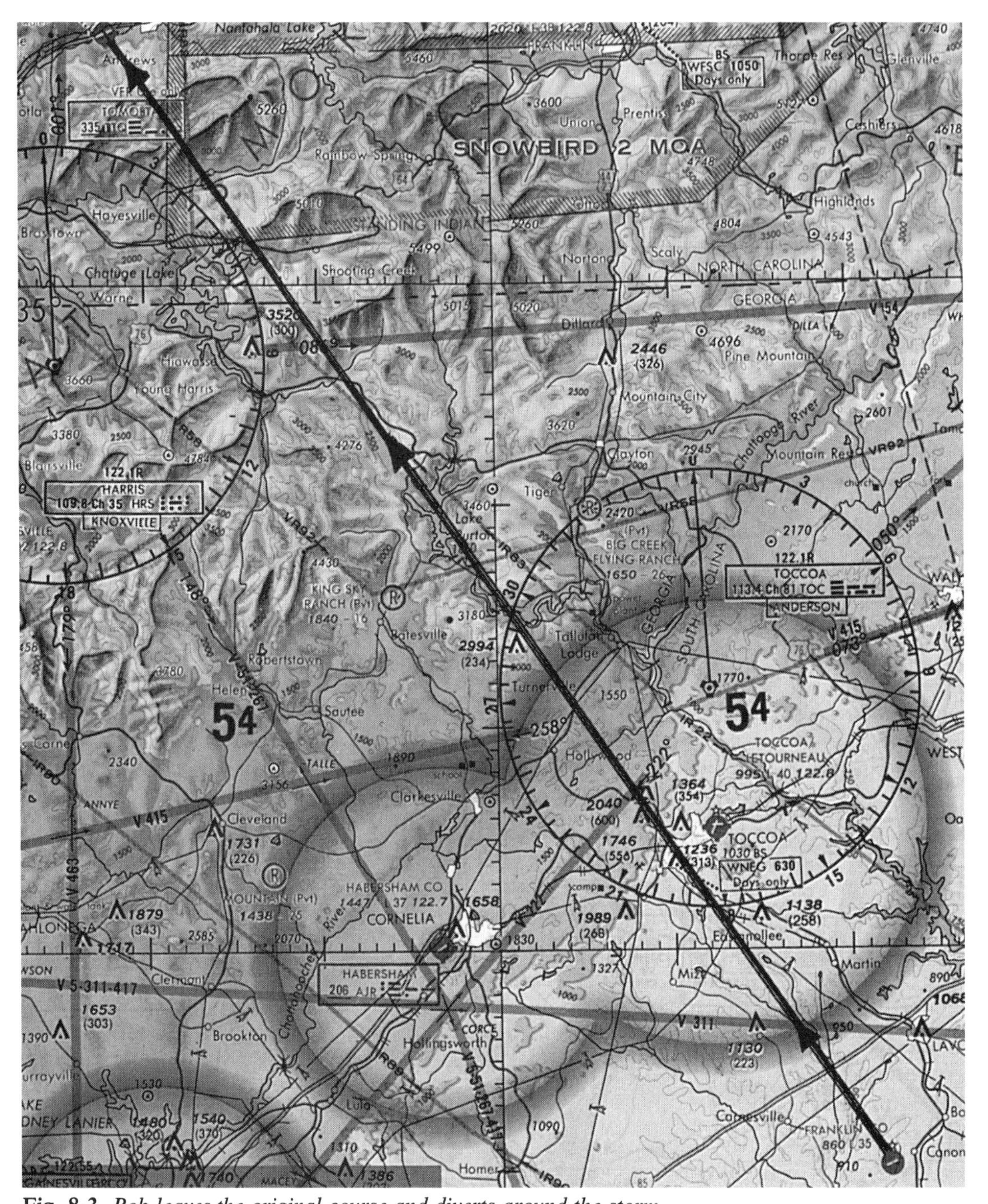

Fig. 8-3. *Bob leaves the original course and diverts around the storm.*

MOODY 1	8000	MON-FRI 0700-2300 OCC SAT-SUN BY NOTAM	ZJX CNTR
PINE HILL EAST, WEST	10,000	MON-FRI 0700-2300 SAT 0800-1500	ZTL CNTR
QUICK THRUST E	100 AGL TO BUT NOT INCL 500 AGL	INTERMITTENT SR TO SS	ZJX CNTR
QUICK THRUST G	10,000 TO 14,000	UP TO 14 DAYS ANNUALLY	ZJX CNTR
QUICK THRUST I	100 AGL TO 14,000	BY NOTAM	ZJX CNTR
QUICK THRUST L	12,000 TO 14,000		ZJX CNTR
SNOWBIRD 1	12,000 TO 17,500	INTERMITTENT 0800-1800	ZTL CNTR
SNOWBIRD 2	2000 AGL TO 11,000	INTERMITTENT 0800-1800	ZTL CNTR
TIGER B	10,000 TO 17,500	INTERMITTENT MON-FRI 0800-2200	ZJX CNTR

*Altitudes indicates floor of MOA. All MOA's extend to but do not include FL 180 unless otherwise indicated in tabulation or on chart.

Fig. 8-4. *The Snowbird 2 MOA information line. This information is found on the top flap of the Atlanta Sectional chart.*

Point of Decision: It was Saturday and some MOAs are used less on weekends. Bob was a crossroads: Fly into the MOA with eyes wide open or call someone to ask if the MOA is "hot."

Bob determined that he was now closer to the Harris VOR than to the Toccoa VOR. He tuned in 122.1 on the communications side of the radio and 109.8 on the navigation side.

"Knoxville Radio, this is N5957L, listening on the Harris VOR, over."

"57L, this is Knoxville, go ahead."

"57L, roger, is the Snowbird 2 MOA 'hot' this afternoon?"

"Negative, 57L. No military operations have been reported over the Smokies today. I do have a pilot report from a Cessna flying in Snowbird. He reports moderate turbulence below 10,000."

"Roger, Knoxville. What are the winds aloft for the area at 6 and 9 thousand?"

"At 6,000, winds forecast to be 300 at 25, and 9,000 has 310 at 35."

"57L, copy the weather. Thank you very much."

Bob saw that the area of dark clouds was now aft of the left wing. There were mountain tops greater than 5,000 feet high ahead. Bob had an altitude of 6,000 feet. The clouds now appeared to be only 1,000 feet above the airplane.

Point of Decision: The wind reported for the area was 25 knots, but the wind would increase its velocity as it spilled over the mountain tops (FIG. 8-5). A venturi effect often occurs when air is forced up and over a ridge. The wind at the top of the ridge can be several times stronger than that which is reported. On the leeward side of the mountain, strong downdrafts can be present. It was possible that the pilot of the Cessna who reported moderate turbulence was in just such a situation. In order to avoid the turbulence, a pilot must fly several hundred feet above the mountain. The clouds, however, would prevent a climb much higher than Bob is currently holding. Bob was at a crossroads: Fly a direct course now to Murphy, which would cross two mountain ridges, each greater than 5,000 feet high, or divert once again around the mountains.

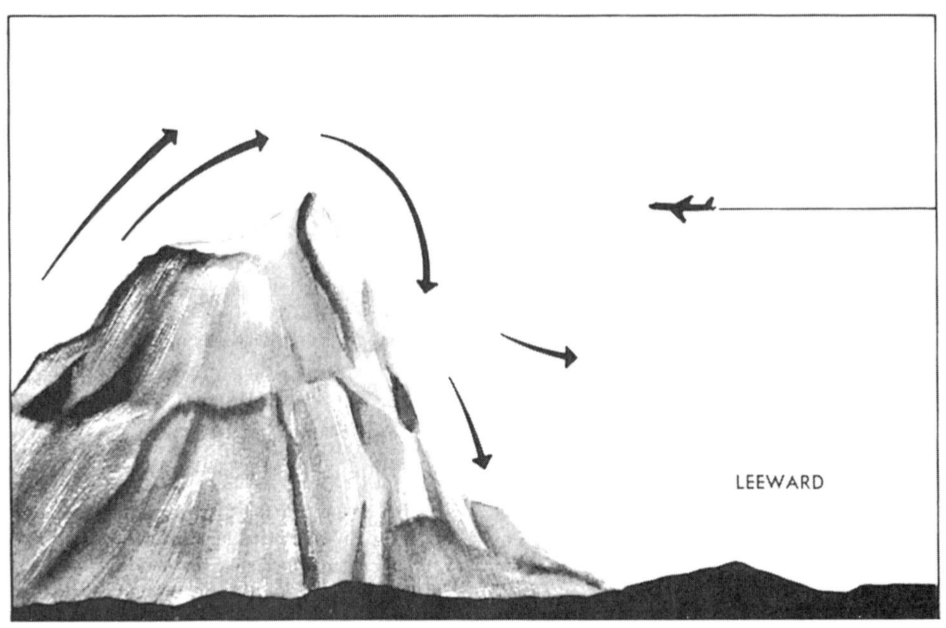

Fig. 8-5. *Strong downdrafts can be present on the leeward side of a mountain. The airplane may not be able to maintain altitude when attempting to cross over the mountain.*

Bob turned west and formulated a plan. He would follow highway 64 to the town of Murphy and then turn and fly up the valley to the Andrews-Murphy airport (FIG. 8-6). This would keep him off the mountain ridges and away from the clouds.

The ride became more turbulent as they neared the edge of the mountains. Bob spotted Chatuge Lake and felt good about his decision not to fly directly over the mountains. He turned the OBS of his VOR and centered the needle with a FROM indication. The radio was still tuned to the Harris VOR. The airplane was on the 360-degree radial now, almost over the city of Murphy.

The clouds had been steadily lowering throughout the flight. Also, Bob had flown over higher terrain. The clouds and terrain had been squeezing him into a smaller and smaller range of available altitudes. Bob turned north again over the town of Murphy (FIG. 8-7) and looked up the valley that led to the airport. The cloud bases were ragged. The mountains on either side shielded out the sunlight, so the area was noticeably darker. The path to the airport was a tube: clouds on top, mountains on each side, the valley floor at the bottom. Bob spotted the four-lane highway and railroad tracks that leave Murphy and go up the valley to the airport. In fact, the chart shows the highway going right past the airport. Bob thought that all he had to do was follow that highway and he would be on his vacation at last.

With only about eight miles to go, Bob saw a whisp of cloud come past at about the same altitude as the airplane. Bob noticed that clouds had completely capped the valley, and he started to descend. The clouds up ahead were very dark now; it might

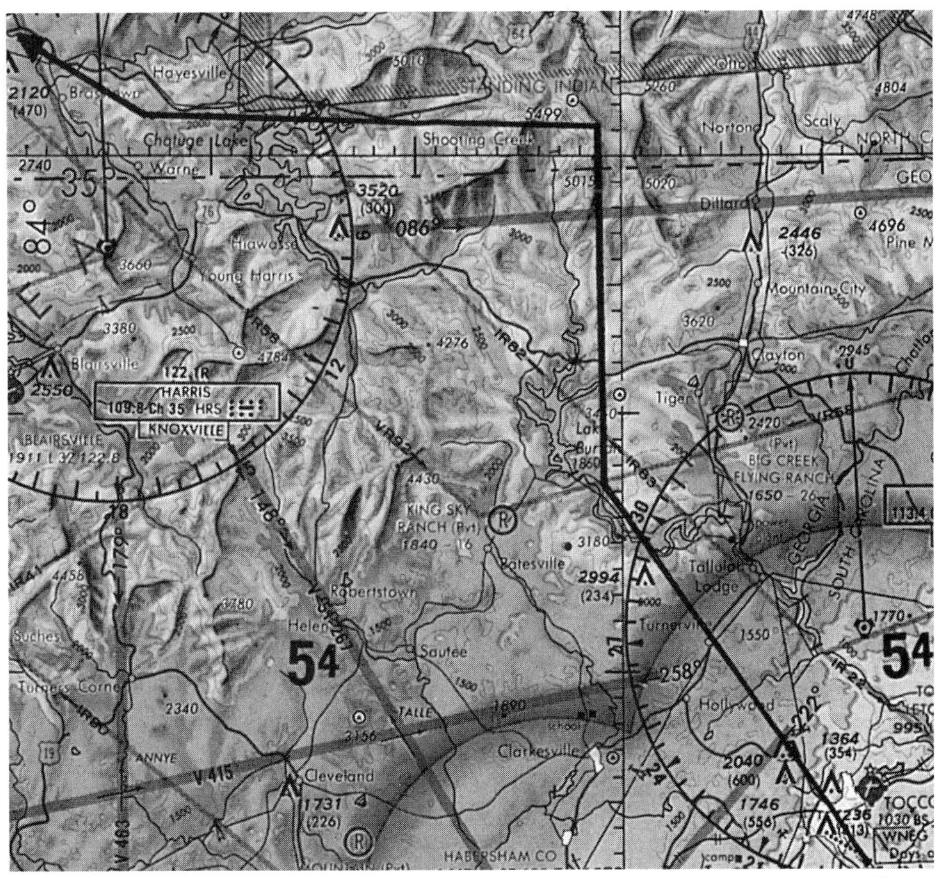

Fig. 8-6. *Bob turns west to fly parallel with the mountain ridge and on to the town of Murphy.*

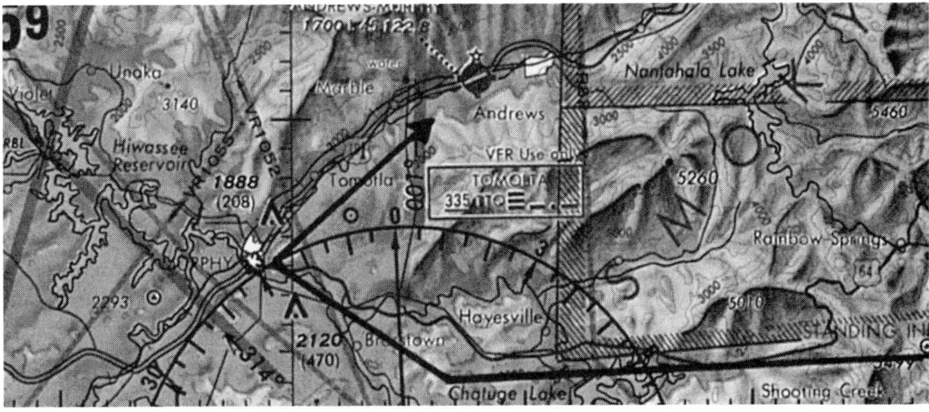

Fig. 8-7. *Bob turns and flies up the valley. Mountain ridges are on both sides and low clouds are above.*

even be raining. A jolt of air turbulence hit the plane, and Bob gripped the wheel tightly. The highway seemed to lead into an area where the clouds were even lower.

Point of Decision: The clouds were coming down. The ground was coming up. The visibility was getting worse. The destination that had been yearned for could only be about five miles away. Bob was at a crossroads: Descend still further or turn around.

Bob pulled back the power and descended for a better look. It was dark and it was bumpy, but the airport was close. Bob remembered that he had a rental car waiting at the airport. He remembered he had made dinner reservations at his wife's favorite restaurant. A voice from the back seat interrupted, "I'm tired of this. When are we going to be there?"

"We're almost there, kids," Bob's wife said and then continued, "All that zigzagging you did back there has made us late. I told you to guarantee the room for late arrival."

Another cloud passed by the window, and then for only a moment they were in the cloud. Then back out. Bob remembered that the temperature/dewpoint spread at Knoxville had only been four degrees. Under the clouds, the temperature here was now 75 degrees. The temperature/dewpoint spread couldn't be more than a few degrees. Bob saw some skud clouds below the airplane. If the spread were close, there could be more low clouds and even ground fog ahead.

Big Point of Decision: The airplane was now on the edge between VFR and IFR. The airport must be just ahead. The highway that leads to the airport was still visible below. There was certainly pressure to land from the back seat. If the airplane were turned around now, it would ruin all the plans for this evening. Bob was feeling the pressure from all sides. Bob was at a crossroads: Should he press on even if that would mean descending even lower or turn around and fly out of this tube?

Bob had made pretty good decisions to this point. The original plan had been altered at almost every step, but he had made necessary adjustments. Even the alterations had been altered. Bob had done a good job of keeping up with changing situations and changing plans accordingly. But now he faced the biggest challenge. The family members had no idea that Bob was contemplating a 180-degree turn. If he did turn around, it would come as a shock to them. They had looked forward to this trip and they would be extremely disappointed. Bob could also lose some money if he turned around now. He already had a deposit on the rental car. If he went to another airport now, where would they stay overnight? Bob made his choice.

Bob banked the airplane left. "Where are you going?" his wife gasped.

"We're on our way to a safe vacation."

The nearest airport was Blairsville. Bob flew to that airport (FIG. 8-8). He rented another car and still made it to dinner in Murphy.

The path taken at each point of decision develops a chain. Every decision affects the next decision. Each new path taken sets up different circumstances that present new challenges and therefore the need for even more decisions. Flying presents an ever-changing set of events that must each be analyzed and acted on. When making

Fig. 8-8. *Bob diverts to a safe landing at Blairsville.*

decisions, pilots should attempt to widen their options rather than limit them. In the example, Bob did not fly along blind to events that surrounded him; he took action. While in flight, he attempted to know as much as he could in order to make good judgments. Not all his decisions were as good as he might have liked, but he was functioning under a certain set of circumstances that influenced what he did. Stress producers were placed on him from his job, his family, his schedule, and the weather (at least the engine ran perfectly!). He managed all these factors and still made a safe decision, although it wasn't the most popular decision at the time.

There is no limit to the number and types of situations in which a pilot may find himself. Adverse factors can build up and lull a good pilot into making bad judgment calls. Watch for the Points of Decision. Ignore all but the flying-related factors. Screen out all outside pressure and stress and take the path that will give the greatest options and the safest course of action.

9
Weather Decisions for IFR Pilots

MAKING THE JUMP FROM VFR TO IFR FLYING IS THE BIGGEST SINGLE accomplishment in flying. It is generally understood that the check ride for the instrument rating is the toughest other than the ATP. But forget about the check ride; the real world of IFR flying can be more frightening. It is unfortunate, but many student pilots are taught only to pass the check ride. The check ride becomes the goal. The primary motivation should instead be to acquire the greatest skills, knowledge, and safety. By doing this, the check ride is easy and becomes secondary. But facts are facts. Humans want the path of least resistance, so many instructors teach students just to pass the check ride. For the private pilot check ride, you can get away with it, but the instrument rating is another story.

When a student pilot first flies into a radar environment, he is advised to tell the controller that he is a student pilot. The controller is then supposed to give a little consideration to the fledgling pilot. But in the world of IFR, there is no provision for the "student" instrument pilot. The first time a pilot flies IFR and goes into the clouds, that pilot is expected to perform with the same precision as anyone else in the system. Twenty-year airline veterans and IFR rookies must have the same proficiency.

There is no way that an IFR flight instructor can present to the student all the possible contingencies that could arise in the instrument environment. The IFR pilot must think. If the prospective IFR pilot is taught only a rote set of instrument approaches known to be used on the check ride, then the student is cheated. The pilot with *instrument rating* typed on his certificate is really not ready for the real world until he starts to think like an instrument pilot.

I was in San Francisco several years ago and saw two street performers juggling. Both jugglers were riding unicycles while tossing a bowling pin, a bathroom plunger, a rubber chicken, a hammer, and a flaming torch back and forth between them. All the items were constantly in motion and ever changing. The jugglers had to control every item with equal accuracy. If one juggler could only handle the pin, plunger, hammer, and chicken, he would inevitably be burned by the torch.

Flying an airplane IFR in today's system is like juggling. Instead of household items to catch and throw, the pilot has altitude, heading, timing, radio communications, and many other inputs to monitor and control. Most pilots can handle one thing at a time with excellence. If all the instrument pilot had to do was think about holding altitude, then IFR flying would be as easy as juggling a single light bulb. But that is certainly not all there is to worry about. The IFR pilot is being bombarded constantly with new and changing attacks on the mind. The mind must accept, process, and then act on hundreds of different items. An instrument pilot must play an inner game of mental juggling.

Instrument training starts with the basics of attitude control. Many instrument students do not understand the need for repetitive basic attitude instrument drills. Timed turns, vertical *S*, partial panel, and unusual attitude recoveries are not all that stimulating. Instrument students want to get on with the "good stuff," like ILS approaches. But attempting an instrument approach without good basics is like juggling with one arm in a sling. To discover why this is true pilots should not look outside but inside themselves. A pilot must learn to think like an instrument pilot.

In the beginning of instrument training, it takes almost 100% of the mind's attention just to keep the wings level and maintain the assigned altitude while flying under the hood. The capacity of the mind becomes completely used up. If the mind receives even one more input, it will reject the input as if it did not exist. This is why good VFR pilots miss radio calls, forget MDAs, and get behind the airplane.

What actually happens can be dismantled into three parts: scanning, understanding, and action. The instrument scan is the method in which the eyes look over the instruments in order to receive the valuable information they offer. Since the situation of the airplane is ever changing, there is no single path the eyes can follow around the panel that will always offer the best information. The instrument scan is a very personal thing that is only developed after hours of practice. In a sense, it is a skill that cannot be mastered; but when a pilot gets close, he will be able to read every instrument efficiently and interpret each bit of information that each instrument offers. But that is not enough.

Just laying eyes on an instrument does not necessarily mean the pilot gets the message. The pilot must understand what the instrument is saying. A single instrument offers little information when it is solo. Instrument combinations paint a bigger picture. A complete understanding of how the instruments work, including their limitations, is essential to understanding the message. But that still is not enough.

The job is not complete until the pilot takes appropriate action to solve any situation the instruments present. Here is where a mental chain of events begins. What is seen by the eyes and processed by the brain must take effect in the hands and feet. When the airplane dips below assigned altitude, a trend is first shown on the Vertical Speed Indicator (VSI). The eyes see the needle below the VSI zero mark and relay the information to the brain. The brain recognizes this as a problem and asks the hands to pull just a little on the control wheel. This should all take place within a fraction of a second and without taxing the brain very much.

In the initial phase of instrument training, teaching a pilot to make a standard rate turn under the hood is not as important as teaching the pilot's mind to recognize and monitor the turn. Eventually, the mind will be able to control the turn, making small adjustments where necessary, with less and less brain power. The less brain power used, the more free the mind is to take on new problems. The mind will have more capacity to control altitude, talk on the radio, or find a particular page in the approach chart book while at the same time monitoring the turn.

The goal is to reach a level when aircraft control is almost instinctive. When a baseball player sees a ball get hit, he does not have time to stop and analyze what the first step should be. He must run to the ball without really thinking. A pilot must fly the same way. However, a ball player survives on instinct for only a few seconds. The instrument pilot must react instinctively at all times while in flight. When turbulence dips one wing, the pilot raises it without consciously thinking about it. When the altimeter wanders off by 75 feet, the pilot returns to assigned altitude without burdening the rest of the thought process.

With training and practice, the airplane's attitude can be controlled with only a small portion of the mind's potential. With the airplane under control, the pilot has time left over to plan ahead. This ability is the true difference between an IFR and a VFR pilot. The skill is a "mental auto-pilot." The more room left over in the pilot's mind, the more able that pilot will be to fly a difficult approach, figure out a holding pattern entry, or unravel air traffic nightmares.

Flying single pilot IFR will demand more from the pilot than anything else in aviation. Take a look inside the mind during a typical instrument approach:

While en route to the destination airport, the pilot holds a heading that will keep the CDI needle glued to the middle of the VOR. The altitude never waivers more than 50 feet even though the air is turbulent and the ride is rough. The DME is clicking off the miles to the home airport. The mind at this moment is controlling only a few items. The pilot is only juggling a small number of objects. The properly trained instrument mind has plenty of room left over after completing these few tasks to perform a few other tasks. Because the mind has more capacity for work than is currently demanded, the mind has time to think about cylinder head temperature, the next radio frequency, and resetting the DG. The mind is ahead of the airplane.

The airplane's number is called out over the center frequency and the controller says, "expect an ILS to runway 7." This is the message from controller to mind to pick up the pace. The controller has handed the pilot an additional item to juggle, but the mind takes it in stride. Because only a small portion of the brain is handling the aircraft control chores, the rest of the brain can think about the upcoming approach. It is not uncommon for a pilot to have trouble finding an unexpected chart. The mind can be so absorbed in flying the airplane that the pilot will forget the alphabet and therefore be unable to turn to the proper page in the chart book. This is a great example of a capacity-exceeded mind.

When all things are working, however, the flying duties may take up only 15% of the available brain power. This percentage will decrease the better instrument pilot you become. Eighty-five percent of the brain is still open for inputs so attention can be directed to setting up the approach. The proper frequencies are found, tuned in, and identified. The Marker Beacons are checked, NDB verified, and control tower frequency selected. Then the mind should work overtime. The pilot's imagination should develop a picture of what is taking place around him. The pilot must form a "mental radar screen" just as if he were sitting by the controller. The pilot cannot see through the clouds but only a few feet ahead; but the mind sees through the clouds and pictures the airplane's location in relation to the instrument approach to be flown, the airport, and any traffic in the area.

Soon the approach clearance is given; but the mind still has capacity to handle the extra input, and the pilot repeats the entire clearance back smoothly. Now the localizer needle starts to move, the mind clearly takes on the new challenge, and the intercept is made. At this point, the pilot is juggling 10 or 12 items. The closer the airplane gets to the airport, the more objects will be presented to the pilot. The objects include: airspeed control, taking the time over the Final Approach Fix, putting the landing gear down, power changes, rudder control, bracketing the glide slope and localizer, landing lights on, fuel on fullest tank, Decision Height and missed approach procedure memorized. The unprepared mind would have dropped four or five items by now. Without instrument mental training, a holding pattern, an intercept, and certainly an instrument approach may be impossible. If the mind does not take on new inputs as they arise and deal with them, it is hard to catch up. A pilot who is mentally unprepared for an instrument flight will be disorganized, disoriented, and dangerous.

This level of mental skill is required even when all equipment is working properly. Pilots should anticipate unusual circumstances that might arise while instrument flying. The day will come when each IFR pilot will have to do an NDB approach with only the clock and magnetic compass because of vacuum failure. Or the glide slope will quit in the midst of an ILS approach. Or the alternator will fail, leaving you with borrowed battery time and hopes. Or any number of other situations that would not be a worry in VFR conditions. At these times, the mind's mental juggling skills will be life saving.

The regulation writer was correct when devising the IFR recent flight experience rules. Juggling takes practice. To be an instrument pilot is a great human accomplishment. To be successful, the IFR pilot must understand charts, clearances, instrument indications, and the human mind.

When I trained to be an instrument pilot, 99 percent of my flying was done in VFR conditions using the IFR hood. After I passed the instrument rating check ride, I was scared to death to fly in the clouds. By law I could fly into anything, and I was proud of that fact; but inside I knew that my skills and experience were not equal to the challenge of instrument flight. On my first solo instrument flight, I was a nervous wreck. My former IFR flight instructor called me one morning and said he had a "mission" for me. A package needed to be delivered to a small airport about 100 miles away and apparently nobody wanted to fly there and back. Always looking for flight time I told him I would love to do it, and I drove to the airport. The weather was VFR but there was a scattered layer of clouds at about 4,000 feet. Eager to use my new instrument rating, I filed a flight plan and requested 4,000 feet as my en route altitude. For about 80 miles I ran into and popped out of clouds. Every time I plunged into the white stuff I was tense. I wanted to fly in the clouds but hated it. I developed a real phobia. I determined that single pilot IFR was just more work than it was worth. Years later I finally got some real IFR training and slowly got a grip on the situation. Nobody in those early days had spoken to me about personal minimums.

IFR pilots talk about the "minimums." They refer to the lowest altitude and lowest visibility that a pilot can fly and still make a successful landing at the end of an instrument approach. The minimums for an Instrument Landing System (ILS—category 1) approach are sometimes as low as 200 feet above the ground. That means a pilot can fly lower than the height of a water tower without seeing the ground, and that is normal! To do that with safety takes great skill. Most new IFR pilots have not yet developed that level of skill. The instrument rating, then, is a license to learn as well. Each pilot should honestly view his skill level and develop some "personal minimums." The law might say it's all right for a new instrument pilot to fly when it is 300 overcast and one half mile visibility, but the smart pilot will work up to that. Pick a day when the weather is 1,000 overcast and three miles visibility. This weather will allow for plenty of work in the system, yet the approach will not be in doubt. Learning to smoothly work within the system is more important than shooting endless approaches.

POINTS OF DECISION

IFR pilots make decisions at every juncture, just as VFR pilots do. The difference is that the stakes are much higher for IFR pilots. The danger resulting from a poor decision made in planning an IFR flight will be multiplied. Let's look in on an IFR flight and see where decisions must be made.

David is a newly instrument-rated pilot. He is planning to fly from the Warren County Memorial Airport in McMinnville, Tennessee, to the Dalton Municipal Airport in Dalton, Georgia (FIG. 9-1). David's first decision is to be in no hurry. He is flying alone to visit relatives but has no particular schedule to follow. Before leaving home, he makes sure to bring all the equipment he feels is required for a single-pilot IFR flight. He fills his case with current approach charts for both the departure and destination airports, current en route charts, an Atlanta Sectional Chart, the Airport/Facility Directory, flight plan forms, blank paper, and a clipboard.

David rents airplanes from the same Fixed Base Operator that he received his private and instrument training from. Today he is taking N714QN, the very same Cessna

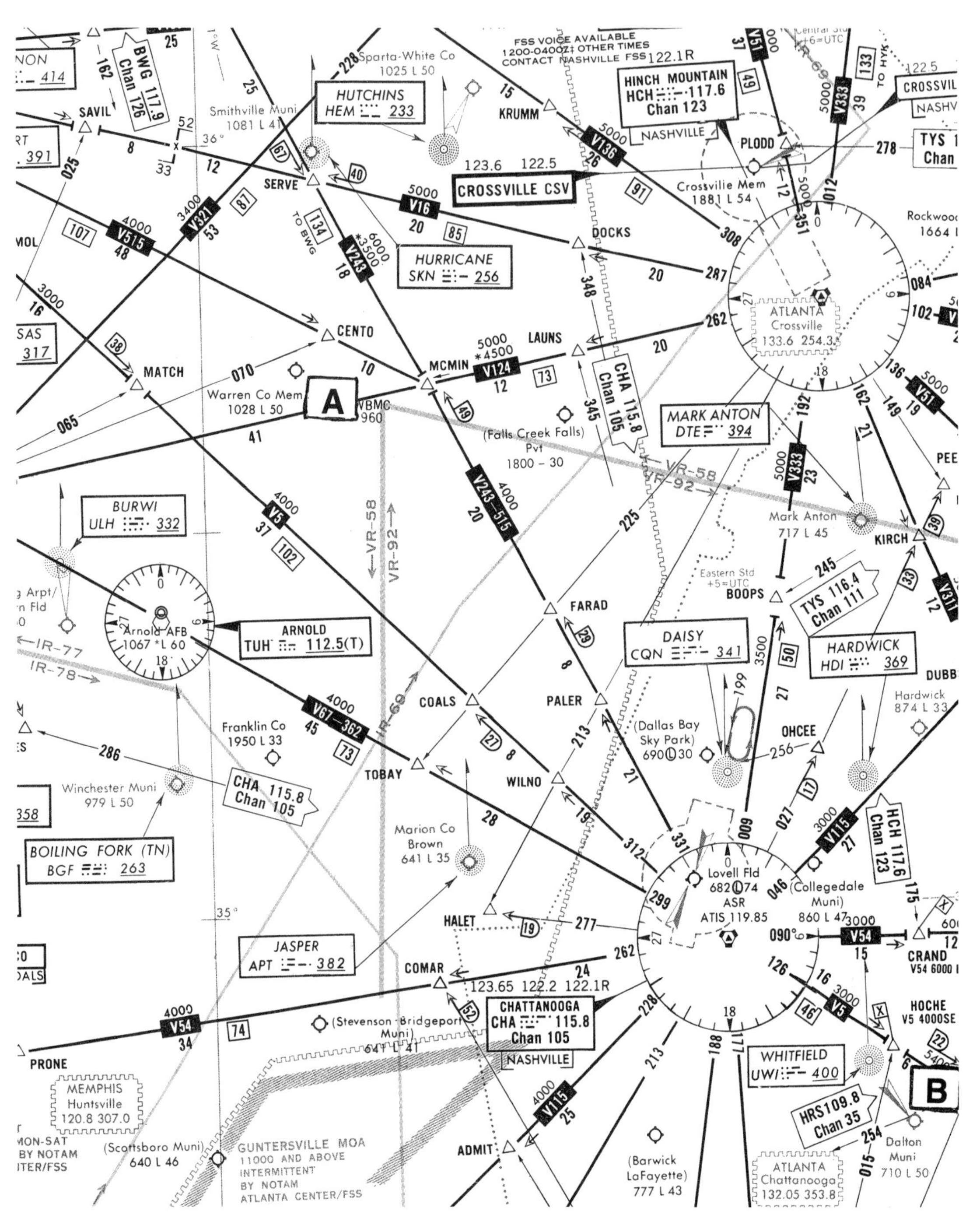

Fig. 9-1. *IFR cross-country from Warren County Memorial Airport (A) in McMinnville, Tennessee, to the Dalton Municipal Airport (B) in Dalton, Georgia.*

172 in which he passed the instrument rating check ride last year. David fills out all the paperwork to rent the airplane and gets the keys. He heads for the pilot briefing room.

The FBO has a new DUAT computer and David is getting pretty good on it. He sits down, activates the DUAT program, and types in his personal access code and password. Soon the entire weather computer is at his disposal. He asks the computer for current weather at various reporting locations around the area. He asks for SA reports at Crossville, Chattanooga, Huntsville, Anniston, and Atlanta. By checking the Airport/Facility Directory, David spots another piece of valuable weather information. His destination airport, Dalton, has a new AWOS-3 automatic weather observing station (FIG. 9-2). David asks the computer for the weather in Dalton even though there is no human weather observer stationed there. Soon the computer's printer is clicking away with the weather David wants.

§ **DALTON MUNI** (DNN) 6 SE UTC-5(-4DT) 34°43'18"N 84°52'09"W **ATLANTA**
710 B S4 **FUEL** 100LL, JET A OX 1, 3 TPA—1510(800) **H-4H, L-14H, 20E**
RWY 14-32: H5000X100 (ASPH) S-30, D-42, DT-80 MIRL **IAP**
RWY 14: ODALS. VASI(V4L)—GA 3.50°TCH 34'. Trees. **RWY 32:** VASI(V4L)—GA 3.5°TCH 37'. Trees.
AIRPORT REMARKS: Attended 1330Z‡-dusk.
WEATHER DATA SOURCES: AWOS-3 127.65 (404) 278-7010.
COMMUNICATIONS: CTAF/UNICOM 122.7
ATLANTA FSS (ATL) TF 1-800-WX-BRIEF. NOTAM FILE ATL.
® **CHATTANOOGA APP/DEP CON** 125.1 (1100-0500Z‡) **CLNC DEL** 120.25
ATLANTA CENTER APP/DEP CON 133.8 (0500-1100Z‡)
RADIO AIDS TO NAVIGATION: NOTAM FILE CHA.
CHATTANOOGA (H) VORTAC 115.8 CHA Chan 105 34°57'40"N 85°09'12"W 135° 20.1 NM to fld. 1030/01E.
WHITFIELD NDB (MHW) 400 UWI 34°47'22"N 84°56'46"W 139° 5.6 NM to fld. NOTAM FILE ATL.
ILS 110.9 I-DNN Rwy 14. (Loc only).

Fig. 9-2. *Airport/Facility Directory entry for Dalton Municipal Airport.*

Point of Decision: David now has the current weather at area locations, but for IFR flight planning the forecast weather is also needed.

David is not finished. He returns to the computer's "menu" and this time asks for the FT (terminal forecast) and FD (winds and temperatures aloft) for the same airports. He successfully receives forecasts for all the locations except Dalton. Robot weather observers are not smart enough to predict the future—yet. Chattanooga is the closest reporting station to Dalton, so close attention is paid to the forecast. The ceilings all over the area are low. Chattanooga is forecasting the cloud heights to be only 600 feet AGL during the time period from one hour before David plans to get to Dalton until one after that time.

Point of Decision: Is this ceiling below David's "personal" minimums? A look at the Dalton approach charts shows that there are two approaches available at Dalton. Both are non-precision approaches. One is an NDB and the other is a Localizer (LOC) approach (FIG. 9-3). The Minimum Descent Altitude (MDA) for the NDB approach leaves the airplane 572 feet above the ground. This would only be 28 feet

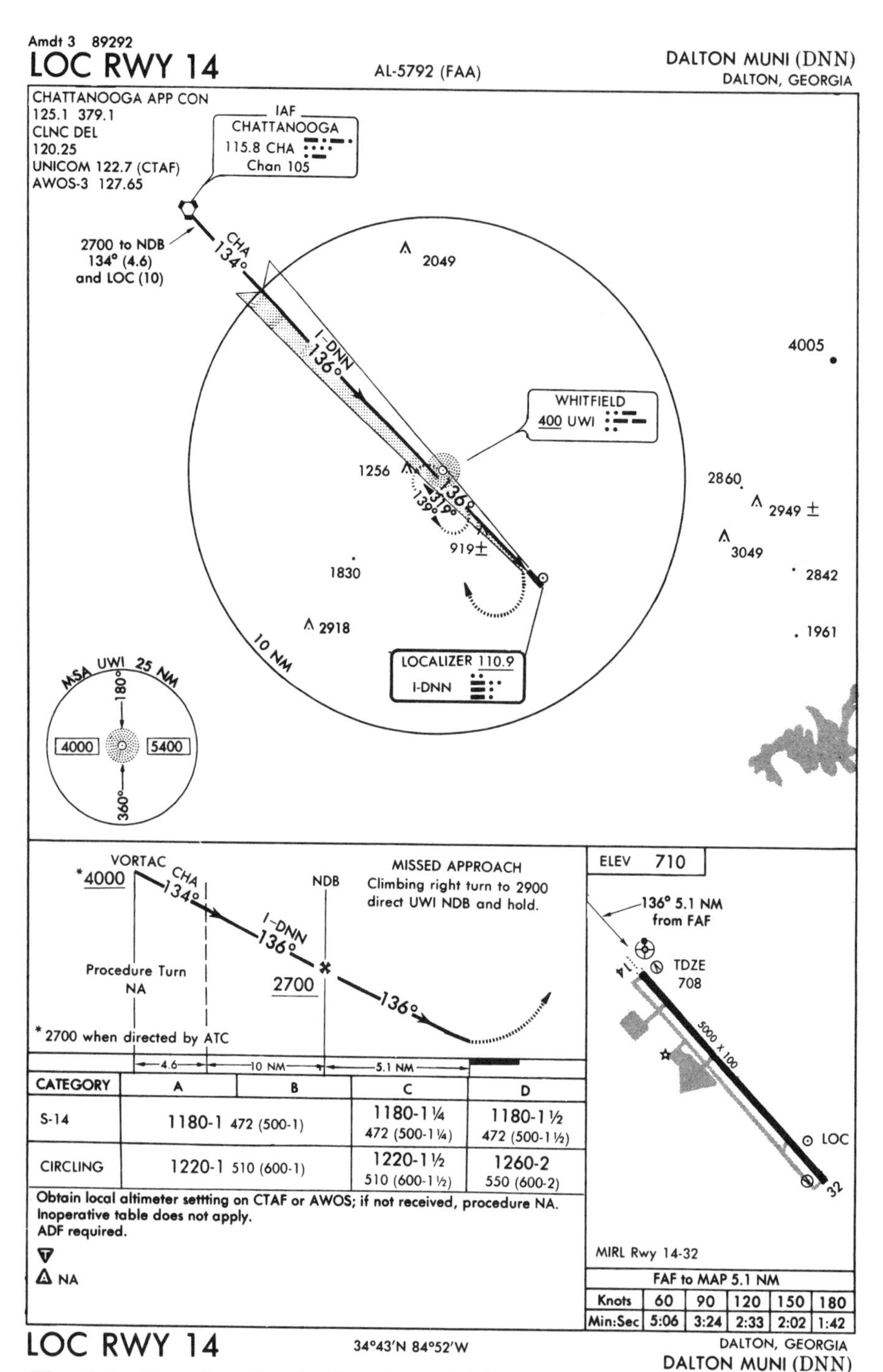

Fig. 9-3. *The chart for the Localizer (LOC) Runway 14 approach at Dalton Municipal Airport.*

below the cloud bases, assuming that 600-foot ceiling was correct. This leaves very little room for error. The LOC approach has an MDA that will put the airplane 472 feet AGL or 128 feet below a 600-foot ceiling. The Localizer is better but not great, especially since the prediction of 600 feet is from Chattanooga, not Dalton.

David determines to make the trip despite the fact that this will be the lowest IFR weather in which he has flown solo. David starts to make out the flight plan. In Block 8 of the flight plan, Route of Flight, he writes in: RNC (the three-letter identifier for Warren County found in the Airport/Facility Directory) direct to MCMIN intersection, V243-515 CHA, direct UWI. UWI is the three-letter identifier for the NDB that is used to shoot the LOC approach to Dalton. This is a case where the navigation aid near the airport and the airport itself have different three-letter identifiers. The navigation aid that must be flown to is the Whitfield NDB (UWI), but the airport the approach goes to is Dalton (DNN). David places the identifier DNN in the next block, 9: Destination airport. This tells the Air Traffic Control computer that he intends to fly to the navigation aid and use it to find the airport. David continues to make out the plan and comes to Block 13: Alternate Airport.

Point of Decision: Will this trip require an alternate to be filled? Yes. The regulations require the airport of destination to have a forecast (one hour before to one hour after intended arrival) better-than-2,000-foot ceiling and 3 miles visibility in order to leave Block 13 blank. A 2,000-foot ceiling with 3 miles visibility is actually good VFR conditions, but the regulation is conservative. If a pilot arrived at the destination and the weather was as good as 2,000 and 3, he would have absolutely no problem shooting an approach and landing. But what if the forecast is significantly in error? The writer of this regulation feels that the chances are almost zero that a forecast of 2,000 and 3 will be in error to the point where the weather is actually below approach minimums when the pilot arrives. Any time the weather is below 2,000 and 3, a second plan must be made.

On VFR flights, it is a good idea to think about alternates. If the flight passes by two other airports along the way, it would be "money in the bank" to look them over ahead of time. If while en route the engine begins to run rough, the pilot would already know where to go. But legal IFR alternates are altogether different. The real reason for IFR alternates is to provide a plan in case the two-way radio communications become inoperative. The alternate chosen must meet certain weather minimums and may not be the closest airport to the destination. On IFR flight plans, there can only be one alternate airport.

David remembers that the forecast for Chattanooga was calling for a 600-foot ceiling. Six hundred feet is much worse than 2,000 feet, so an alternate is automatically required. The visibility alone can trigger the need for an alternate as well. If the forecast had been 5,000 feet and 2 miles visibility, an alternate would have been required as well.

Point of Decision: Which alternate should be used? This is a decision that only the pilot can make. A briefer at the FSS can offer some suggestions based on weather, but the pilot must make this call. Sometimes a low cloud system will spread out and cover a large area. In this case, a legal alternate may not be within the fuel range of the airplane. The ATC computer will take an alternate into the system that the airplane can't actually reach. In other words, the FAA will never do your planning for you. If you incorrectly choose an impractical alternate based on range the FAA will take it, and if the radios ever quit, you will be in real trouble. Choose alternates realistically!

To be considered as an alternate, an airport must have a qualified weather observer on the airport at the time of arrival. If the airport has a precision approach, the weather cannot be worse than 600 feet AGL and 2 miles visibility. A precision approach is anything with an electronic glide slope. For civilians this means an ILS approach. There are other precision approaches available, but an ILS is the most common. If the airport has a non-precision approach, then the weather cannot be worse than 800 feet and 2 miles visibility at the time the flight arrives. David looks back over the forecast he took off the computer. He asks himself: If I really had to fly to an alternate, where could I go and not get stranded? He remembers that one of his college roommates was from Cleveland, Tennessee, and the Hardwick Airport in Cleveland has an NDB approach. Hardwick is only about 30 miles north of Dalton.

Point of Decision: Can David use Hardwick as the alternate? No. In the landing minimums section of the Hardwick Field NDB approach to runway 3 (FIG. 9-4) there appears the letter *A* inside a triangle. Next to the triangle appear the letters *NA*. This signifies that this airport cannot be used as an alternate. The reason it cannot be used is that there is no certified weather reporting service or remote monitoring facility (like AWOS). Why is the lack of weather reporting so important at the alternate? There is no requirement for a weather observer at the destination airport. The reason would be important if a missed approach took place at the destination.

Before a pilot, flying in IFR conditions, leaves the area of the destination airport he must know for a fact that he will be able to land at the next airport to which he flies his plane. If a pilot flies to an alternate that has no weather observer, he cannot be sure the weather at the alternate is any better than the airport where a missed approach was made. Valuable fuel could be wasted flying to an airport where a landing cannot be completed. When a pilot misses an approach at the destination and decides that he needs to go to the alternate, he must ask for the weather at the alternate first. The controller will find out the weather or allow you to vacate the frequency long enough to call Flight Service. Only after the weather report verifies that a landing can be made at the alternate should a pilot spend fuel to get to the alternate. In this case, Hardwick Field would be an alternate unknown and therefore unusable.

David spots the *NA* indication and eliminates Hardwick from consideration. The next logical alternate David considers is Chattanooga. He turns in the approach chart book to Chattanooga and finds an ILS approach to runway 2 (FIG. 9-5). If David were forced to make a missed approach at Dalton, then Chattanooga would be a good choice because it is only about 20 miles away. Also, landing to the north at Chattanooga would be an easy transition coming from Dalton. The weather at Chattanooga at the time the flight would arrive there is forecast to be 600 feet. The precision approach alternate minimums require 600 feet. Even though it is right at the mini-

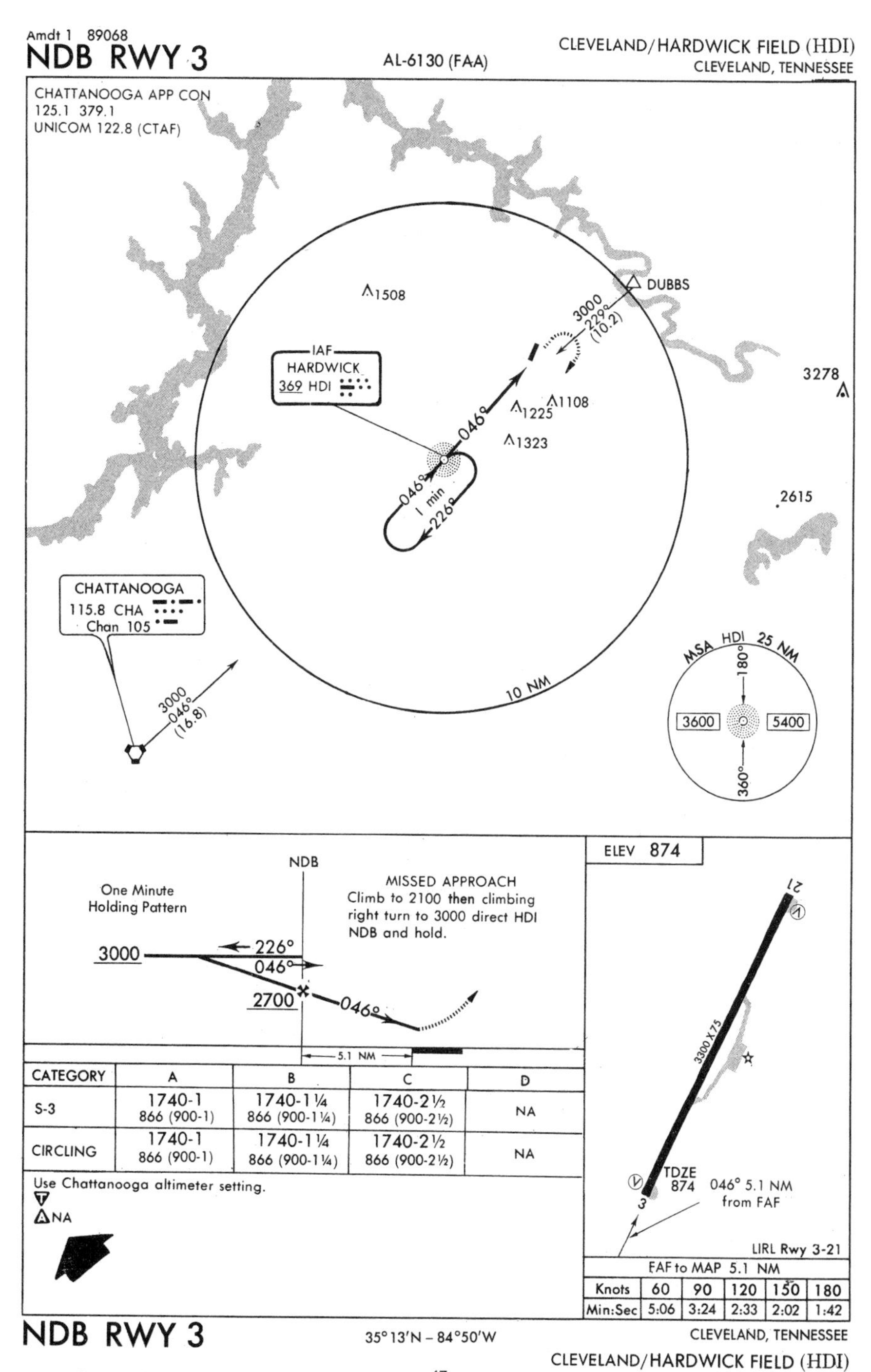

CATEGORY	A	B	C	D
S-3	1740-1 866 (900-1)	1740-1¼ 866 (900-1¼)	1740-2½ 866 (900-2½)	NA
CIRCLING	1740-1 866 (900-1)	1740-1¼ 866 (900-1¼)	1740-2½ 866 (900-2½)	NA

EAF to MAP 5.1 NM					
Knots	60	90	120	150	180
Min:Sec	5:06	3:24	2:33	2:02	1:42

Fig. 9-4. *The NDB approach at Hardwick Field at Cleveland, Tennessee. The arrow points out the "A triangle" symbol and the letters* NA.

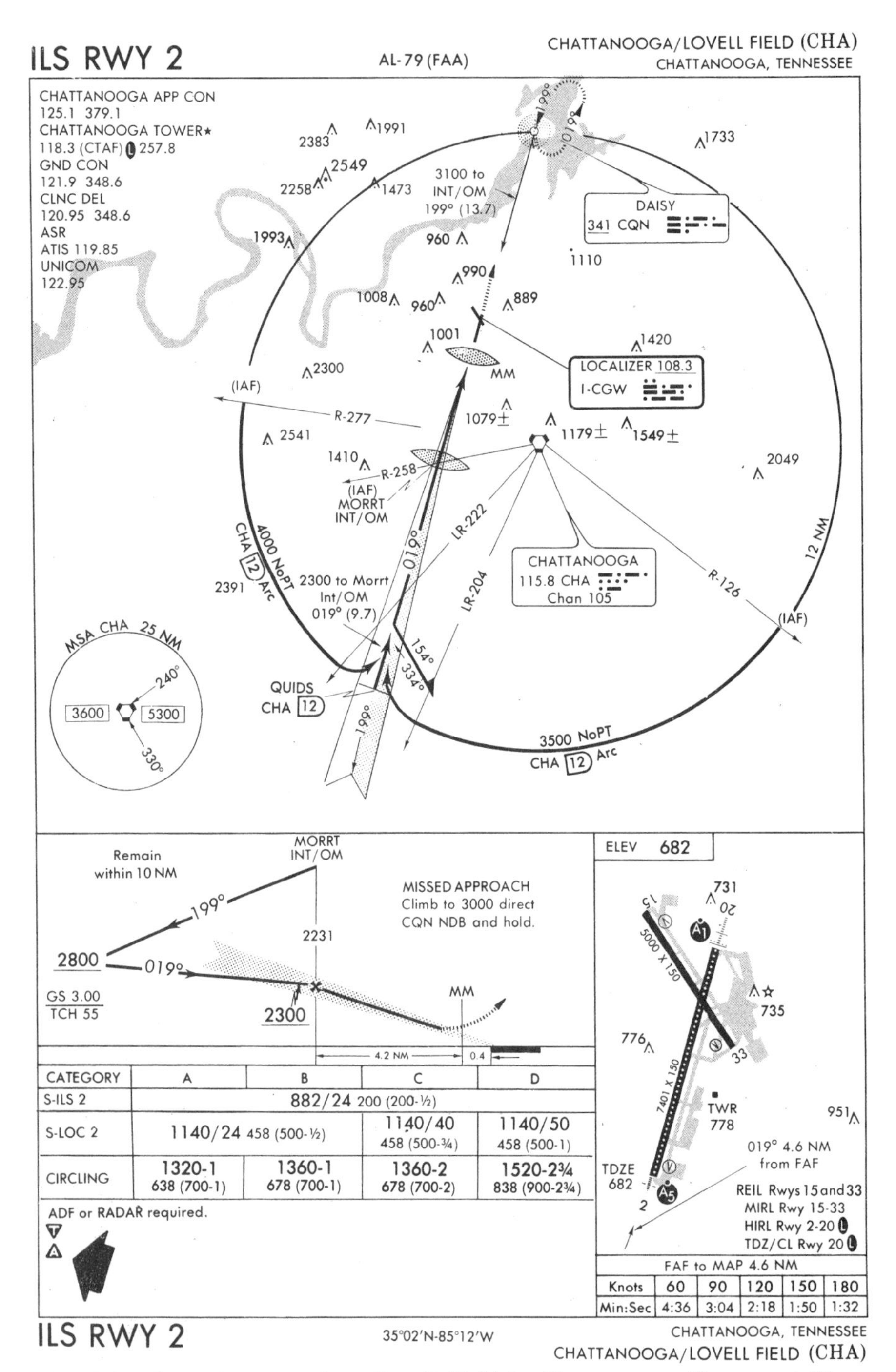

Fig. 9-5. *The ILS approach at Lovell Field in Chattanooga, Tennessee. The arrow indicates the "A triangle" symbol.*

mum, it does qualify. David decides on Chattanooga as the alternate, but then sees the letter "A" in the triangle. This time there is no *NA* next to the triangle, so this means something different. This symbol means that Chattanooga has non-standard alternate minimums.

Point of Decision: Can David use Chattanooga as the alternate? On the surface it looked all right, but the letter *A* in the triangle means that more information is required before a final decision can be made. The symbol means that the pilot must look further. David turns to the front of his approach chart book (Jeppesen charts have this information on the back of the approach chart itself). In the corner of several pages in the front of the book is the *A* in a triangle symbol. David looks up Chattanooga on this list (FIG. 9-6) and sees that a unique situation exists at this particular airport. Chattanooga has a notation that shows all its ILS approaches for categories A, B, and C require not a 600-foot ceiling as is the standard, but a 700-foot ceiling and 2

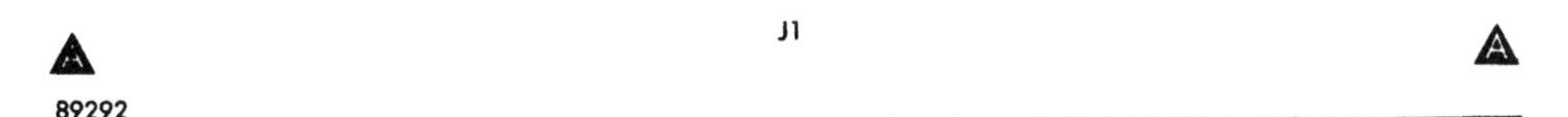
J1

89292

INSTRUMENT APPROACH PROCEDURES (CHARTS)

IFR ALTERNATE MINIMUMS
(NOT APPLICABLE TO USA/USN/USAF)

Standard alternate minimums for nonprecision approaches are 800-2 (NDB, VOR, LOC, TACAN, LDA, VORTAC, VOR/DME or ASR); for precision approaches 600-2 (ILS or PAR). Airports within this geographical area that require alternate minimums other than standard or alternate minimums with restrictions are listed below. NA - means alternate minimums are not authorized due to unmonitored facility or absence of weather reporting service. Civil pilots see FAR 91. USA/USN/USAF pilots refer to appropriate regulations.

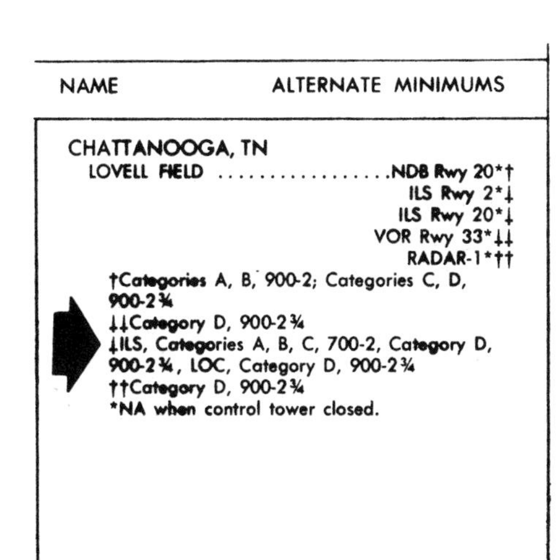
NAME	ALTERNATE MINIMUMS
CHATTANOOGA, TN	
LOVELL FIELD	NDB Rwy 20*†
	ILS Rwy 2*‡
	ILS Rwy 20*‡
	VOR Rwy 33*‡‡
	RADAR-1*††

†Categories A, B, 900-2; Categories C, D, 900-2¾
‡‡Category D, 900-2¾
‡ILS, Categories A, B, C, 700-2, Category D, 900-2¾, LOC, Category D, 900-2¾
††Category D, 900-2¾
*NA when control tower closed.

Fig. 9-6. *The IFR Alternate minimums page is located in the front of the NOS chart book. Here the listing for the ILS approach in Chattanooga is shown by the arrow.*

miles visibility. The forecast at Chattanooga called for 600 feet, but the alternate minimums require 700 feet. Chattanooga cannot be used as an alternate. No information is given as to why Chattanooga requires non-standard alternate minimums, just that they exist.

David has considered two alternates and has not found a good one yet. Crossville, Tennessee, was another airport from which David received a forecast on the computer. Crossville is forecasting a ceiling of 700 feet during the time of the flight. David looks up the approach charts for Crossville. He finds two approaches. One is a VOR/DME—A approach, but this is non-precision. Non-precision approaches require the forecast to be 800 feet. With 700 feet predicted in the Crossville area, this approach cannot be the basis for the decision to use Crossville. David also finds an ILS approach to runway 26 (FIG. 9-7). The ILS will work as long as the glide slope is operating because all that is required is 600 feet. If the glide slope is not in service, the approach will change to a LOC approach, which is a non-precision approach. Since the forecast is for 700 feet and non-precision approaches require 800, the decision about Crossville hinges on that glide slope.

David looks in the Airport/Facility Directory and discovers that any NOTAMs about Crossville will be on file at the Crossville Flight Service Station. David accesses the computer again and asks for NOTAMs listed at Crossville. The computer gives no information about the ILS glide slope, so David assumes it is in operation.

Point of Decision: Is Crossville then a legal alternate? Maybe. Before David can know for sure, there is one more item to check. The ILS approach has the letter *A* in the triangle, so more information is available. In the alternate minimum listing for Crossville (FIG. 9-8), the information only reads, "NA when Control Zone not effective." So now the decision hinges on whether or not the Control Zone will be in effect when the flight arrives there.

Back to basics reminds David that a Control Zone can be in effect only when a weather observer is on the field. At Crossville the Flight Service Station employees act as the weather observers; but the FSS is not open 24 hours a day. The Airport/Facility Directory indicates that the Crossville FSS is open from 1200 Zulu time until 0400 Zulu time (FIG. 9-9). Also, the En Route IFR chart indicates FSS from 1200–0400 Zulu. Only during these times can this airport then be used as an alternate. Crossville is in the Central time zone, where the conversion to Zulu time is plus 6 hours for Standard time. This means that the Crossville FSS is open from 6 o'clock AM until 10 o'clock PM Central Standard time. The flight that David proposes will fall within that time frame, so Crossville would be a legal alternate.

It has taken a lot of research, but David has found an alternate that will work, and he writes CSV in block 13 of the flight plan. He double-checks the entire flight plan and then accesses the DUAT computer one more time. David transfers his handwritten IFR flight plan (FIG. 9-10) to the computer (FIG. 9-11). He indicates in the remarks section of the flight plan that he received his weather briefing over the DUAT computer. The flight plan must be filed on the computer at least 30 minutes before departure, so now David has time to check over the airplane.

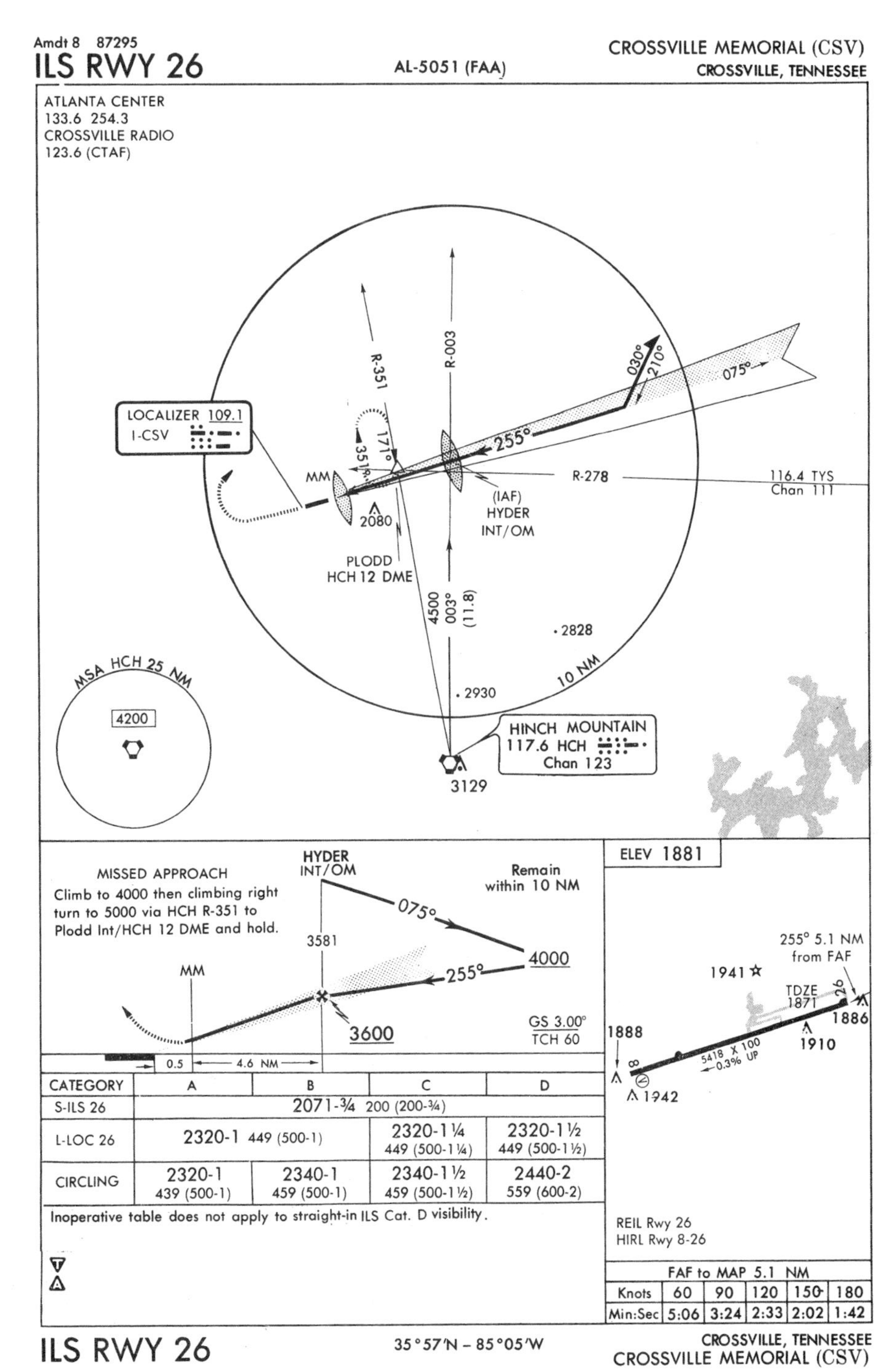

CATEGORY	A	B	C	D
S-ILS 26	2071-¾ 200 (200-¾)			
L-LOC 26	2320-1 449 (500-1)		2320-1¼ 449 (500-1¼)	2320-1½ 449 (500-1½)
CIRCLING	2320-1 439 (500-1)	2340-1 459 (500-1)	2340-1½ 459 (500-1½)	2440-2 559 (600-2)

Inoperative table does not apply to straight-in ILS Cat. D visibility.

FAF to MAP 5.1 NM					
Knots	60	90	120	150	180
Min:Sec	5:06	3:24	2:33	2:02	1:42

ILS RWY 26 35°57′N – 85°05′W CROSSVILLE, TENNESSEE CROSSVILLE MEMORIAL (CSV)

Fig. 9-7. *The ILS approach at Crossville Memorial Airport in Crossville, Tennessee.*

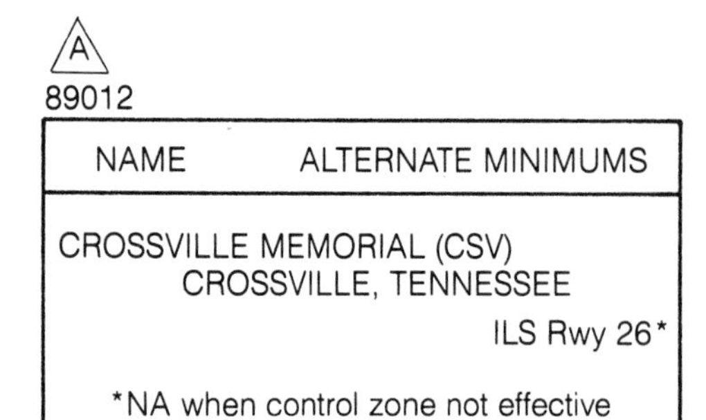

A
89012

NAME	ALTERNATE MINIMUMS
CROSSVILLE MEMORIAL (CSV) CROSSVILLE, TENNESSEE	ILS Rwy 26*

*NA when control zone not effective

Fig. 9-8. *The IFR Alternate Minimums listing for Crossville, Tennessee.*

§ **CROSSVILLE MEM** (CSV) 3 W UTC-6(-5DT) 35°57'04"N 85°05'06"W **ATLANTA**
1881 B S4 **FUEL** 100LL, JET A **H-4H, L-14H, 21D**
RWY 08-26: H5418X100 (ASPH) S-33, D-62 HIRL 0.3% up W. **IAP**
RWY 08: VASI(V4R)—GA 3.0°TCH 50'. Trees. **RWY 26:** REIL. Trees.
AIRPORT REMARKS: Attended 1400Z‡-dark.
COMMUNICATIONS: CTAF 123.6
CROSSVILLE FSS (CSV) on arpt. 123.6 122.5 122.2 LC 484-9541 (1200-0400Z‡). NOTAM FILE CSV.
NASHVILLE FSS (BNA) TF 1-800-WX-BRIEF (0400-1200Z‡).
RCO 122.5 122.2 (NASHVILLE FSS)
® **ATLANTA CENTER APP/DEP CON** 133.6
RADIO AIDS TO NAVIGATION: NOTAM FILE CSV. VHF/DF ctc NASHVILLE FSS.
HINCH MOUNTAIN (L) VORTAC 117.6 HCH Chan 123 35°46'51"N 84°58'43"W 335° 11.5 NM to fld. 3040/02W.
ILS 109.1 I-CSV Rwy 26. BC unusable.

Fig. 9-9. *The Airport/Facility Directory entry for Crossville, Tennessee. Arrow indicates the hours that the Flight Service Station is open and therefore when the Control Zone is in effect.*

Form Approved OMB No 2120-0026

U.S. DEPARTMENT OF TRANSPORTATION
FEDERAL AVIATION ADMINISTRATION
FLIGHT PLAN

(FAA USE ONLY) ☐ PILOT BRIEFING ☐ VNR ☐ STOPOVER | TIME STARTED | SPECIALIST INITIALS

1 TYPE	2 AIRCRAFT IDENTIFICATION	3 AIRCRAFT TYPE/ SPECIAL EQUIPMENT	4 TRUE AIRSPEED	5 DEPARTURE POINT	6 DEPARTURE TIME PROPOSED (Z)	6 DEPARTURE TIME ACTUAL (Z)	7 CRUISING ALTITUDE
VFR / X IFR / DVFR	714 QN	C-172	110 KTS	RNC	1530		5,000

8 ROUTE OF FLIGHT
RNC → MCMIN, V243-SIS CHA → UWI

9 DESTINATION (Name of airport and city)	10 EST. TIME ENROUTE HOURS	10 EST. TIME ENROUTE MINUTES	11 REMARKS
DNN	1	05	Wx Brief on DUAT

12 FUEL ON BOARD HOURS	12 FUEL ON BOARD MINUTES	13 ALTERNATE AIRPORT(S)	14 PILOT'S NAME, ADDRESS & TELEPHONE NUMBER & AIRCRAFT HOME BASE	15 NUMBER ABOARD
6	00	CSV	DAVID LENOIR O/F RNC 615-555-1234 RNC	1

17 DESTINATION CONTACT/TELEPHONE (OPTIONAL)

16 COLOR OF AIRCRAFT
WHITE WITH BLUE STRIPE

CIVIL AIRCRAFT PILOTS. FAR Part 91 requires you file an IFR flight plan to operate under instrument flight rules in controlled airspace. Failure to file could result in a civil penalty not to exceed $1,000 for each violation (Section 901 of the Federal Aviation Act of 1958, as amended). Filing of a VFR flight plan is recommended as a good operating practice. See also Part 99 for requirements concerning DVFR flight plans.

FAA Form 7233-1 (8-82) CLOSE VFR FLIGHT PLAN WITH ____________ FSS ON ARRIVAL

Fig. 9-10. *David's handwritten IFR flight plan to Dalton.*

```
 1 – F/P Type> IFR   2 – A/C ID> N714QN   3 – A/C Type> C172/U   4 – TAS> 110
 5 – Dept Apt> RNC   6 – ETD> 1530   7 – Fl Lvl> 50
 8 – Rte> RNC MCMIN V243 CHA UWI
 9 – Dest Apt> DNN   10 – ETE> 0105   11 – Remarks> WX BRIEF FROM DUAT
12 – Fuel> 0600   13 – Alt Apt> CSV
14 – Name> DAVID LENOIR
     Addr> O/F RNC
      Tel> 615-555-1234
     Base> RNC
15 – Num Abd> 1   16 – Color> WHITE WITH BLUE STRIPE
17 – Contact>

Enter Block Number(s) to correct or F to File Flight Plan...?
```

Fig. 9-11. *David's DUAT IFR flight plan to Dalton.*

When David first arrives at the airplane, he checks the fuel level. He turns on the Master Switch and watches the fuel gauges leap across their dials. He does not actually trust the dials, however. He switches off the Master Switch and climbs up on the wing. The tanks are not full. David can stick his finger down inside the tank and touch the fuel, but he is not certain how much fuel has been burned out.

Point of Decision: This is a short trip and well within the airplane's fuel range. Should David get fuel, even if it is only a few gallons? Definitely! Never go into the clouds with less than a full load of fuel. If the loading of the airplane requires less than full tanks, the pilot should rethink the entire situation. The fact is that IFR is an unknown. Many things could happen that would force the pilot to fly longer or farther than expected. Take all the fuel possible when going into the clouds.

David goes to the line shack at the airport and asks that the tanks be topped off. The lineman grabs a clipboard off the wall and looks down a list. "4 Quebec November was topped before the last flight. It has only .8 burned out. That should be plenty of fuel for you," the lineman argues.

David does not take no for an answer. Never let the lineman determine if you need fuel. The tanks are topped off.

The Warren County airport does not have any direct link to air traffic control. There is no Clearance Delivery, Ground Control, or Control Tower on the field. The Airport/Facility Directory entry for Warren County lists Memphis Center for Approach and Departure Control. There is no weather reporting facility at Warren County, so the only way David can determine the height of the clouds is to estimate or ask a pilot who has just come through the clouds. No other IFR flights have arrived, so David guesses that the ceiling is between 800 and 1,000 feet.

Point of Decision: How should David receive his IFR clearance? Without Ground Control, Tower, or even a Remote Communications Outlet (RCO), there are only two ways available to get the clearance: take off VFR and receive it in the air or get a void time clearance. The decision depends on radio reception over the airport. How high must an airplane be over Warren County in order to establish two-way radio communications? This is an unknown. If a VFR takeoff is attempted, the airplane might not be able to get high enough to talk to Memphis Center without entering the clouds. David cannot enter the clouds unless he has a clearance first. The ceiling is no higher than 1,000 feet. The risk is too great.

David decides to get a void time clearance from the FSS. This method is clumsy and time consuming, but it is the best decision since the clouds are so low.

Point of Decision: When accepting a void time clearance, the pilot must be completely ready for flight. When a void time clearance is issued, a block of airspace is reserved above and around the airport. No other airplanes will be allowed into the airspace until the departing flight has been identified. Unfortunately, the controller will not allow one pilot to reserve airspace for any length of time, so he gives the pilot a "window." The window of time allows the pilot to take off without ever talking to anybody on the radio and to fly up into instrument conditions. After a radio reception altitude is reached, the pilot identifies himself and the trip continues as normal. The controller will issue a time when the IFR window will again be closed.

The pilot must get his wheels off the ground prior to the time issued or the clearance becomes void. If a pilot is not completely ready for flight when the void time is given, there may not be enough time between the moment the pilot hangs up the phone and the time the clearance becomes void to prepare for flight. Get the preflight inspection completed, load all passengers and luggage, and prepare all charts for flight before calling the FSS for the void time clearance.

David prepares the airplane for IFR flight, then calls the toll-free number of the Nashville FSS. He has allowed enough time between filling the flight plan and making the telephone call, so the flight plan should be ready. When the FSS briefer answers the telephone, David asks to receive an IFR clearance on N714QN from McMinnville to Dalton. The briefer puts David on hold. The FSS does not have the clearance. The briefer must call Memphis Center and get all the information. The FSS is just the middle-man in the communication process. The controller in Memphis gives the clearance over the phone to the briefer in Nashville. The briefer then takes the pilot in McMinnville off hold and relays the clearance.

"ATC Clears Cessna 714QN to the Dalton Airport as filed, climb on course to 5,000, squawk 0523, Departure frequency will be Memphis Center on 126.75, clearance void if not off by 25, time now 10."

David reads back the clearance verbatim and hangs up the phone. The controller has given 714QN exactly 15 minutes to get off the ground. At 25 minutes after the hour, this clearance will be canceled. The time of issue was 10 minutes after the hour. David synchronizes his watch with the controller's watch.

The plane is ready and David starts the engine. He does not want to feel rushed into low IFR conditions, but he is racing the clock. He is careful not to miss any checklist items. He taxis to the end of runway 5. The Cessna has dual two-way radios that should each be tested for operation prior to takeoff. David tunes in the unicom frequency of 122.8.

"Warren County unicom, this N714QN for a radio check."

"4QN, that radio is loud and clear."

David throws the switch on the audio panel that allows him to transmit on the number two radio and says, "O.K. Warren County, how is this radio?"

"4QN, that radio is loud and clear as well. Have a good trip, David." (Everybody on your hometown unicom knows each other. This is true across the U.S.)

By testing each radio in this way, David is verifying that they work. With a void time clearance from an uncontrolled airport, there is no requirement that David talk to anyone until he calls Memphis Center, but that will not be until he is already in the clouds. That would be a bad time to discover that your microphone is broken.

Still tuned to 122.8, David keys the microphone and declares, "Warren County Traffic, Cessna 714QN is departing runway 5." David looks at his watch; it is 21 minutes after the hour. He writes that time down on the flight plan, switches on the transponder, and adds fuel power to the engine.

The takeoff is smooth. The airplane enters the clouds at 700 feet above the runway. There would have been no opportunity to contact Memphis Center for the initial flight plan at that low altitude. The decision to get a void time was correct. David is flying in solid IFR conditions. After passing through 2,000 feet, he contacts Memphis Center on 126.75, which was already dialed into the number two radio.

"Memphis Center, this is Cessna 714QN IFR off Warren County, leaving 2,000 for 5,000 on course."

"714QN, this is Memphis, Ident."

David hits the ident feature on the transponder. "Ident 714QN."

"4QN, you are radar contact 08 miles east of the Warren County airport, resume own navigation."

David eventually levels off at 5,000. During the climb, he tunes in the VOR frequency at Chattanooga. At 5,000, he listens to the three-letter identifier and verifies Chattanooga.

Point of Decision: If David is receiving the Chattanooga VOR, he can ask the controller if he can turn and fly directly to the VOR rather than flying to the MCMIN intersection. The flight plan had to show the intersection because the pilot could not have been sure that the VOR could be received from this distance. This points up an important fact that many pilots miss: You very seldom fly an IFR trip exactly as you filed it. The flight plan must follow some basic guidelines that allow the ATC computer to accept it. To follow the guidelines, courses are often required that are out of the way. After the pilot is airborne, he can "work out" the trip one on one with the controller to save time and fuel. In this way, the flight plan only has one purpose: to fool the ATC computer into letting you in the system. Once in the system, you negotiate your own deal with the controller.

"Memphis Center, this is 714QN with a request."

"4QN, go ahead."

"Memphis, 4QN is receiving Chattanooga suitable for navigation, request direct."

"4QN, proceed direct Chattanooga, maintain 5,000."

David has successfully cut off the corner of his flight plan (FIG. 9-12). He will never fly exactly on Victor 243-515 now, but it no longer matters. He has worked out his own deal to save time and fuel.

After 20 minutes en route, David starts to see some light precipitation on the windshield. He has the DUAT weather printout under his chart on the clipboard, so he pulls it out for a look. The temperature at 6,000 was predicted to be just above freezing. The Outside Air Temperature gauge, however, reads −7°C. David quickly leans forward to enable himself to look out and down the leading edge of the wing. There is a trace of ice forming.

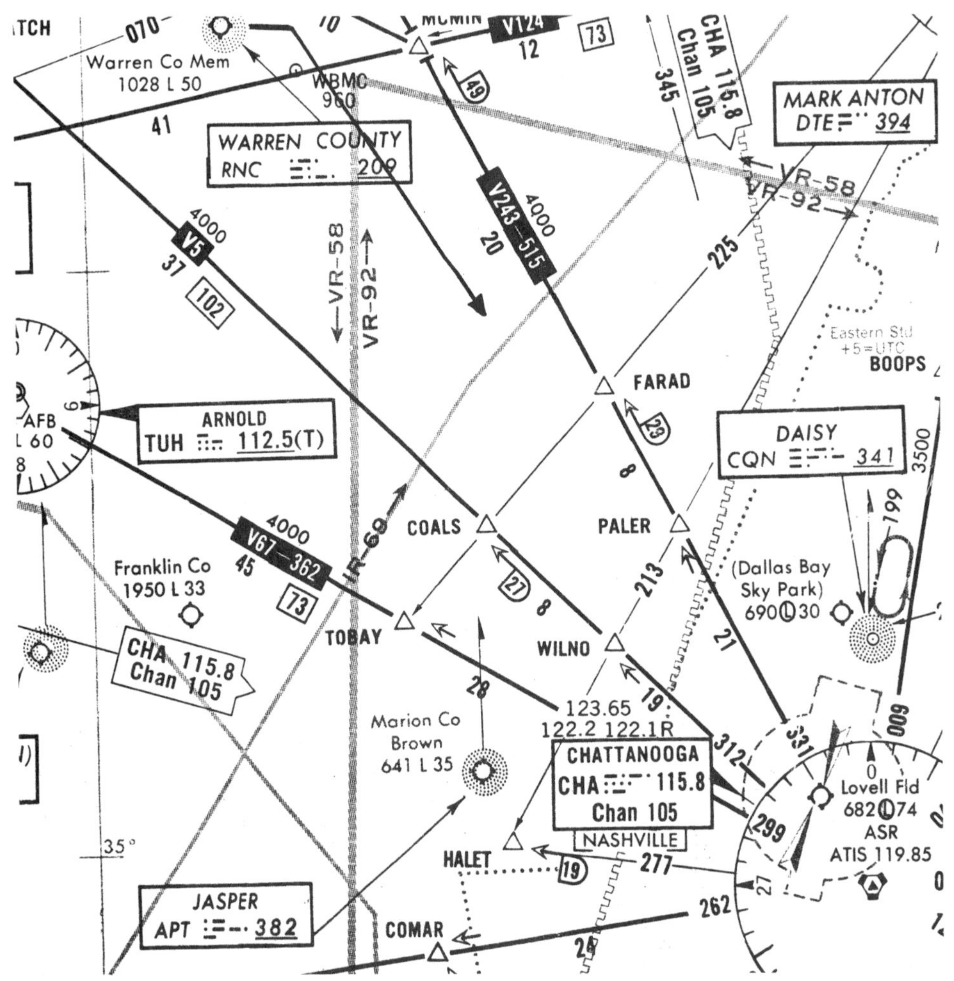

Fig. 9-12. *By identifying the Chattanooga VOR early, David is able to negotiate with the air traffic controller and get a shorter course.*

Point of Decision: What should be done about the ice on the wings? The Cessna has no anti- or de-icing equipment. Light rain is falling and adhering to the airplane. Logic would say the pilot should descend to an altitude where the temperature is above freezing. The Minimum En Route Altitude (MEA) for this area is 4,000. If a standard lapse rate was in effect, the plane would need to descend lower than 4,000 to reach above freezing temperatures. The other alternative is to climb. If the airplane can reach an altitude that is so cold that the precipitation is already frozen, then no more would stick to the airplane. David has reached his first real decision crossroads: Should he ask for a descent or a climb or should he stay at the same altitude?

"Memphis Center, this is 714QN. I have a pilot report to give you and a request, over."

"Go ahead 4QN."

"Yes sir, 4QN has picked up a trace of ice at 5,000 and would like to request 7,000."

"4QN, we are coordinating a handoff for you to Chattanooga Approach in five miles. We will relay your request."

It was important to identify the ice problem early. David is now stuck at 5,000 while the controllers coordinate the handoff and altitude change. All the while the airplane is picking up more ice. If David had made his decision later, he could have been forced to pick up even more ice. Of course, he could change altitudes now if he declared an emergency, but he decides to give the controllers a little time.

"714QN, climb and maintain 7,000 and contact Chattanooga on 125.1. Have a good flight."

"Leaving 5 for 7 thousand, and over to Chattanooga on 125.1, 4QN."

Repeating the frequency back was a good decision. If David had misunderstood the controller to say 126.1 and just said "roger" and switched frequencies, he would now be talking to nobody. The Chattanooga controllers are expecting him to call so they would wonder what happened. It can be a real mess. Repeating the frequency back gives the controller the chance to correct you if you did not get the correct frequency the first time.

"Chattanooga Approach, 714QN out of 5,000 for 7,000."

"Roger 4QN, resume own navigation direct Chattanooga VOR, then flight plan route."

David reaches 7,000 and reports level. The ice is still on the wings, but there does not seem to be any further accumulation. The ride is smooth, but there has been no sight of the ground since takeoff back at Warren County. Then the unexpected happens.

"714QN, proceed direct Chattanooga VOR and hold Southwest on the 210 degree radial, 7,000."

The controller has had a conflict. Probably there is another approach beginning at Dalton and there must be better spacing. The controller has described a procedure whereby David will fly to the VOR (FIG. 9-13). When the FROM indication shows for

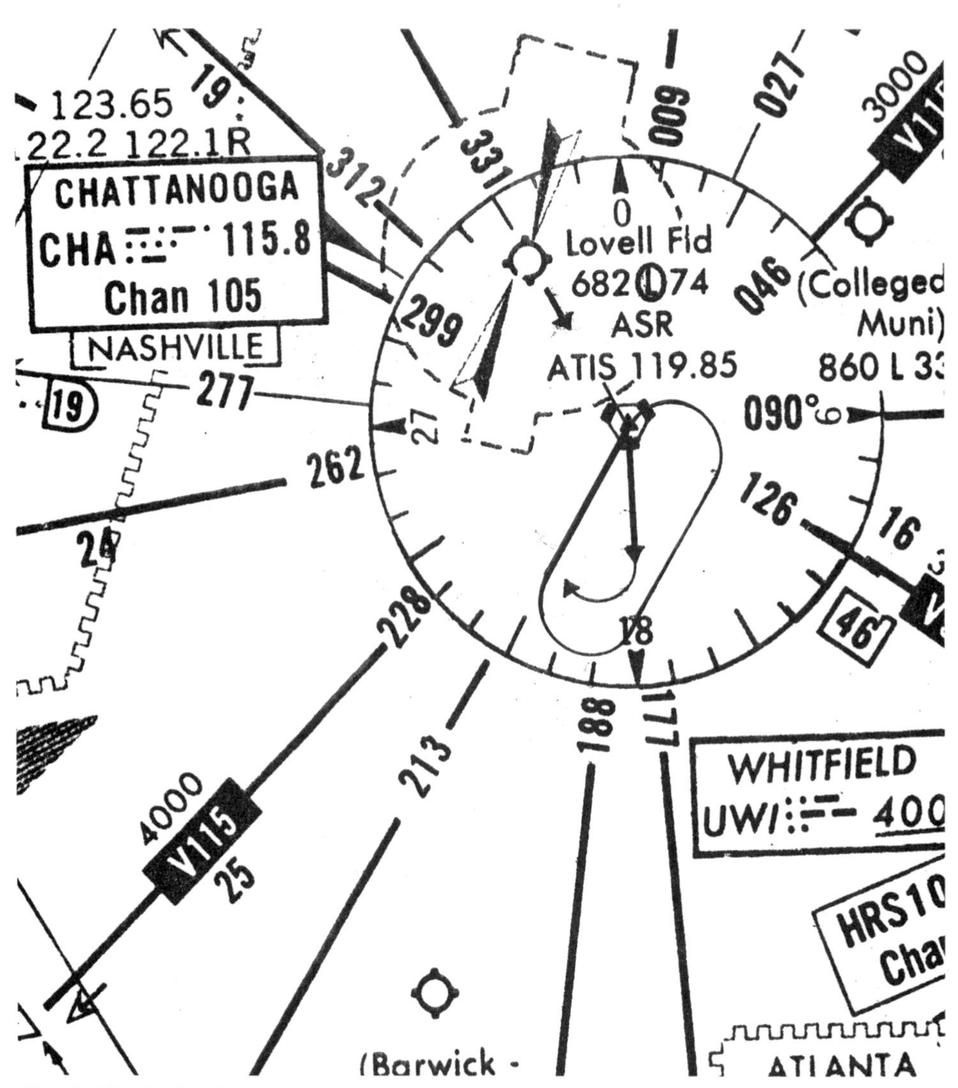

Fig. 9-13. *The holding pattern assigned by Air Traffic Control over the Chattanooga VOR. Teardrop hold entry procedures shown.*

the first time, he will make a right-hand turn and begin a teardrop hold entry. The turn is to the right because the controller said nothing about direction. When nothing is said, the standard right-hand holding pattern is assumed.

He will turn to a heading of 180 degrees. One hundred eighty degrees is 30 degrees off the holding radial of 210 degrees. David holds a heading of 180 outbound for approximately one minute. Then he will turn right again and intercept the 210-degree radial and track it inbound. The inbound heading will be the reciprocal of 210 or 030 degrees unless any wind correction is needed. But wait, something is missing. The controller has not issued an Expect Further Clearance (EFC) time.

Point of Decision: Without an EFC, the pilot places himself in a dangerous position. If while holding without an EFC the radios go dead, you will not know what to do next. You cannot hold forever; the airplane will eventually run out of gas. You cannot leave the holding fix just any time you want to because you could fly into a traffic conflict. David is at a crossroads: Does he ask the controller for an EFC or does he fly the hold without saying anything?

"Chattanooga, 714QN will hold southwest on the 210 radial at 7,000 feet, requesting an EFC."

"4QN, expect further clearance at 05 time now 50."

David again looks at his watch to verify that his time is the same as FAA time. With the EFC in hand, David can hold. If the radio quits now, he will continue holding until 5 minutes after the hour and then proceed on. The controllers will clear the airspace in front of him at 5 after. Never accept a hold without an Expect Further Clearance time. If for any reason the controller will not give an EFC, deny the hold. Who is in charge up here anyway? Of course, the pilot is in command. If the controller cannot accommodate a pilot's request, he will tell you. The pilot and controller should work together. But the pilot can request anything at any time.

The ride starts to get a little rough. Being inside the clouds, the pilot has no view of what he is about to run into. When flying IFR but in and out of the clouds, the pilot can occasionally see ahead and therefore make a decision as to whether or not he wants to fly through what he sees. Embedded in the clouds, the pilot is blind. Radar are the only eyes that see through the clouds. Very few Cessna 172s have onboard radar, and David's rented airplane is not an exception. His only hope of seeing ahead is to have someone who has radar describe it to him.

"Chattanooga, this is 714QN. Are you painting any precip echoes along my course? over."

"714QN, there is an area of moderate returns about five miles wide and 12 o'clock to your position."

"Chattanooga, 4QN requests a vector around the weather."

"4QN, fly heading 180."

"180 for 4QN, roger."

The heading that David has been given does not assure him that this will keep him completely clear of the precipitation. The heading is a suggestion based on the controller's view of the situation. When David accepts the turn, it is understood that this is just an attempt to avoid the worst part of the radar echoes. When thunderstorms are widespread, the pilot may not fly on any particular route. The pilot, if in the clear, can ask for "deviations around the weather." This means that the pilot will pick his way, zig-zagging if necessary, to avoid plunging into a storm. If a storm sits right on an airway that a pilot has been cleared to fly, there is no reason why he has to fly through the storm just to remain on course. Ask for a deviation. The controllers will help you work it out and avoid trouble. Remember: You seldom, if ever, fly what you file.

If a pilot ever gets caught and is surrounded by heavy precipitation and has no onboard radar, he must work with the controller even more. "Put me through at the best spot," the pilot might say. This is a request for the controller to look at the position of the airplane and the positions of the echoes and then determine what path will keep the airplane in the area of echoes the least amount of time. When the controller gives a heading, the pilot understands that it is only a suggestion. It becomes part of the clearance when the pilot accepts the heading.

Attempt a storm penetration only as an absolute last resort. If you must go throug[illegible] follow these rules:

1. Tighten your seatbelt, and put on your shoulder harness. Secure all loose objects in the cabin.
2. Cross the storm at right angles. This will reduce your time in the storm to a minimum.
3. Avoid altitudes where icing could be critical. Icing is a huge problem in thunderstorms and no altitude will be completely immune. Try an altitude where the outside air is colder than $-15\,^{\circ}\mathrm{C}$.
4. Turn on all anti-ice equipment. Even a Cessna 172 has a pitot tube heater and carburetor heat. Also, turn on the cabin heat full strength and make sure the forward defrost vents are open.
5. Reduce speed. Of course pilots want to get in and then get out as quickly as possible, but flying through a thunderstorm above Maneuvering Speed (V_a) is like driving your car 60 mph over speed bumps.
6. Turn off any automatic pilots or wing levelers. The jolts inside a storm will be too rapid for the automatic pilot. The device could tear itself up while continuously fighting for an impossible attitude. You must hand-fly through a thunderstorm. This means instrument skills must be sharp.
7. At night, turn up all lights in the cockpit. The brighter the cabin, the less effect a lightning bolt will have on the pilot's eyes. If lightning strikes the airplane, in theory, there should be no adverse effect since the airplane is flying free and is not grounded. But radios have been burned up and holes punched in airplanes by lightning strikes.
8. No matter how bad it gets, do not turn around. The shortest distance out is a straight line, so hold the heading. Turning while in the storm adds extra stress to the airplane as well.
9. Do not attempt to hold a particular heading or altitude. "Ride the waves" through. This will put less stress on the pilot and airplane.
10. Do not look outside. Pilots need the best instrument scan of their lives in this situation, and looking outside will increase the possibility of temporary blindness from a passing lightning bolt. Also, looking outside can scare you to death.

I cannot emphasize enough that thunderstorm crossing is something you do when every other course of action has been attempted. I have earned a few dollars while in thunderstorms, and I was never paid enough. There have been times when I told myself that if I ever got out of this situation alive I would never fly again. But I always went up again.

Fortunately, David worked out a vector with the Chattanooga approach controller that would keep him clear of the storm.

"4QN, the precip echoes are at your 8 o'clock position, turn left and resume own navigation direct Chattanooga."

David follows the instructions and enters the hold over Chattanooga as requested. It takes a teardrop entry, but before he can complete another turn the controller says, "714QN, you are clear present position direct to Whitfield, track inbound on the Localizer, you are clear for the Runway 14 Localizer approach to Dalton. Report passing Whitfield."

"Roger Chattanooga, cleared for the Localizer 14 approach, report Whitfield, 4QN."

Point of Decision: David is at 7,000 feet, which is a higher altitude than was originally planned for. The controller has said the magic words, "clear for the approach." When the controller says that, the pilot goes by the approach chart from then on. The minimum altitude over the Chattanooga VOR is 4,000 feet (FIG. 9-3). Without saying so in actual words, the controller has cleared David to descend. Looking at the approach chart, 2,700 feet is the minimum altitude over the Final Approach Fix (FAF), which in this case is the Whitfield NDB. David is at another decision crossroads: Is it possible to get down that fast or will he have to ask for a descent while still in the hold over Chattanooga?

David quickly determines that he must lose 4,300 feet in the distance between the VOR and the NDB. That distance is found on the approach chart to be 14.6 nautical miles. Traveling approximately 110 knots during the descent, the distance will be covered in 8 minutes. That means David will have to lose an average of at least 537.5 feet per minute.

David decides that the rate of descent required to make 2,700 by the NDB is not excessive and begins the approach from the VOR. David will soon have three radio frequencies to juggle. He must monitor Chattanooga approach until released by that controller. He would like to find out the weather at Dalton, and he would like to know if there is any traffic at Dalton. David leaves the number one radio on 125.1, which is still Chattanooga. On the number two radio, he then tunes in the AWOS radio frequency of Dalton on 127.65. He cannot just leave the approach controller in case the controller calls him with a traffic advisory or other instructions, so David must monitor two frequencies at one time. He throws the switch labeled "both" on the audio panel to the speaker position. Then he holds the volume knob of the number two radio. This way he can listen to the AWOS, but if Chattanooga calls his airplane number he can quickly turn down the volume on AWOS and hear the controller. AWOS is the computer-generated weather observation from an unmanned facility. The computerized voice synthesizer broadcasts the current conditions. David listens in. The voice does not sound like a machine; it sounds real. The computer says, "Dalton Municipal Airport. Dalton Municipal Airport. Automated Weather Observation. 1910 Zulu. Sky

Condition: clouds below 500. Visibility one mile. Temperature 48. Dewpoint 40. Wind 270 at 12. Altimeter 30.06."

Point of Decision: The AWOS has just reported that clouds exist over the airport at below 500 feet. The MDA of this approach is 1,180, which will bring the airplane to 472 feet above the ground. The visibility reported by AWOS is exactly on the minimum of one mile. David is at a crossroads: Should he miss the approach now and save fuel or continue the approach?

David decides to continue toward the airport. The position of the AWOS on the field is not known. The weather could be different when the approach breaks out than where the weather is being reported. The decision to descend below the MDA to a landing is the pilot's decision based on what he can see at the Missed Approach Point (MAP). David changes the number two radio frequency from AWOS to the Common Traffic Advisory Frequency (CTAF) of 122.7 in anticipation of a change during the approach. The Localizer frequency, 110.9, is set in number one navigation and the Chattanooga VOR frequency, 115.8, is in number two.

The airplane reaches 2,700 feet prior to the NDB, so David levels off. He has intercepted the Localizer and is working on a bracket that will hold course accurately. He slows the plane to 90 knots. David has the Automatic Direction Finder (ADF) switch on the audio panel turned to the speaker position. He turns up the volume just enough so he can identify the station and listen to the morse code during the approach. The ADF does not have an "off" flag like the VOR does. If the NDB station were to go off the air or the ADF receiver to stop working during the approach, the only way David will know this is if he is listening to the morse code. Since the ADF is required for this approach, he listens as he nears the station. Soon the ADF needle starts to move through the wing tip. Quickly David moves his eyes from the ADF to the clock. The second hand is passing the 3 o'clock position. According to the FAF to MAP timing chart, the approach will take 3 minutes and 24 seconds at a ground speed of 90 knots (FIG. 9-14). David reduces power and begins the descent to MDA.

Point of Decision: The time from FAF to MAP is based on ground speed. The airplane has been slowed and is now indicating 90 knots. But the AWOS reported the wind from 270 degrees at 12 knots. This is a quartering tailwind, which will increase the airplane's ground speed. The airplane is actually traveling faster than indicated. David is at a crossroads: Should he recalculate the approach time or go with 3:24?

David sees that there is an approximate difference of 50 seconds between the time using 90 knots and the time using 120 knots. In the middle of an approach there is no time to take out pencil and paper and do an interpolation problem, so he uses best estimates. He figures he may be traveling around 100 knots across the ground, so he takes approximately one third of the 50 seconds because 100 would be one third of the way between 90 and 120. One third of 50 is a little more than 15 seconds. At a faster speed, the airplane will get to the airport sooner.

If the time estimate is not reduced, the pilot runs the risk of overflying the runway while in the clouds and never seeing the airport. David must shave off 15 seconds from the time to give himself the best chance of making the approach. Three minutes

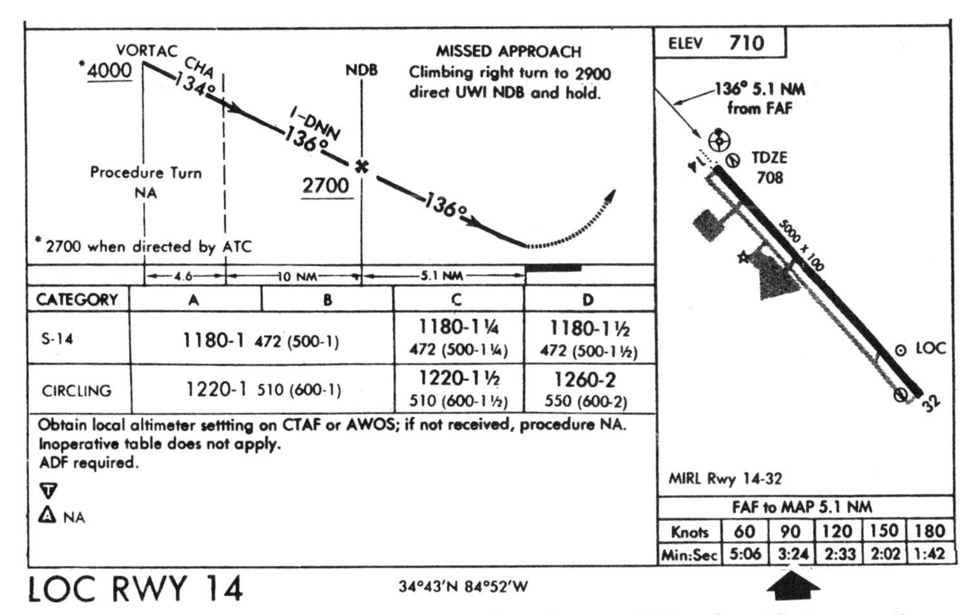

Fig. 9-14. *Enlargement of the Dalton Localizer Runway 14 Landing Minimums, Airport Sketch, and Timing Table.*

and 24 seconds minus 15 seconds equals three minutes and nine seconds. The time the ADF needle swung through the wing tip signifying station passage was at the 3 o'clock position. The second hand must go around the dial three times back to the 3 and then to the 5 o'clock position for an elapsed time of three minutes and 10 seconds. That is the time when David must make the final descent decision.

"Chattanooga, 4QN is Whitfield inbound."

"Roger 4QN, contact advisory frequency, report IFR cancelation this frequency or on the ground through Flight Service, report back this frequency in case of a missed."

David throws the switch on the audio panel from transmitter number one to number two. This allows him to talk on the CTAF that he previously tuned in. This method will save him some time at a very busy point in the approach.

"Dalton traffic, this is Cessna 714QN inbound for landing Localizer 14 approach."

There is no response from the radio.

Unlike what the profile view of the chart shows on non-precision approaches, the MDA should be reached as soon as practical. The diagram shows a sloping approach that never flies level. But flying level is important because this gives the best opportunity to see the airport. David levels off at the MDA with just over one minute to go until the MAP. He is still in the clouds. Then a break and he can momentarily see the ground. He is quickly back in the clouds. He must be right at the ragged cloud base. The only chance of seeing the airport will be if a high spot in the clouds is over the approach end of the runway. David looks at the clock; there is only 10 seconds to go. He must see the runway or at least the runway lights. So far, he has not seen either. The time has run out.

Point of Decision: David is probably just over the runway threshold but still in the clouds. The time has run out. He has come a long way for this moment. David is at a crossroads: Should he descend below MDA without the airport in sight or make a missed approach?

David pushes the throttle full forward and begins to climb. He had memorized the Missed Approach instructions before descending to MDA. This is a critical time. A missed approach should be considered an emergency. The airplane is low to the ground but still in the clouds with its exact position unknown. There is no time now to fiddle through charts to find out what to do; the pilot must already know. In this case, David makes a climbing right-hand turn and climbs to 2,900 feet. He switches back to the number one radio.

"Chattanooga Approach, Cessna 714QN is missed approach at Dalton."

"Roger 4QN, hold as published. What are your intentions?"

Point of Decision: David can now ask to fly the approach a second time. If in his mind he feels that the approach could have been flown more accurately and that a better job this time could make a difference, he could take that option. But if the approach was flown well and it made no difference because the clouds were just too low, then attempting another approach here would be a waste of fuel. David is at a crossroads; Should he attempt another approach or go to the alternate?

David feels that he did all he could have done on the approach and still stay above MDA. Trying another approach would be a hit-or-miss gamble. He makes a direct entry over Whitfield.

"Chattanooga, I would like to proceed to the alternate."

"Roger 4QN, climb and maintain 3,000 direct Chattanooga."

David turns the OBS on the number two radio, still set to Chattanooga, so that the needle centers with a TO indication. He turns the airplane and heads direct to Chattanooga.

Point to Decision: The alternate that David filed was Crossville. But the decision to use Crossville was based on legal requirements. The controller now thinks David intends to fly all the way to the alternate since that is what David said when asked his intentions. The first vector he gave on the way to Crossville was to Chattanooga VOR. Why not attempt an approach at Chattanooga even though it is not the listed alternate? Chattanooga is on the way and they have an ILS approach, which can bring the plane lower than in Dalton. If a missed approach must be made at Chattanooga, David can still go on to Crossville. David must make a decision: Chattanooga or Crossville?

"Chattanooga approach, 714QN is level at 3,000 with a request."

"Roger 3,000 4QN, go ahead."

"Chattanooga approach, I would like to attempt an ILS at Chattanooga."

"Roger 4QN, expect vectors to the ILS runway 2 approach."

The ILS will bring the airplane down to within 200 feet of the ground at Chattanooga. David flies this approach and breaks out of the clouds at an altitude higher than the Decision Height (DH). From that vantage point he verifies that he has the runway in sight, the visibility is above minimums, and he can make a normal approach. David sees the ground for the first time since the takeoff from Warren County and then briefly near Dalton. He lands safely in Chattanooga.

David made many good decisions during this flight. He was always planning ahead. He had no problems with any pieces of equipment. But what would have happened if things had not gone so well? Lets go back in time to when David first took off:

"Memphis Center, this is Cessna 714QN, IFR off of Warren County, leaving 2,000 for 5,000 on course."

The radio does not respond. David figures that he is still too low to communicate, so he waits a little longer.

"Memphis Center, this is Cessna 714QN, IFR off of Warren County, leaving 3,000 for 5,000 on course."

Still no answer on the radio. He double-checks that the microphone is plugged in properly and that the frequency is correct. He calls Memphis again and again with no response.

David can only assume that he has experienced two-way radio failure. Even though he is close to Warren County, he cannot land back there because there is no way to tell the controllers his intentions. He must fly to the destination airport. David has the IFR clearance that he copied down on his clipboard. He reads the clearance again: ATC clears Cessna 714QN to the Dalton Airport as filed, Climb on course to 5,000, squawk 0523, Departure frequency will be Memphis Center on 126.75. Two things in that clearance become vitally important: the altitude and the route. The altitude is 5,000, and he will fly that altitude unless another IFR altitude listed on the chart for his route is higher. The route approved was "as filed." Another extremely important statistic now is the time off. David had written the time down when he rolled onto the runway. He had listed on the flight plan a time en route of one hour and five minutes. One hour and five minutes after the time off would now become the time to shoot an approach in Dalton. Without the knowledge of the departure time, David will not know when the controllers expect him to shoot the approach.

David changes the squawk code from 0523 to 7700 and waits for one minute. Then he changes over to 7600. Now the controllers are aware of his problem. All he has to do is remain calm and follow the rules.

A pilot should never give up on establishing some type of communication. David tunes in the Hinch Mountain VOR in the number two radio, throws its switch to speaker, and turns up the volume. The controllers, who know that radio failure has occurred, may try to contact him by some other method. The Memphis controllers seeing the 7600 squawk code may have called the Nashville FSS and asked them to attempt a contact on area VOR stations. Nashville is the "parent" station for Hinch

Mountain. If the FSS calls over Hinch Mountain, David wants to be ready. If they do make contact, David can communicate again by pressing the ident button of the transponder. The controller may say, "714QN, if you can hear me ident" or "714QN, you are cleared for the approach. If you understand ident." This method is crude but better than silence.

David had hoped to cut off the corner and fly directly to the Chattanooga VOR, but now with no two-way communications, that deal cannot be made. David flies to the MCMIN intersection and turns to join Victor 243-515.

Near the FARAD intersection David notices a light precipitation and a trace of ice on the wings. But without communications he is trapped in the ice. The controllers expect David to be at 5,000 because that was the last altitude given in the clearance. The controllers could have placed traffic at 6,000 and above to stay out of David's way, but David cannot know that now. If the ice accumulation starts to get dangerous, he will have to take action anyway. If David's Mode C is working properly, the controllers will see the climb and hopefully have time to vector any traffic out of the way.

Near the PALER intersection, the ride starts to get rough. The Cessna has no onboard radar and David has no way of asking for more information. He is helpless. He is headed right for a storm that he is unaware of and does not know which way is best to get around it. The airplane enters heavy precipitation. David turns on carb heat and pitot heat. He rides the waves, holding heading and altitude as much as he can. Soon things begin to smooth out again.

Crossing the Chattanooga VOR, David realizes that his time estimate had been in error. He is still about 20 miles from Dalton, but one hour and five minutes since takeoff has already expired. In this situation, it works as an advantage because if he is on time or later he will not have to hold until the time expires. David begins the Localizer approach to runway 14 at Dalton, but he has no idea of what the altimeter setting or weather is at the airport.

David levels off at the MDA with just over a minute to spare before MAP. He sees the ground momentarily but immediately goes back into clouds. When the time expires from FAF to MAP, he cannot see the airport, so he executes a missed approach. The worst possible thing has happened short of complete electrical failure. A missed approach with no two-way radio communications.

David would like to request an ILS approach at Chattanooga because it is closer than Crossville, but there is no way of telling the controllers in Chattanooga this. David climbs back to 5,000 and heads for Crossville. The time spent determining the legal alternate must pay off now. David must land at Crossville. There is no contingency plan if a missed approach is forced there.

The meticulous preflight planning pays off. David flies to Crossville and lands after an excellent, though nerve-racking, ILS approach. David ends up a long way from where he intended to be, but he is on the ground and out of the clouds.

10 Airmanship Put to the Test: Emergencies

WHEN AN EMERGENCY SITUATION OCCURS, A PILOT'S SKILLS, KNOWLEDGE and experience must all be tapped in an instant to solve the problem. The DC-10 pilot that brought his airplane in to land when all hydraulic systems failed practically had to rewrite the book while in flight. He had no control through the roll axis because the ailerons would not work. Using differential thrust on the wing-mounted engines, he yawed the plane into runway alignment. The plane crash-landed, but many were saved by the pilot's quick thinking and flying skills.

We all hope that we will never be placed into a situation where our safety depends on a quick decision during an emergency, but we must be prepared. In an emergency, even the coolest person will feel panic start to creep into the decision-making process. Panic is more the enemy than the actual problem in some cases. It is a good practice to talk about what options a pilot might have in an emergency. It is easier to develop a plan of action for an emergency before the fact than to develop a plan during the fact.

When an emergency takes place, there will be little time to think things through and to determine the best action. It would be better to fall back on things previously considered than to try to "reinvent the wheel" in the midst of an emergency. This chapter is an "armchair quarterback's" view of certain emergency, possibly life-threatening, situations. Ideas are presented to foster thought on how to meet these and similar emergencies. Airmanship involves planning.

ENGINE FAILURE

Other than structural failure and fire, the engine stopping unexpectedly is a pilot's greatest fear. Fortunately, the occurrence of engine failure is extremely rare. I have only known two pilots who have had the engine just stop on them. One had the engine quit immediately after takeoff—the worst time. The flight was in early March. This particular flight was the first time the engine had been started for many months. The airplane had been tied down in the grass all winter. With very little preflight inspection, the pilot and his son got in the plane and started the engine. The engine showed absolutely no signs of a problem during taxi or run-up. The pilot looked both ways, announced his departure on unicom, and began the takeoff roll. Soon after the plane became airborne, the engine coughed and quit. The pilot landed in a plowed field that was just off the end of the runway, and the nose gear collapsed.

Later, an FAA inspector drained several filler cups of water from the sump drain of the gas tanks. A winter's worth of condensation had formed in the tanks. There was still enough fuel in the lines and in the carburetor to allow the engine to start and taxi. By the time the plane was airborne, however, that fuel was gone, and the only thing remaining was water.

The other case of complete engine failure occurred on a local flight when all the oil drained from the engine's oil pan. The plane had just had an oil change, and the drain plug had not been reinstalled properly. Slowly the lubrication left the engine and eventually it stopped. This flight ended on Interstate Highway 24.

No one was hurt in either accident. Actually, some confidence can be derived from these two accidents. Both could have easily been prevented, and both engines stopped by no fault of their own. The importance of a good preflight inspection cannot be over-emphasized. Engines that are cared for usually do not just quit. The chances of the engine stopping are greater during power changes, so make all throttle movements smooth and easy. Pilots should be completely familiar with the operation of the engines in the airplanes in which they fly. Pilots do not need to be mechanics, but they should be able to recognize problems that can threaten airworthiness.

Include the seldom-seen engine instruments in the cross-check. Problems detected early can be dealt with more safely. Rapidly rising oil temperatures are a sign of real trouble. If the pilot catches the gauge moving toward the red line early, a precautionary landing can be made. Use the entire instrument panel. Ask questions about what each engine instrument actually reads and what needle indications are indicative of what problems.

If the engine ever loses power, but does not actually quit, do not try to make it come back to life by advancing the throttle. First, put the mixture to the full rich position. A common mistake is forgetting to replace the mixture control to the rich position during descent from cruising altitude. At a higher altitude fuel can be saved by leaning the fuel/air mixture to the proper ratio. During the descent, however, the air will get thicker and thicker. If the fuel flow is not also increased, an extremely lean mixture will result. The engine will run hotter and in a severe case the engine will run rough or stop altogether. Having too rich a mixture will cause the engine to run rough as well. Fuel boost pumps used for start and takeoff will enrichen the mixture at high altitudes if not turned off. Check your own aircraft manual for the proper procedure.

Next, check for carburetor ice. Pull the carb heat control to the hot position and let the engine run for several seconds. With the control in this position, heated air is sent to the carburetor. The air is heated in small planes by exposing intake air to a hot exhaust pipe. The heated air will hopefully melt any ice that is blocking the air's path to the engine. The engine will take in approximately 12 to 15 times more air than fuel, so a clear passage is essential. If after the carb heat control has been placed in the hot position the engine begins to run rough, the chances are good the intake system had ice accumulation. The ice is melting and being ingested into the engine, making the engine run unevenly. When the ice is gone, the engine should run normally. Afterwards, run the carb heat in the hot position periodically to prevent the problem from recurring. While on the ground, taxi with the carb heat control in the cold position because the heated air is usually not filtered. Unfiltered air can introduce dirt into the engine, especially when taxiing.

One magneto may develop a problem that causes the entire engine to run poorly. Reduce the throttle and do an inflight magneto check. If one magneto is grounding out, the engine will run rough even when both magnetos are in operation. Isolate the bad magneto and fly to an airport running on just the good one.

It is possible for an intake or exhaust valve in the engine's cylinders to break. If this occurs, the seal in the compression stroke will be broken. That cylinder will not produce any power and will drag the other cylinders down. If this happens, the pilot will see a rapid reduction of RPM and lots of vibration, since the engine is no longer running with a smooth delivery of power. Reduce the throttle and get on the ground. Determine if the current altitude can be maintained. If altitude can be maintained, the best decision would be to land at the nearest airport for repairs. If the power available will not allow the plane to hold altitude and an airport cannot be reached, use the power that is available to control a stabilized descent to an off-airport landing. Do not stretch it, hoping to make the airport.

On the ground the existence of a broken valve can be easily verified. Making sure the magnetos are properly grounded, swing the propeller through its rotation. At various points, the propeller will become harder to swing. This happens when a compression stroke is taking place in one of the cylinders. The reason it becomes harder to swing is that in addition to moving the propeller, the air is being compressed. If a valve is broken, there will be no cylinder seal on the compression stroke, and therefore no resistance when swinging the propeller through.

If the engine does quit altogether, do not panic. Of course that is easy to say but very hard to avoid. Many fatal accidents have occurred because the pilot was so shaken by the engine stopping that he was not able to function. If the engine quits, the airplane just becomes a heavy glider. There is no reason, depending on terrain, that an engine out has to be a tragedy. I am asked all the time, "What will you do if the engine quits?" Many people believe that the engine is the only thing keeping the airplane up and that if it quits the airplane will plummet to Earth. I reply, "I intend to fly the airplane back down to a normal landing." The wing is the thing! As long as the wings produce lift, pilots will have time to manage the situation. If a pilot panics and allows the airplane to stall or stop flying, then time will run out quickly.

There are many memory prompts that can be used for engine failure. I like the three F's: Fly, Find, Fix. In an emergency, your powers to think may be reduced to jello! If you have some memory gimmick to fall back on, it is better than running the risk of going completely blank.

Fly. This means do not allow the airplane to enter a stall. Fly the speed that will allow the plane to glide the longest distance from its altitude. Check the airplane manual for best glide speeds, both flaps up and flaps down.

Find. Then look for a good place to land. When planning any flight, think about the terrain that must be crossed. Avoid extended flights over mountainous areas. This will increase the possibility of having a suitable place to land.

Choose a landing site and then consider these factors: Wind, Altitude, Terrain, Obstructions. (The factors spell out WATO. That is not a word but is another memory jog.) Given the choice between a severe cross wind or tail wind landing, and a normal into-the-wind landing, most pilots will take the normal approach. This will allow the pilot to apply previously acquired judgment to this new situation. However, the pilot might not have a choice and must take what he can get. Next, consider the altitude from which the airplane must descend. Altitude is time. The more time available, the more options the pilot will have to choose from. Engine failure after takeoff allows no time for much of anything but flare and touchdown on whatever is in the way. If the plane is at a cruise altitude and several minutes are available, more landing sites will become possible. Do not spot a field several miles away, however, and begin a long glide. First, the plane may not be able to glide that far. Second, the field may not look as good close up as it did from far away. Plan to stay in close proximity to where the engine failure occurred. Choose a landing site that is easy to see. Circle down to land if necessary.

Answering the question "How long must the field be?" is difficult. Judging distance from the air is tough because of the perspective. Pilots should estimate landing distance in this way. Make a short field landing at the airport and notice where the plane comes to rest. Take off again, and from traffic-pattern altitude look down at the length the landing took. Now compare that distance to the open fields within sight of the traffic pattern. This will increase judgment and lead to better decisions concerning the required length of a landing site. Also, determine how rough the terrain is at the landing site. Land with the run of a plowed field. Plan the approach and landing on a path that provides the least resistance. That means do whatever is necessary to miss rocks, ditches, houses, trees, anything. Also, look to see what obstructions the plane must clear to get to the landing site.

The debate is endless as to what is better. Should a pilot land in a field or on a highway? If the pilot chooses the highway, should the landing be made with or against the traffic? Small, two-lane highways usually have unseen power lines crisscrossing over them. I would choose a field before I would choose a narrow highway. Large, four-lane interstate highways have less power lines and should be considered. I think landing with traffic would be best. But nothing is a sure thing. A small airplane once landed safely on a highway only to rear end a car on the highway. The lady in the car saw the plane in her rear view mirror and in her panic she hit the brakes. Maybe consider the median strip between the lanes of traffic.

What about ditching in the water? The surface of water is flatter than the tops of trees, so water might be an option. Water is not soft, however, and the pilot would also have to consider the passengers on board. The amount of fuel in the tanks might be a consideration, too. Nearly empty gas tanks might allow the airplane to float. What type of landing should be made when a water landing cannot be avoided? Landing gear up or down? If the plane has retractable gear, I would attempt the landing with the gear up. If the landing gear were to get caught in the water, the plane would probably get flipped inverted. With a fixed-gear airplane, go in nose high and stall the tail in first.

If there is no open field in which to attempt a forced landing, and only trees to choose from, land in the top of trees. Two pilots tracking to the Crossville VOR found themselves on a collision course with the trees on the top of Hinch Mountain in Tennessee. They landed in the tree tops and the airplane came to rest approximately 30 feet in the air, still hung up in a tree. Neither pilot was hurt in the crash, but one did suffer a broken leg when he fell out of the tree. The VOR was later named the Hinch Mountain VOR to remind pilots that there was a mountain at that location.

Another method of landing in trees is to place the airplane's fuselage between the trunks of two trees. In theory, the momentum of the plane will be arrested by the force of the wings coming off. My first flight instructor told me to use this technique only as a last resort. He said he knew a man who put an airplane between two trees and walked away without a scratch. The problem was that these two trees stood alone on the side of a huge, flat field that was longer than the runway at the airport.

Before any off-airport landing, verify that everybody has seat belts and shoulder harnesses tight and that the doors are cracked open. Having the doors open will reduce the chance of getting trapped in the plane after touchdown or impact whichever the case may be. Before each takeoff, the pilot should brief the passengers on how to get out of the seat belts and the airplane. This does not have to be an airline-type disaster message, but you do not want passengers trapped in the airplane after a forced landing because they do not know how to operate the seat belt release.

Make a traffic pattern to a forced landing if at all possible. Fly a downwind, base, and final approach to the landing site. By doing this, the pilot can call on his training to guide him. All students have had a flight instructor simulate an engine failure in the traffic pattern. Use the judgment acquired from those practice sessions to help land safely in the field. If the pilot attacks the landing site with an unusual approach path, there can be no judgment to call on because the pilot is seeing the maneuver for the very first time. The simplest flight maneuvers are hard until they are practiced. It only makes sense to go with what you know when there is only one chance to get it right.

Pilots should observe the terrain for possible landing sites at the end of the runways at their home airports. A takeoff from a familiar place should provide no mystery about what lies just beyond the runway. Next time a takeoff is made (and the engine is running perfectly), look for a place to land when the runway has just been passed. Then, in the future, if the engine should quit at that spot, you will already know what to do. Engine failure after takeoff will not allow the pilot any time to look around—have a plan already in mind. If the engine fails on takeoff and there is still runway in front of the plane, land on the remaining runway. Avoid intersection takeoffs. Use the whole runway.

Fix. If there is time, try to determine the problem. The engine might have stopped because one tank has run dry. Switch tanks, hit the boost pump, and the plane is on its way again. Develop a pattern in which all the engine controls can be checked for proper position. In addition to the fuel selector valve, the mixture control, carburetor heat, and magneto switch should be checked. If the airplane has a bad right magneto and the switch is inadvertently turned to the right setting, the engine will stop. Turn the magneto switch to the left position and restart the engine.

If all efforts to restart the engine fail and if there is still time available, make a radio call. This certainly is an emergency, but do not waste valuable time switching the radio to 121.5 MHz if the radio is already monitoring an air traffic control frequency. Any control tower, Flight Service Station, or approach control will relay a MAYDAY call received on their frequency to search and rescue personnel.

Once on the ground, call home and tell whoever answers that you have had a small problem and to go ahead and eat dinner. Then call the airport.

ELECTRICAL SYSTEM FAILURE

An electrical system failure might not be as urgent as a complete engine failure but that depends on when and where it happens. While in VFR conditions during the day, if the electrical system fails it is not a great problem. Avoid areas where two-way radio communications are required, and land as soon as practical. The engine is in no danger. The magneto system will ensure that the engine continues to receive a spark. A pilot can turn off the Master Switch while in flight and the engine will never miss a beat. If the electrical failure occurs at night, the problem becomes being seen. Without electricity, all position, anti-collision, and landing lights will not work.

If the electrical failure occurs while flying in instrument conditions, now there is a big problem. Without electricity, the communications and navigational radios will not work. Without the navigation radios, it will be impossible to determine position while in the clouds. The situation is much worse than loss of two-way radios in instrument conditions. In that situation, the pilot could still navigate to a position and then shoot an instrument approach. With no electricity, the pilot has very few options. There are no Federal Aviation Regulations that pertain to this situation because there is no clear-cut way out. Pilots caught in this situation will have to use every ounce of talent, skill, experience, and luck they can locate to get out of this mess. Before going into clouds, instrument pilots should find out the answer to this question: Where is the nearest VFR weather conditions? If a pilot knows that better weather exists to the north, he should turn the airplane and head north. The magnetic compass and flight instruments will still work (except an electric turn coordinator). Hopefully, the airplane will pop out into the clear before the fuel runs out. Once in the clear, stay in the clear and land. While en route in IFR conditions, fly a VFR altitude. This is a suggestion, not a regulation. If the flight conditions are solid IFR, then nobody is likely to be flying VFR altitudes. This should reduce the chance of crossing another IFR flight's path. Remember, without navigation radios, the pilot in the clouds has no idea where he is. It is possible he is passing through extremely dense airspace without ever knowing it. If the controllers still have the flight on radar, they will vector other traffic out of the way; but there is no guarantee that the plane will remain in radar contact. Without a transponder to reply to the radar interrogations, the target will be harder to identify and no altitude information will be given.

If the nearest VFR conditions are more distant than the range of the fuel on board, the problem goes from bad to worse. Fly toward flat terrain. It is a good idea to take a sectional chart along on IFR flights just for this purpose. Sectionals show elevation; IFR charts have only limited information and no color coding. Now here is the tough part. Remember, there are no good solutions to this problem. Hopefully, the pilot knows his approximate location when the radio failure (or complete electrical failure) occurs.

From a known position, fly over level terrain. The pilot can't know for sure that he is over level terrain, but by using best estimates of distance by figuring direction, speed, and elapsed time, a location can be approximated. Then start a slow 200- to 300-foot-per-minute descent. Hopefully, the plane will break out of the bottom of the clouds prior to hitting the ground. After flying into the clear, land! Land anywhere, do not press luck any further. One idea is to fly out over the ocean or another large body of water if one is in range. The surface of the water is flat, and in the case of the ocean a properly set altimeter will read zero when the pilot should flare. All these ideas represent slim odds. These are only suggestions. What an individual pilot does in a similar situation will depend on the factors surrounding the event. This situation makes a hand-held, battery-operated, walkie-talkie-type transceiver a life saver.

The best idea is to monitor the electrical system gauges to detect any problems (FIG. 10-1). The Ammeter is the instrument that gives information on the status of the battery. If the Ammeter needle deflects to the minus sign, this represents a discharge of the battery. In other words, the alternator or generator on the airplane is not supplying enough current for the electrical demand. The electrical items that are turned on require a certain amount of current flow. If the items can't get the flow from the alternator, they will steal from the battery to make up the difference. Batteries only have so much charge to give, so eventually the battery will be dead and no electricity will be available. If the pilot sees this situation early, conserving the battery can avoid an all-out electrical failure.

A discharge indication of the Ammeter might mean that an alternator has not

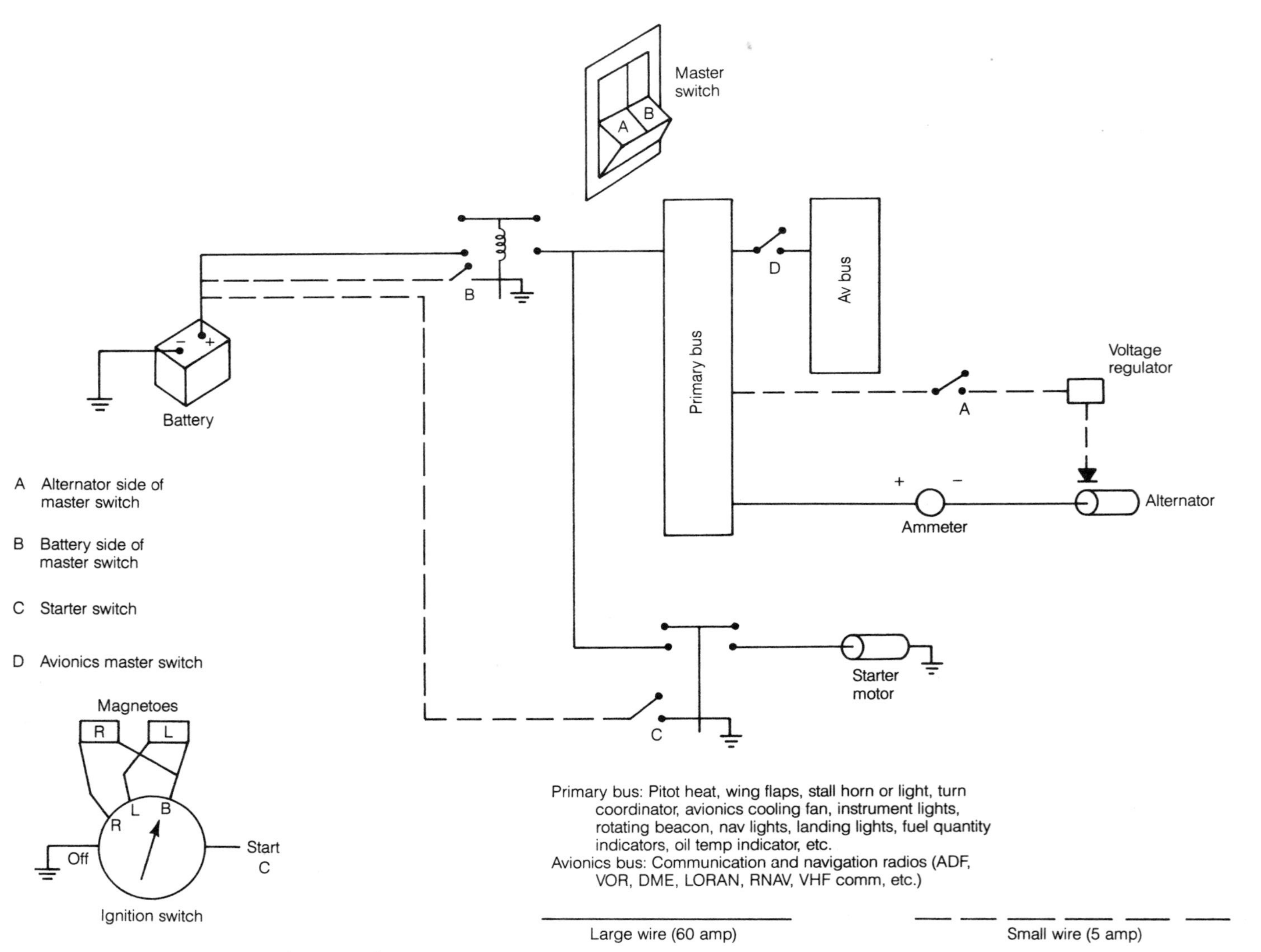

Master switch
A
B
Primary bus
D
Av bus
Voltage regulator
A
+
−
Ammeter
Alternator
Battery
−
+
B
A Alternator side of master switch
B Battery side of master switch
C Starter switch
D Avionics master switch
Starter motor
C
Magnetoes
R
L
R
L
B
Off
Start
C
Ignition switch
Primary bus: Pitot heat, wing flaps, stall horn or light, turn coordinator, avionics cooling fan, instrument lights, rotating beacon, nav lights, landing lights, fuel quantity indicators, oil temp indicator, etc.
Avionics bus: Communication and navigation radios (ADF, VOR, DME, LORAN, RNAV, VHF comm, etc.)
Large wire (60 amp)
Small wire (5 amp)

Fig. 10-1. *Generic electrical system diagram.*

properly come on line and is not functioning at all. Try to activate the alternator with a surge. Turn off all radios or open the Avionics Master Switch; then turn the Master Switch off and back on again. This may bring the alternator to life. The Ammeter should momentarily show a charge as it replaces the current used up from the battery while the alternator was on vacation, but then it should return to zero.

If battery discharge occurs in IFR conditions, and efforts to restore the alternator fail, turn off all electrical equipment except a single radio. Advise the air traffic controller of the problem. Divert to the nearest instrument approach that will get the airplane on the ground. If the nearest approach is farther away than 30 to 45 minutes, work with the controller to go silent. The pilot must have electricity to fly the instrument approach, so saving current until that time is the number one priority. Leaving one radio on while en route could deplete the battery to the point where there will not be enough charge to fly the instrument approach.

The pilot should inform the controller of the severity of the problem and request a heading that will aim the airplane toward the instrument approach. Then turn off everything. The battery is not in use, saving itself for the moment of truth. After a predetermined time interval, turn one radio on. Contact the controller again and ask for the airplane's position. Hopefully, the controller has been watching the airplane all along on radar. If the airplane is near enough to the approach, vectors can begin and the approach be made. If there is still some distance to cover, ask for any heading corrections and go silent again. Repeat the process until in range for the approach.

If the Ammeter shows a continuous charge, a different problem could be taking place. Alternators require a small current flow in order to produce a larger current. The small current is metered out by the voltage regulator. But if the voltage regulator fails, unregulated amounts of current get passed into the alternator. This could set up a chain reaction where larger and larger amounts of current are fed to the alternator. The alternator in turn produces larger and larger output. The system begins to feed itself. The current flow will be much greater than demanded by the electrical items in use. The overflow heads for the battery. The battery overcharges and begins to cook and boil. The alternator is running away, overheating, and could start a fire. The pilot must be aware that a situation like this could develop and take action to stop it.

Every airplane's electrical system is a little different, so for the exact procedure to fix this problem ask a mechanic. However it is done, the current delivery to the alternator must be stopped. In most airplanes, the alternator can be cut out of the system by turning off the alternator side of the Master Switch. This stops the overcharge dangers, but now the electrical system is on borrowed time. The battery will slowly drain away. In a severely critical situation, with the battery going dead, the pilot might consider turning back on the alternator side of the Master Switch to charge the battery back up. Doing this would only put the pilot back in danger from the original problem, and that might be worse. This is a toss-up decision.

Sometimes the Ammeter needle might race repeatedly from side to side, moving from complete charge to complete discharge and back rapidly. This could be caused by severe vibration from the engine, but it could be indicative of a problem in the system. The Alternator produces alternating current, but the equipment in the airplane uses direct current. The system uses rectifiers and diodes to straighten out the current into one useful direction. If the rectifiers are not working properly, the current will escape and go both ways instead of correctly down a one-way path to the equipment. The Ammeter senses the current as it alternates direction back and forth and displays it on the needle. This is not an emergency but should be looked into.

Include a check of the Ammeter in the pre-takeoff runup. Switch the alternator side of the Master Switch to the OFF position and watch to see if the Ammeter needle swings to the discharge. Then verify that the needle jumps into the charge side when the alternator switch is switched back on. This will tell the pilot that the alternator is properly online supplying current and that the Ammeter readings are correct. Include the Ammeter in the instrument scan. Do not let the first indication of electrical problems come from dimming lights or the smell of boiling battery acid.

FIRE

If a pilot sees smoke while inflight, there will be panic. Occasionally, I fly past smoke from a fire on the ground and smell the ashes. If I am with an instrument student who is under the hood, I always tell the student there is smoke from the ground. I do not want him to detect that burning smell and think the airplane is on fire.

If smoke or actual flame is seen by the pilot, action must be taken immediately. The first question that must be determined is: Is it an electrical fire or an engine fire? All good decisions are made from a position of knowledge. The course of action in a fire depends on the source. Electrical fires smell like smoldering wire insulation. It is a good idea to burn a wire, like the kind used in the airplane, and smell it. This will train the nose to distinguish electrical and engine fires.

If the source is determined to be electrical, turn off the Master Switch immediately. Remember, the engine runs just fine without the electrical system, so turning off the Master Switch will not induce a forced landing. After the Master Switch is off, wait until all the smoldering smell is gone or no smoke is visible. Turn off all electrical equipment. If the flight is being conducted in VFR conditions, then leave well enough alone and land. Get light gun signals if you must, but do not try to fix the electrical system in the air. If the electrical fire takes place while flying in IFR conditions, there might be no choice but to do some mechanic work in flight. After the smell and smoke are gone, turn off all other electrical equipment, then turn on the Master Switch. Wait to see if any smoke or smoldering smell recurs. If the smoke does come back, turn the Master Switch back off. This is a very serious problem in the Master Switch circuit. The pilot will have to follow a procedure discussed earlier in the chapter to get out of the clouds without electricity. The choices are fire or IFR with no electricity. These choices are terrible and worse! If after the Master Switch is turned on the smell or smoke does not return, try for one radio. Turn on the one radio most needed to get back on the ground. Then wait again to see if the problem is in the radio. If the smell returns, turn off that radio and try another radio. Keep trying until something is figured out that will work.

If the source is an engine fire, you must get on the ground fast. A decision must be made to keep the engine running or shut it down. If the pilot knows that the flames are contained in the intake of the airplane's induction system, the best thing to do is to allow the engine to run. This will allow the flames to be sucked up into the engine. This situation occurs sometimes when engines are over-primed for start up. Fuel will leak from the carburetor and can ignite if the engine should backfire. But while in flight, from the pilot's point of view, it might be impossible to determine the actual location of the fire. Certainly if flames are visible from under the cowling, the engine should be shut down. The fuel may even be feeding the fire. Take no chances. Pull the mixture control to the idle cutoff position and turn the fuel selector valve to OFF. Yaw the airplane so that flames do not come back toward the cockpit. Choose a suitable landing site, put the plane on the ground any way possible, and get out!

A fire can also start on brakes. It is not uncommon for pilots at busy airports to land long and fast with faster traffic on short final. A controller will often say, "Keep your speed up," to slower, single-engine traffic. This pressures pilots into hotter landings with quick turnoffs. High-speed taxiway turnoffs are used so pilots will not have to slow down as much before exiting the runway. But anytime the taxiway intersects the runway at a 90-degree angle, the braking action required to slow to a safe turnoff speed is increased. During a hard brake, all the force of momentum is concentrated on those small airplane brakes in a very short time. The brake disks can be seen glowing red hot at night sometimes. It is possible for the brake disc and pad to ignite. This could blow or even ignite the tire. The heat could damage the brake lines, causing a brake fluid leak. The brake fluid could burn and feed the fire.

When taxiing off after a hard brake, check to make sure there is no smoke. The wheel pants can hide the fire. If fire is detected, stop and deplane all passengers. Then a decision has to be made: Should the pilot shut down the engine and get out or should he stay with the airplane with the engine running? This decision hinges on whether or not the airport has crash/fire/rescue trucks and equipment on hand.

If fire assistance is available, I would declare an emergency over the tower frequency or ground control. With the engine running, the propwash might push the flames away from the fuselage until the fire trucks arrive. Waiting for trucks in a burning airplane has high risks. Remember that wheel fires are usually located under gas tanks. Do not hesitate to pull the mixture and get out. If the brake is on fire, do not attempt to put the fire out with the fire extinguisher. Metal fires cannot be blown out by the propwash or put out by a small extinguisher. Hopefully, the fire trucks will have enough chemical to put the fire out and save the airplane. If all this takes place at an airport that does not have fire trucks, the decision is different. Push the flames with the propwash just long enough to get the passengers out. Then pull the mixture and follow the passengers. Again, do not attempt to put the fire out with a hand-held extinguisher. To do so would mean getting too close to the fire. The risk does not justify the probable results. The plane at this point might burn completely if no one is coming with real fire equipment to put it out. The loss of an airplane is a high price to pay for a landing that requires excessive braking.

If the brakes are hot when the airplane is parked, do not set the brake. With the brake pads clamped on the hot disc, the disc will cool unevenly and this could cause the disc to warp. The brakes will later wear unevenly and could pull to one side during the next landing deceleration.

Pilots should be aware of the type of fire extinguisher that is carried on the plane if there is one. Not all chemicals placed in extinguishers are the same or do the same jobs. The extinguisher should be checked during every preflight inspection. It should be properly charged and secured to the plane (FIG. 10-2). Do not leave a fire extinguisher, even a small one, lying loose in the cabin because the bottle or canister could become a projectile in turbulent weather conditions. The canister could hit someone or be punctured.

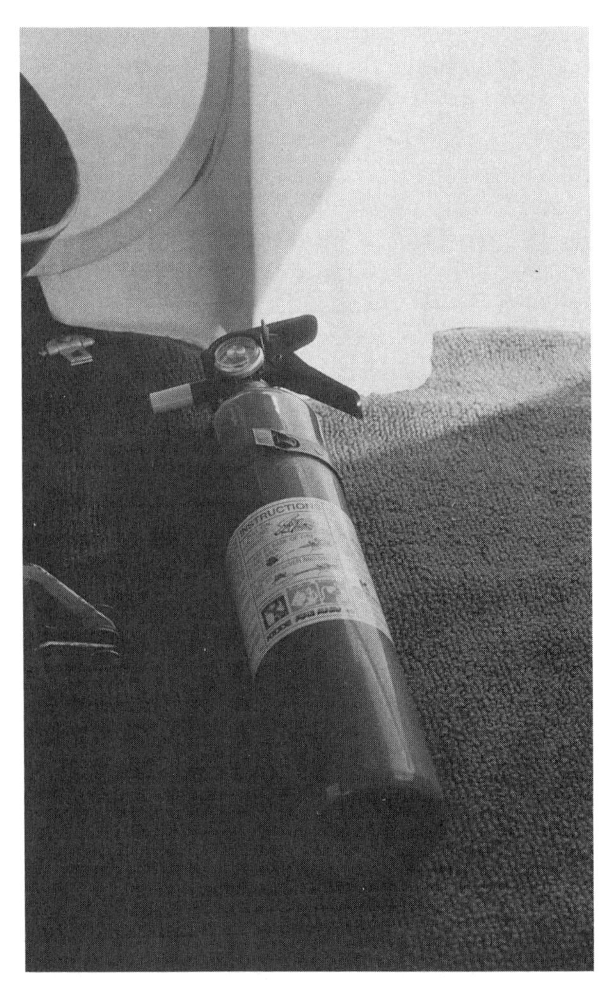

Fig. 10-2. *Fire extinguisher mounted in the baggage compartment of a Cessna 150.*

Chemicals used in fire extinguishers vary, but they can usually be divided into two groups: Carbon Dioxide and Halon. The CO_2 types stop a fire because the Carbon Dioxide molecules, which are not flammable, push the flammable oxygen molecules aside and away from the combustion source. Of course, more oxygen molecules are free to move in again and reignite. Halon stops a fire in a different way. Halon attacks the oxygen molecule and breaks it down. The breakdown causes the oxygen molecule to lose its flammable characteristics, and the fire goes out. There is a large problem, however, with this method. The oxygen that is burning is the same oxygen that is needed by humans to breath. Spraying Halon in a closed space, like a small airplane cockpit, will soon make the space free of oxygen. Once the fire is out, be prepared to quickly ventilate the area so humans can start breathing again.

VACUUM SYSTEM FAILURE

The Attitude Gyro and Directional Gyro are normally operated by a vacuum or a suction system. If the system fails, both instruments will slowly fail as well. Like several other system failures previously discussed, the loss of vacuum is much more critical when it occurs while flying under IFR conditions.

The heart of the system is an air pump that runs off the engine. The pump creates a low pressure area. The higher pressure outside the pump tries to rush in and fill the void. The air is only allowed to rush in through air lines, past the flight instruments, and then to the pump. The air drawn in comes first through a filter. The filter is usually mounted in the cockpit, behind the instrument panel. After the air is filtered, air lines deliver the moving air to the rear of both the Attitude Gyro and Directional Gyro instruments. Once inside the instrument, the air is squeezed down to get the fastest speed and directed across the gyro. The gyro itself has small scoops cut out all around the circumference of the wheel. The scoops cup the air like the buckets on a water wheel. The gyro is gimbaled so it is free to move through any axis. After the air has done the job of pushing the wheel around, it is led out the back of the instruments. The air then travels through the vacuum pressure gauge that indicated the pressure drop to the pilot. Most gyro systems operate with a 4- to 7-inch pressure differential. If the suction was too low, the gyros would not spin as fast and therefore precession would be a problem. The air moves through a relief valve, then to the pump. The pump passes the air overboard.

The shaft that connects the pump to the engine's accessory case is deliberately made to fail. Should the pump ever bind, the shaft will twist apart before the pump breaks. This is so the airplane's owner only buys a new shaft rather than an entire new pump, which costs about $700. The practical problem is that the pilot can never know when the shaft will break and the system stop working. The shaft is not even included in routine maintenance checks. The first time anybody will know there is a problem is when it breaks.

When the vacuum system fails, the air will stop flowing. The gyros, however, will not just stop; they will coast to a stop by winding down. After an airplane is shut down, the gyros can still be heard spinning for several minutes. The same is true when vacuum failure occurs in flight. The gyros spin down and in doing so get less and less reliable to provide stable information. In VFR conditions, this is annoying. In IFR conditions, it can be deadly. Instrument flight instructors simulate a gyro failure by covering up both the Attitude and Directional gyros. This forces the pilot to rely on other instruments for direction, pitch, and bank.

With practice, the pilot can adapt to using the Magnetic Compass instead of the Directional Gyro, and the combination of altimeter, airspeed, and VSI instead of the Attitude Gyro. But this does not deliver a real life situation. If the vacuum system fails, it does so gradually. Covering the instruments creates an instant problem and the student knows exactly what the problem is. In actuality, the Attitude Gyro precesses so slowly that the deflection of the horizon is barely perceived by the pilot. It looks as if a slight turn has begun. The instrument pilot, flying in the clouds, cannot correct this misconception with outside reference and so he follows the gyro. The pilot will be misled into an ever-steepening bank in an effort to right the airplane to the Gyro. Sensations of turning are sent to the pilot's brain, but instrument pilots are trained to ignore these sensations and believe the instruments. But in this case the instruments are liars.

The only hope for the pilot now is to notice the conflicting readings that are presented by the Attitude Gyro and the Turn Coordinator. The Attitude Gyro will show a slight turn, whereas the Turn Coordinator will show a steep turn. The pilot must determine now which is correct and which is not. A look at the vacuum gauge will tell the story. If the vacuum system has failed, the needle will have fallen to zero (it is also possible for it to fail and fall to the high side) just as it does when the engine is shut down. The Turn Coordinator in most cases is an electric gyro that does not rely on vacuum to operate. The gyro instruments are not all operated on the same system just for the purpose of verification during a system failure. When a Turn Coordinator fails, a red flag will be visible. The absence of the flag will verify that the electric instrument is operating when the vacuum instrument has failed. With the operating instrument verified, the pilot can level the airplane's wings and safely continue the flight.

LANDING GEAR EMERGENCIES

Retractable landing gear systems today are extremely reliable (FIG. 10-3). If the landing gear ever does have a problem, there is a manual override to the system that allows the pilot to get the gear down anyway. Usually, the first time a landing gear problem is discovered is on downwind when the gear is first extended. If the gear does not go down and lock the first time, leave the traffic pattern. Fly away from the airport and get some altitude. Do not try to wrestle the gear down as you turn on base and then base to final. Once away from traffic, there will be more time to think through the problem. Go through the manufacturer's recommended procedure for manual gear extension.

Most light airplane retractable systems are combination electric and hydraulic.

Fig. 10-3. *Retractable landing gear and gear doors.*

An electric pump will push hydraulic fluid one way or the other through lines to the landing gear. The hydraulic pressure will either push out or pull up the gear or both. If the gear is held in place against gravity with hydraulic pressure, the pressure is merely released. Then the gear will freefall into place. If it takes pressure to push the gear into place, a gear hand pump will be provided. Just add hydraulic pressure with hand-pump pressure rather than electric-motor pressure. If for any reason this procedure does not successfully put the gear down, remember that the pilot is never alone. Get on the radio. Even at small airports where unicom is the only form of communication, help can be found. Have whoever answers the call get a mechanic or another pilot with experience in the airplane. The more heads working on the problem the better.

When dealing with pent-up hydraulic pressure such as is the case with retractable landing-gear systems, a subsystem must be in place to monitor the pressure in the system. The pressure-sensing devices will have a high and a low threshold. When the gear is in transition, the pump motor is increasing the pressure. When the landing gear stops moving, the pump continues to run to add force to the fluid. But the high pressure sensor will detect when the pressure is sufficient and shut off the pump motor. If the sensor does not work, the motor will continue to run and could eventually burn up the motor.

When the gear is in transition, look to make sure the gear went where you wanted it to go, but also listen and verify that the pump motor did in fact shut off. While in flight, listen for the pump motor to come on in short bursts. If this happens, the low pressure sensor has determined that pressure is not high enough and turned on the pump just long enough to bring the pressure back up to where it belongs. If these short pump operations begin to occur more often, it could be a sign of a hydraulic leak. When the pressure is high, it may squirt fluid out. The absence of fluid will cause the low-threshold pressure switch to turn on the pump and repressurize the system. The higher pressure causes another leak and another pressure loss. The cycle begins again. Eventually, the fluid could be pumped over, leaving the system dangerously low. Manual hand-pump gear-extension systems bring fluid to the hand pump from a low position in the hydraulic reservoir. The electric pump draws fluid from a slightly higher position. In theory, this prevents a leak from causing the pump to drain the reservoir. This means there should always be enough fluid in the system for the hand pump to work.

Systems that work the opposite way hold the landing gear up with pressure. If a leak develops in this system and the pump motor sensor does not activate, the landing gear might slowly start to extend. If the pilot sees this happening, he should go ahead and fully extend the landing gear while there is still enough fluid to push the gear into the locked position. If the pilot waits too long, the gear will partially extend and when a free-fall extension is attempted, the gear will not have very far to fall. This means the gear might not have enough momentum to push through the one-way locks. The gear would then be down but not locked. The only hope of extension now is to induce load factors on the gear. A steep turn might throw the gear down and locked. Violent yawing from side to side might cause centrifugal force to swing the gear out and locked. Try just about anything.

All landing gear systems have some form of warning device to help the pilot remember to extend the landing gear before touchdown. The device may be as simple as a mirror so the nose wheel can be seen from the cockpit or as sophisticated as an airspeed system that automatically drops the gear when the speed of the airplane drops below a predetermined level. Think of these as backup systems. Talk out loud about the position of the landing gear when on takeoff, and definitely before landing. Verify the gear is down and locked when it is first extended. Then verify the gear a second time on short final approach. When I roll out on final and see the runway number, I have taught myself to use that as a reminder to verify the landing gear one more time.

If the landing gear just cannot be extended and a belly landing or a partially extended landing must be made, take your time to get ready. Here decisions will have to be made that pertain to the specific airplane. Should a belly landing be made on grass or on a hard-surface runway? Is an all-wheel-up landing better than a two-wheel-down landing? I suppose that depends on which two wheels it is. Talk this one over with other pilots who are familiar with the particular airplane involved. If a grass landing is best for the plane, get out and walk around the sides of the runway (take a hand-held radio if it is a controlled field) and look at the grass. Determine if the grass is level. Pace off a possible landing path to check for obstructions. This information could prove very valuable if you were to find yourself one day with stuck landing gear.

The number-one mission of a belly landing is to get the pilot and passengers down safely. The airplane comes second. But if there is enough time to plan ahead and enough runway on which to belly land, the pilot might attempt to also save the engine. While on final approach and with the landing site absolutely made, shut down the engine. Raise the nose and lower the airspeed so that the propeller will completely stop. Be very careful here not to get so slow that a stall is imminent. With the propeller stopped and the mixture control back, take the key and bump the starter. Try to leave the propeller parallel with the ground, so when the landing occurs the propeller blades do not touch the ground. This will not work with a three-bladed propeller. Again, this maneuver should not be attempted if it will in any way jeopardize the possibility of a safe landing. Engines are not cheap, but they are replaceable. The pilot and passengers are not.

MULTI-ENGINE PROBLEMS

When manufacturers first placed a second engine on an airplane, the idea was to enable the plane to fly faster and safer. If the engine quits on a single-engine airplane, it would be nice to have a spare to call on. But believing that two engines are always better than one is a big misconception. There are plenty of pilots who have been injured or killed attempting to solve an engine-out problem in a multi-engine airplane. These pilots probably would have survived had the engine failure happened in a single-engine. When all the pilot has is one engine and that engine stops running, what happens next is evident. The pilot will glide to Earth. The pilot does not have to make any decisions except where the touchdown will take place. When a pilot has two engines and one fails, however, there are several more decisions to be made. Having an extra engine might tempt a pilot. Having an extra engine to use "just in case" the other fails is not as simple as it sounds.

On multi-engine airplanes, the thrust does not pull through the center of the airplane. Thrust is pulling from two different locations: one on each wing. If a car is driving 55 mph on a paved road but the driver allows the right side wheels to drop off the pavement into sand, what will happen? The car will yaw severely to the right. The wheels in the sand cannot get a grip and therefore the thrust provided is reduced. At the same time, the left wheels are producing the same thrust as always. The left side of the car tries to outrun the right side of the car. Since the car is all in one piece and will not allow one side to go faster than the other, the car sways.

The same is true with an airplane that has two engines. If one engine suddenly loses power, it will produce less thrust. The good engine, which is still providing thrust, will move ahead. The plane will pivot toward the bad engine (FIG. 10-4). This is still not a problem the pilot cannot overcome. The pilot can use the rudder to hold the airplane straight even though the engine wants to cause the plane to turn. The pilot can reduce the power on the good engine, thus reducing the turning force. If one of the engines fails in flight, the pilot should secure the dead engine by turning off fuel and

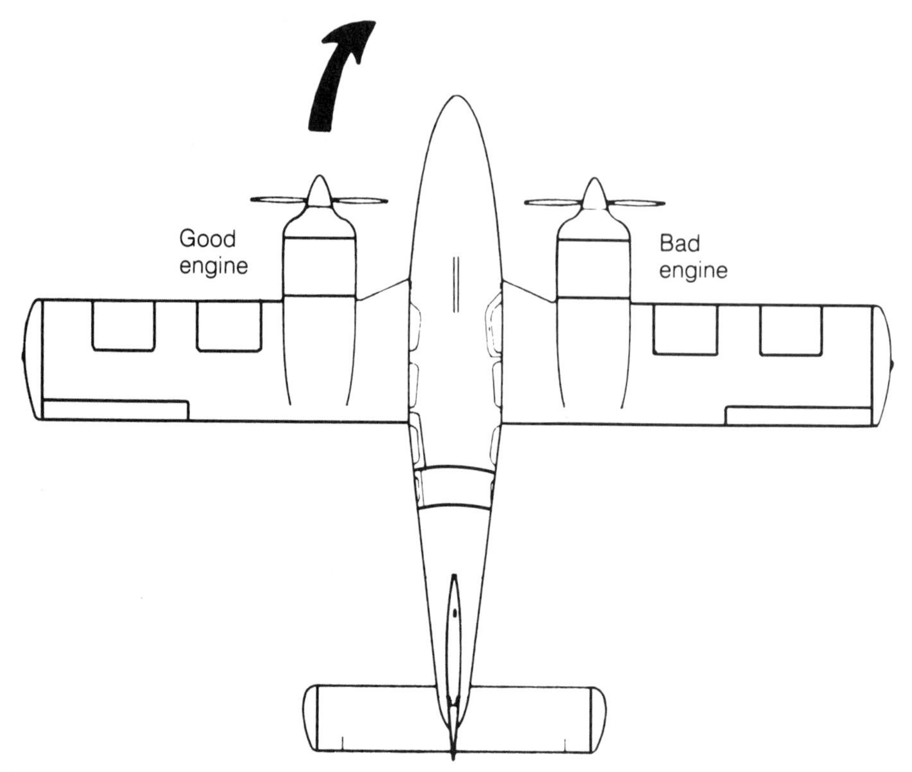

Fig. 10-4. *If the right engine quits while the left engine continues to run, the airplane will yaw to the right. Left rudder would be required to bring the nose of the airplane straight again. At this time, no right rudder is needed and the pilot's foot rests on the floor; thus the term: Dead foot/Dead engine.*

ignition systems. Then, with the proper amount of power on the good engine and the proper amount of rudder to hold the plane straight, the pilot heads for an airport and a safe landing. This situation is better than gliding to an uncertain future when a single-engine airplane loses its only powerplant. But in this situation it was assumed the multi-engine airplane had plenty of speed.

If the speed of the multi-engine airplane is slow, however, the pilot has less options but more decisions. The rudder required to hold the airplane straight against the turning effect of the good engine requires airflow. The airflow strikes the deflected rudder, placing a force on the vertical stabilizer. When the tail moves one way, the nose of the airplane moves the other way. The faster the airflow, the greater this force will be. When a pilot has only one good engine, the force of yaw provided by the rudder has to be very great. When the right engine quits, the left engine causes the airplane to turn to the right. The pilot then adds left rudder to offset the right turn and to bring the nose straight. One force pushes right (engine) and one force pushes left (rudder). This works fine as long as the forces are equal and therefore balance out.

But when the speed gets slow, the rudder cannot provide enough force to offset the engine. If there comes a time when the right turning force cannot be counterbalanced by rudder, the airplane will yaw to the right uncontrollably.

A multi-engine airplane begins a takeoff roll, while on a parallel runway a single-engine airplane starts to take off. Both airplanes leave the ground at the same time. Both still have plenty of runway ahead. The right engine on the multi-engine plane quits. The only engine on the single-engine plane also quits. Which pilot has the best opportunity to avoid an accident? At this moment the single-engine pilot is in a safer situation because his choices are made. He will land on the remaining runway straight ahead and stop.

The multi-engine pilot might believe that since he has a spare engine it will be all right to continue flying. The point of decision is: Use the good engine to fly once around the pattern and land normally or put the airplane back on the ground on the remaining runway. The second option will "look" bad on a short runway. Putting the airplane back down at this point might cause the airplane to run off the far end of the runway and into the approach lights. The pilot might attempt option 1, but the airplane cannot deliver option 1. The airplane is too slow to provide the rudder with enough offsetting force. The engine force will easily overpower the rudder force, and the airplane will yaw out of control. The single-engine pilot walks away; the multi-engine pilot who thought he was safer does not.

The speed at which the rudder can no longer counterbalance the engine is called Velocity—Minimum Control (V_{mc}). The actual speed of V_{mc} varies from plane to plane. And on any one airplane the V_{mc} speed will change. The placement of the center of gravity, the density altitude, the ability of the pilot to feather the dead engine, all these factors and more affect V_{mc}. When learning to fly a multi-engine airplane, decision making must be fast and accurate. Fly every takeoff in the mind before doing it for real. While on the takeoff roll, if one engine shows any sign of a problem, pull back the power on both engines. This will eliminate any unwanted turning effects while the plane decelerates to a stop. The best idea for takeoff is to stay on the ground until accelerating through V_{mc} if this is possible. In this case, the worst thing that could happen if one engine quit would be to pull all power off and roll. Once V_{mc} is exceeded, rotate and fly. But the decisions are not completed. V_{mc} is a control speed only. V_{mc} guarantees that the pilot can keep the nose straight without an uncontrollable yaw. V_{mc} does not guarantee any climb performance. On a hot day, the chances are high that V_{mc} speed will be a descent. A pilot with engine failure on takeoff but who is flying at a speed faster than V_{mc} might only be able to control the airplane as it descends back to Earth. The plane will come down, but the pilot with greater than V_{mc} will at least be able to keep the plane from turning inverted. After takeoff, the pilot needs to accelerate faster than V_{mc} to a speed where a climb is possible on only one engine. When the plane is moving faster than that speed, then for the first time safe flight is possible.

Engine failures on takeoff are rare, but if they happen they will happen quickly. The best decisions are made after the pilot has time for contemplation. A takeoff engine failure will allow little or no time for thought, so decisions must be made early. Considering all the factors that affect aircraft control and performance, decide before takeoff what options are available at what speeds. There is a speed on every takeoff that represents a dividing line. If an engine fails short of that line, the pilot must bring the plane down, even if that means running through the approach lights. If an engine fails beyond that line, then flight is possible. Determine the speed before rolling onto the runway and stick with the decision. A multi-engine instructor can discuss the exact procedures required for a particular airplane. These procedures provide good judgment and are good decision-making skills.

UNUSUAL ATTITUDES

Not all emergencies are induced by mechanical problems. The single most deadly thing a VFR pilot can do is fly into a cloud and get disoriented. Spatial Disorientation, or Pilot's Vertigo, can fool the brain into believing things that simply are not true. The brain gets position information from three sources: the body, the inner ear, and the eyes.

The position of muscles and organs in the body feels normal when gravity pulls them from head to toe. When a person stands on his head, he knows this without looking. The blood rushes to the head, and the body just feels out of place. The brain has become accustomed to depending on the sensations for reliable position information. Unfortunately, while in flight gravity is not the only force that acts on the body. Centrifugal forces and turbulence work together to trick the body into sending false sensations to the brain.

The inner ear is the worst liar to the brain while in flight. The inner ear has three semicircular canals, each filled with fluid. The three canals are fixed like the three axes of an airplane (FIG. 10-5). When motion of the head begins, the fluid in the canal remains stationary for a moment. Extending into the canals are small sensing hairs. When the canal moves and the fluid remains in place, the hairs will bend like blades of grass in the wind. The deflection of the hairs tells the brain that motion has taken place.

If a turning motion continues, eventually the fluid in the canals will start to move and equal the speed of the canal. This will allow the hairs to slowly stand erect again. This tells the brain that no motion is present when in fact the body is still in a turn. If the turn is abruptly stopped, the canal will stop but the fluid will rush on. This will send a strong turning message to the brain when in fact the body is motionless. This sensation can be reproduced by experiment in a rotating chair. When these sensations take place, the brain verifies the motion by using the eyes. If the eyes confirm the motion, then the motion is understood. If the eyes cannot be used to verify a motion, the brain can only rely on the message from the inner ear. While flying in the clouds, the eyes will have no outside reference. The brain will believe the message from the inner ear even if it is in error.

Eyesight is the only information source that is reliable in flight. In the clouds the eyes cannot see the horizon, so the instruments try to paint a picture of what is really

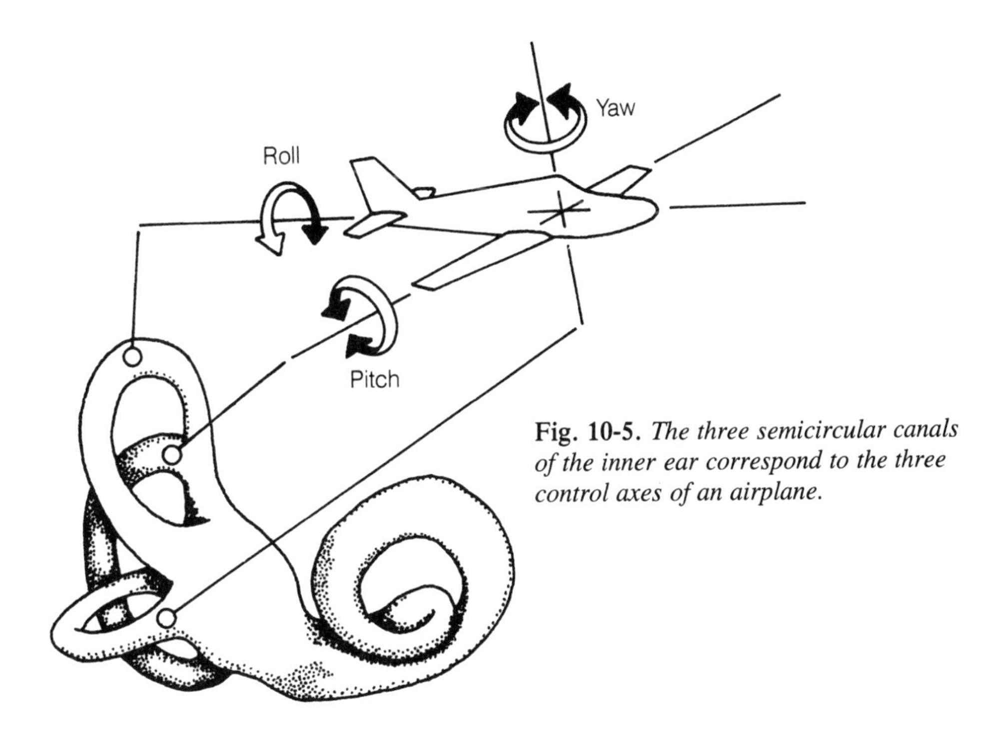

Fig. 10-5. *The three semicircular canals of the inner ear correspond to the three control axes of an airplane.*

out there. While in the clouds, pilots must ignore the messages the brain is receiving and rely on the flight instruments only. This is hard to do. VFR pilots have gotten so disoriented that they tore their airplanes apart in the sky with their violent attempts to recover.

When a VFR pilot, or a non-current IFR pilot, enters the clouds, it is an emergency. If a cloud is entered, get out. The best action is usually to make a 180-degree level turn. The pilot knows that clear air is just behind. What is ahead, below, and above are all unknowns. When the turn is made, use only a shallow bank. Pilots have gotten in the clouds, and in their haste to get out they have turned so steeply that control of the airplane was lost. Watch both the Attitude Gyro and the Turn Coordinator. Mentally place yourself inside the little airplane on the Attitude Gyro and fly that plane. Use the Turn Coordinator to verify the bank is not too steep. Place the wing tip of the Turn Coordinator's airplane on the "hash-mark" of the indicator. This signifies that a standard-rate turn is in progress. Before beginning the turn, notice what the heading is off the tail of the airplane. This is the heading that should be turned to in order to get out. While in the turn, concentrate on the instruments. Do not stare at any one instrument, but use them all together. Work hard to override whatever sensation your body is feeling and fly the little airplane in the Attitude Gyro.

If at any time the plane's attitude is other than what you desire, take the following steps: If the nose is high and the wings are banked, lower the nose to the horizon first. This will prevent the airplane from stalling. If the nose pitch is so high that a stall is imminent, then put the nose at or just below the horizon and add full power; in other words, make a normal stall recovery. After the nose is on the horizon, slowly level the wings. Control any altitude change with a power change.

If the nose is low and the wings are banked, level the wings first. If an attempt is made to raise the nose first, the turn will only be tightened and the situation aggravated. After the wings are level, gradually bring the nose back up to the horizon. During this time, the power might need to be reduced. A high power, nose low condition could cause the entire airplane to overspeed and place it in danger of overstressing. Once the nose is back on the horizon, the power can be reset to maintain altitude.

Do not just rely on this discussion. Spatial Disorientation is something pilots must actually feel to believe. Practice unusual attitude recoveries with a competent instructor. But most of all, stay out of the clouds until you are proficient and on an IFR flight plan.

11
Medical Decisions

ALL AIRPLANE PILOTS GET MEDICAL EXAMS. IN THE PAST THEY WERE JUST just to determine if a person was healthy enough to fly an airplane. Now they are much more. The FAA is using the medical-certificate process for enforcement of several new rules. The basic idea of medical certificates is to make reasonably sure that a pilot while flying an airplane will not become unable to get back on the ground safely due to some illness. There is no guarantee that something like that won't happen despite the precautions, but the FAA cuts down the odds with medical certificates. Medical certificates are issued only by doctors who are authorized Aviation Medical Examiners.

It is up to the individual pilot to maintain his medical certificate. The FAA does not send reminders. While the pilot is exercising his duties as pilot in command of an aircraft, he must keep his medical certificate with him. If the certificate has any limitations, the holder must be observing those limitations. For instance, if a medical certificate indicates in the limitations section that "the holder shall wear correcting lenses while exercising the privileges of his/her airman certificate," then the person must wear eyeglasses or contact lenses. This seems obvious, but the FAA has recently gone on a campaign of "ramp checks" and if a pilot is asked for a medical certificate and does not have it or is not observing the limitations of the certificate, the pilot will get suspended, and maybe fined. Do not get caught without your paperwork.

A Michigan man died at the wheel of a Piper Cherokee 180. He had a heart attack and left his passenger to figure out his own way to get back down. It turned out that the man had no medical or pilot certificates at all. The passenger was a private pilot but had not had a medical exam in 12 years. The plane landed safely.

MEDICAL CERTIFICATION

Medical certificates come in three classes: first, second, and third. The third-class medical certificate is required for solo flight by student pilots, for a private pilot certificate, and for any add-on ratings like the instrument rating. The second-class medical certificate is required to become a commercial pilot and to exercise the privileges of a commercial pilot. To be a flight instructor, or to hold any other piloting job that is included in FAR part 135.1, a second-class medical is required. A first-class medical is required for the Airline Transport Pilot Certificate (ATP) and is usually a requirement for airline employment (FIG. 11-1). Prospective ATPs must have a first-class medical certificate before they are allowed to take the ATP written exam. The pilot must make an appointment with an FAA inspector to get his logbook "certified" and medical certificates checked. After the inspector determines that the pilot's logbook has at least 1,500 legitimate hours of flight time and a first-class medical, he gives him a permit to take the ATP written once.

UNITED STATES OF AMERICA
DEPARTMENT OF TRANSPORTATION
FEDERAL AVIATION ADMINISTRATION

MEDICAL CERTIFICATE First **CLASS**

THIS CERTIFIES THAT *(Full name and address)*
Nathaniel Latham Bost, Jr.

DATE OF BIRTH	HEIGHT	WEIGHT	HAIR	EYES	SEX
10/18/69	73	180	BRown	Brown	Male

has met the medical standards prescribed in Part 67, Federal Aviation Regulations for this class of Medical Certificate.

LIMITATIONS
Holder shall wear corrective lenses while exercising the privileges of his airman certificate.

DATE OF EXAMINATION	EXAMINER'S SERIAL NO
05/03/90	08828-4

EXAMINER
SIGNATURE
TYPED NAME Joseph Shelton Bower, M. D.

AIRMAN'S SIGNATURE Nathaniel Latham Bost, Jr.

FAA FORM 8500-9 (10-73) SUPERSEDES PREVIOUS EDITION

Fig. 11-1. *First class medical certificate.*

Certain medical certificates can also serve as a pilot certificate in the case of student pilots (FIG. 11-2). When a pilot goes to the FAA-approved Medical Examiner for the first time, he receives a combination medical and student pilot certificate. Both are required before a student pilot is allowed to fly solo. The back of the medical/student certificate is very important. This is where a flight instructor must make an endorsement making student pilot solo flights legal. The instructor signs one endorsement for the first solo and again for the first solo cross-country. Medical/student certificates are yellow. Medical certificates are white. Occasionally a student pilot will be issued a medical certificate with no student certificate. The only way this happens is if the medical branch of the FAA in Oklahoma City, Oklahoma, has a question concerning a student's eligibility for a medical certificate. If the question is later solved, the FAA sends the student a new medical certificate but may not send a new student certificate.

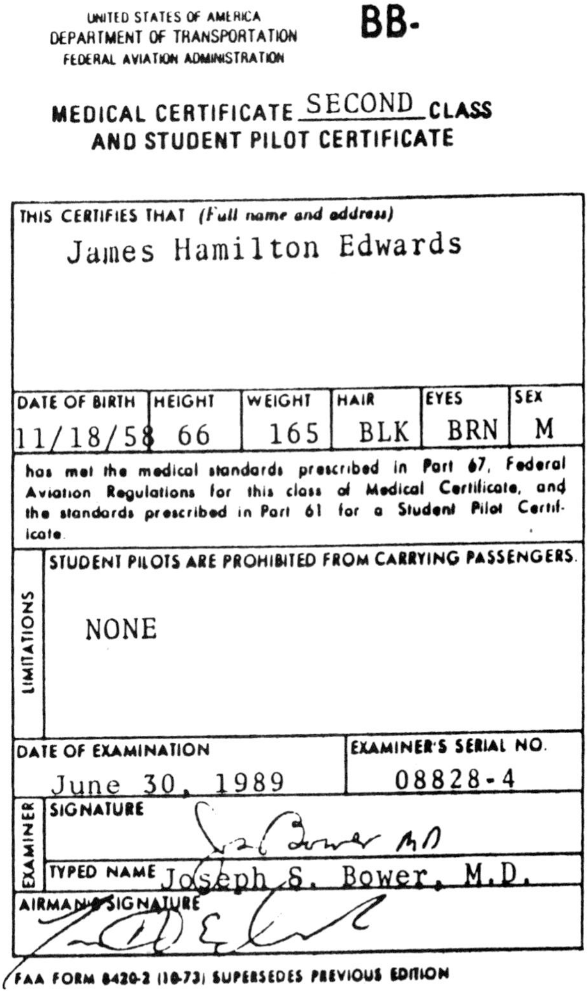

UNITED STATES OF AMERICA
DEPARTMENT OF TRANSPORTATION
FEDERAL AVIATION ADMINISTRATION

BB-

MEDICAL CERTIFICATE SECOND CLASS
AND STUDENT PILOT CERTIFICATE

THIS CERTIFIES THAT *(Full name and address)*
James Hamilton Edwards

DATE OF BIRTH	HEIGHT	WEIGHT	HAIR	EYES	SEX
11/18/58	66	165	BLK	BRN	M

has met the medical standards prescribed in Part 67, Federal Aviation Regulations for this class of Medical Certificate, and the standards prescribed in Part 61 for a Student Pilot Certificate.

LIMITATIONS
STUDENT PILOTS ARE PROHIBITED FROM CARRYING PASSENGERS.
NONE

DATE OF EXAMINATION	EXAMINER'S SERIAL NO.
June 30, 1989	08828-4

EXAMINER
SIGNATURE
TYPED NAME Joseph S. Bower, M.D.

AIRMAN'S SIGNATURE

FAA FORM 8420-2 (10-73) SUPERSEDES PREVIOUS EDITION

Fig. 11-2. *Medical certificate and student pilot certificate combination.*

In this case, a student certificate can be obtained from any FAA inspector or designated pilot examiner. To get the certificate, just fill out the top portion of an Airman Application for Certification and check the box for student pilot.

If you are beginning to fly and are interested in a career as a pilot, it is a good idea to go ahead and get the class of medical certificate required for the type of flying you intend to pursue. It is possible to get a first-class medical on a student pilot certificate. The actual certificate will most likely expire before you ever get the job, but you will know that your health meets the standards before you spend lots of money on lessons. The information about what is possible for a pilot to do would have a great bearing on training decisions. I have had students who were told that the only medical certificate they could ever get was a third-class. This fact alone would rule out any commercial flying.

The first-class medical is good for only six months of pilot operations that require a first-class. After the last day of the sixth calendar month past the examination, the certificate is only good for operations requiring a second-class medical. After 12 calendar months, the certificate can only be used for pilot operations that require a third-class medical certificate. After 24 calendar months, the certificate is good for nothing. At all times during this time periond, the certificate remains a first-class medical. The certificate does not downgrade, only the privileges of its use. The first-class medicals require:

1. Eyesight. Pilots can wear glasses and still receive a first-class medical, but their glasses must correct their vision to at least 20/20. A test is also given for eyesight without correction. Without glasses or contact lenses, the applicant must see 20/100. Tests are also made for near vision, color blindness, field of vision, and diseases.
2. Ear, Nose, Throat, and Equilibrium. The applicant must be able to hear a whispered voice at a distance of at least 20 feet. Also the eardrum, middle ear, inner ear, and equilibrium are tested.
3. Mental condition. The doctor attempts to determine if the applicant has any personality disorders, alcoholism, or drug dependence. There is no mention in the regulations as to how the doctor will meet this requirement.
4. Neurological disorders. The doctor asks questions to determine if the applicant has a history of epilepsy, disturbance of consciousness, or convulsions.
5. Cardiovascular. The doctor determines through medial history and clinical diagnosis if the applicant has ever had Myocardial infarction, Angina pectoris, or any coronary disease. When the pilot is between the ages of 35 and 40, he must have an electrocardiographic examination. The pilot only needs one such exam until after the age of 40; then the exam is required annually. Blood pressure is taken in a reclining position and cannot exceed the maximum limits of the chart provided:

Age	Systolic	Diastolic
20 to 29	140	88
30 to 39	145	92
40 to 49	155	96
50 and older	160	98

6. General medical condition. The applicant cannot have a medical history of diabetes that requires insulin or any other medical condition that the Federal Air Surgeon believes would compromise safety in the air.

The second-class medical is good for 12 calendar months for commercial operations and 24 calendar months for private pilot operations. The medical requirements for a second-class medical are virtually the same as for a first-class. The vision requirements are the same. The only differences are that for a second-class medical, the whispered voice can come from only eight feet, and electrocardiographic examinations are not required at any age.

The third-class medical is good for non-commercial flying and lasts for 24 calendar months. Third-class medicals require uncorrected vision of 20/50. If the vision is poorer than 20/50, the applicant must use correction so that the vision becomes 20/30. This means that no matter how bad your vision is, if glasses can make you see 20/30 you can be a private pilot. The whispered voice need only be heard from three feet and electrocardiographic exams are never needed.

If a pilot ever fails to meet the medical standards, his medical certificate can be denied. If a denial is given, the pilot has 30 days in which to ask for reconsideration by the FAA Medical Branch in Oklahoma. If the pilot does not take action within 30 days, the medical application is considered to be withdrawn. If a certificate is denied because of one or more requirements, it might not be the end of the world. A "Certificate of Demonstrated Ability" could be issued. This is a waiver of the requirements in one individual's case. When he was examined for a student pilot certificate, one of my students discovered that he had a borderline case of color blindness. His medical was issued with the statement, "night flying prohibited." We arranged for the student to "demonstrate" to FAA officials that he could distinguish red, green, and white (the colors on the ATC light gun signals). The student stood in my office, which has a view of the control tower. An FAA inspector called the tower and asked them to shine a light to my office window. The light came on. The student said, "That is green." He was correct. He did the same for red and white and passed the test. The notation about night flying was removed. That was an easy problem to solve, but other waivers are tougher to get. Some waivers require that the pilot remain grounded until all the paperwork is complete, while others allow the pilot to continue to fly. Each case is handled differently.

One of the questions on the medical certificate application deals with a person's driving record. Here is where the medical certificate is used as an enforcement tool.

The state of Florida was tested first. Police records in that state were cross-referenced with the question about driving record on pilot medical exams. The FAA wanted to determine how often pilots lie on this question. What they found was that pilots lie a lot. Now the cross-check is nationwide. I had a young man as a flight student who got caught. He passed his medical exam, and a short time thereafter I let him fly solo. He had his sights set on the airlines and a great career in flying. About two weeks after his first solo, he stormed into my office. He held a letter from the FAA. His medical certificate has been revoked. The reason: He had two drunk driving arrests on his police record. The revocation was for life!

Today if you are caught drinking and driving, you put your flying on the line. I know another student who received a letter concerning speeding tickets that were more than 10 years old! That student eventually got his medical back but spent a month tracking down court records and recommendations. The FAA feels there is a direct correlation between the way pilots drive and and the way they fly.

The eyesight requirements prevent many pilots from going very far in a flying career. Currently there are two treatments that in theory will improve vision. The first is called Orthokerototomy commonly called OrthoK. Orthodontics is a branch of dentistry that specializes in changing the shape of a person's teeth. Orthokerototomy changes the shape of the cornea, or lens, of the eye. The lens focuses an image on the retina (the eye's film) so that vision is possible. When vision is poor, it is usually because the focus of the lens is in front of or behind the focal point of the retina. By changing the shape of the lens, the focus changes and vision improves. The shape change occurs over time by using different contact lenses. The patient starts out with contact lenses that change the shape very little. After the lens has adapted to the small change, a new set of contact lenses are used. Gradually the lens shape is altered. Be careful, however; this is no recommendation. The lens could move back to the original position. Pilots wear these lenses until moments before their medical exam (The FAA requires they be removed for 24 hours prior to the exam). This allows their uncorrected vision to be within limits during the eye test. Many pilots keep flying in this way.

The more radical and risky treatment is surgery of the eye. The procedure is called Radialkeratology. From the center of the Cornea, several incisions are made in a radial pattern. This produces "flaps" in the lens of the eye. The flaps are then refolded in a new shape. The lens then heals with a new shape and a new focus position on the retina. This procedure is not recommended for pilots. In fact, the American Medical Association has suggested to the FAA that anybody having this surgery be denied first- and second-class medical certificates. Patients who have had the treatment have had mixed results and usually have extremely poor vision to begin with.

DRUG TESTING

In the 1990's pilot drug testing is a fact. All pilots involved in any commercial operation must be tested. The FAA has identified three pilot groups that are subject to testing. Group A is made up of all Part 121, or Air Carrier, pilots. Group B are pilots flying under Part 135, Air Taxi or Charter, in a company with 11 or more employees. Group C are Part 135 pilots who work in companies with less than 11 employees. All flight instructors, and even ground instructors, have been placed in Group C as well. Some groups and individual companies already require drug testing, but after April 10, 1991, all pilots in all groups will be tested.

Pilots can argue about the invasion of privacy issue, but the fact remains: The FAA feels that the responsibility of being a pilot is so significant that individual rights can and will be ignored. Pilots are now judged not only by the content of their skills but by the content of their urine. Each pilot in groups A, B, and C must submit to six types of tests:

1. Pre-employment. Every commercial pilot's job interview now is an evaluation of a pilot's drug use. A positive test will cause the employer to look elsewhere for a pilot.
2. Periodic. Pilots must be tested on a regular basis throughout the year during their employment.
3. Random. Since a pilot could "clean up" for the periodic test, an unexpected test is required.
4. Reasonable Cause. If a pilot is suspected of drug use, his employment can be suspended until he proves himself innocent by a drug test.
5. Post Accident. When a pilot is involved in an aircraft accident, a drug test is required to determine if drug use was a cause or factor in the accident.
6. Return to Duty. If a pilot is suspended for drug use by a company, the pilot must prove that he is drug free by a drug test prior to beginning work again.

Each company must designate an "Anti-drug manager" within the company. The manager determines how the company will conduct drug testing. The manager must choose a drug testing laboratory that is approved by the FAA. The U.S. Department of Health and Human Services maintains a list of approved labs. The manager must select a site for the drug testing to take place and be in charge of collecting urine samples. The manager must keep the samples secure until testing and remain confidential about all results. The company must train the employees about the effects of drug use and how to recognize drug use in a person. The drug testing must at least look for marijuana, cocaine, opium, codeine, morphine, PCP, and amphetamines.

The cost of the test will be the responsibility of the company if the pilot works for a company. But what if the pilot is an independent? Free-lance flight instructors and other commercial pilots must pay for their own tests. How does an individual give himself a "random" drug test? The FAA says that individuals working independently for a company with a drug testing program must go to their local Flight Standards District Office (FSDO) and draw a date from a hat. The hat (or other container) will contain every date of the year. The FAA inspector will write down the date that the pilot drew from the hat, but the pilot will not know which date was drawn. Then when the day arrives the FAA will call the pilot and say, "Today is the day! Drop everything and get a drug test done now!"

All pilots are justifiably concerned that the drug tests can be flawed and that the possibility exists for clean pilots to test positive for drugs. If this were to occur, the innocent pilot's career and reputation would be on the line. The best advice to guard against a false positive is to take two tests. When a test is required, give a sample to the manager. Then get in the car and go give a second sample to a different lab. The second test will of course have to be paid for by the pilot. If the first test comes back positive while the second test given on the same day is negative, the pilot will have a better defense.

No provision in these rules speaks to alcohol abuse. Alcohol addiction is supposed to be covered in the airman's medical exam. The fact is that if you take drugs and fly, you will eventually be caught if you ever try to fly for a living. Non-commercial pilots are not currently tested.

MEDICAL DEFICIENCY

The Federal Aviation Regulations require that pilots police themselves in regards to medical problems. If a pilot discovers, between medical exams, that his health has fallen below the requirements of the certificate he holds, he is supposed to take himself out of the game. This would involve a major change in health from the time of the last exam. Most pilots know that when a serious illness or injury occurs, a proper recuperation prior to flight would be required. A larger problem is the use of over-the-counter medications used before flight. Pilots need to be aware that a drug in the system at sea level might not produce any side effects. The same drug in a person's system at 10,000 feet, however, might render the pilot unable to fly. The pilot will not notice an altitude reaction until it is too late.

The best decision when it comes to any medication is: Do not take ANY and fly. The list of everyday medications that could be dangerous in flight include: tranquilizers, pain relievers, cough-suppressants, antihistamines, blood pressure drugs, diarrhea and motion-sickness preventatives, muscle relaxants, and sedatives. When these drugs get into the bloodstream, they can inhibit the acquisition of oxygen. The pilot can suffer symptoms of hypoxia at much lower altitudes than expected.

Over-the-counter medications can affect a pilot's memory, alertness, coordination, and vision. They can prevent the pilot from making calculations and impair his judgment. All these factors have been discussed earlier as essential ingredients to good decision making. All the skill, knowledge, and experience in the world cannot be relied upon if the body cannot process information properly. If you must take a certain medication, talk to a physician about possible effects of the drug and altitude. The best decision is to avoid all medications prior to flight.

PREVENTION

As a pilot you must protect your health. Without a medical certificate you will no longer be a flier. Exercise and stay in shape. Catching a problem early is important because preventive measures might be available that will prevent eventual medical certificate denial.

Hearing loss is common among pilots. Pilots are usually exposed to long durations of steady noise. I sit behind a propeller sometimes up to six hours a day. Years of noise abuse on the ears can cost a hearing loss—and a medical certificate. Loud noises can cause a temporary threshold shift that will decrease hearing ability. Prolonged exposure can cause a permanent threshold shift. When nerve fibers in the inner ear are destroyed because of noise, they do not regenerate. Partial or complete deafness can result. Pilots who are exposed to airplane noise on a daily basis should use ear protection in some form. The simplest and most widely used form of protection are earplugs. It is important that they be inserted properly for best results (FIG. 11-3). Headsets are excellent as well.

Good decision making must include an evaluation of the decision maker. The condition of the pilot is as important to safety as the condition of the weather and airplane.

Fig. 11-3. *Pilot using earplugs to reduce the chance of hearing loss.*

12
The Anatomy of an Accident

VERY FEW ACCIDENTS ARE CAUSED BY A SINGLE FACTOR. MOST ACCIDENTS are the result of an accumulation of bad decisions. The goal of any pilot is to recognize when a chain of bad decisions is forming and break it. In this chapter we will fly with real pilots who made poor decisions. These pilots each reached a point of decision and made the wrong choice. In some cases the pilots made a succession of poor choices, each leading to tragedy. These accidents are all real and are taken from the National Transportation Safety Board's public records. This is not an attempt to place blame on anyone; but by seeing the decision process break down, it will be easier to recognize when it starts happening to you.

THE CLASSIC CASE OF "GET-THERE-ITIS"

A 43-year-old private pilot planned a VFR trip one morning from Wichita to Greenburg, Kansas. He had logged 76 total flight hours prior to the flight in question. The flight was in a Cessna 172.

The man called the Wichita Flight Service Station at 6:20 a.m. and requested a weather briefing for his VFR flight. The FSS records all conversations on the radio and telephone. The discussion between pilot and briefer was taken from the FSS transcript:

FSS Briefer: *''Roger, weather system here this morning is low pressure, still way out west of us, be approaching southwestern Colorado here this morning. Right now, got a lot of moist air up ahead of it.*

Some cloud cover. We've got ceilings running 2,300 overcast here at Wichita, visibility 20, temperature staying up at 44 degrees, and our winds are southeast 160 at 14. Back at Dodge City [near the pilot's destination of Greensburg] *well, they have picked up some lower clouds. They're measured 900 broken, 3,800 overcast, visibility at 15, temperature at 42, dewpoint 36. South winds 180 at 15. The freezing level there about 8,000 feet on the RADAT (temperature balloon) at 6:00.''*

Pilot: "Okay, what's the wind at 3,000 and 6,000—oh, you gave it, yeah, okay."

FSS Briefer: *''Ah, 3,000 would be 170 at 30. 6,000 210 at 35, and nine, 220 at 38. Were you going IFR on that?''*

Pilot: "Yes."

FSS Briefer: *''Oh, okay, their, uh, forecast really hadn't called for what they have got. They were calling for about 1,600 overcast this morning, slight chance of some light rain.''*

Pilot: "Okay, doesn't look like anything real serious moving in before noon or so, does it?"

FSS Briefer: *''Well no, we're just getting the overrunning up ahead of that low pressure and we had a pilot report here on the top at Wichita at 6,500 and a higher layer above. That's probably a multilayer cloud. As the day goes on, it'll probably lower the ceilings.''*

Pilot: "Yeah, I expect to be there and back."

FSS Briefer: *''You know a 1,000 feet or less across the area.''*

Pilot: "I expect to be there and back by 11."

FSS Briefer: *''Well, the lower conditions, you know, those 500-foot ceilings and that'll probably come late afternoon, this evening.''*

Pilot: "All right, I'm not too sure yet whether I'm going. I gotta call a guy, but just wanted to see what it looks like."

The pilot hung the phone up. The conversation shows signs of serious judgment flaws and poor decisions. First, I feel this pilot was determined to make this flight, so he heard what he wanted to hear from the briefer. He did not acknowledge the fact that conditions at an airport near his destination were reported as a ceiling of 900 broken. Then, when the briefer pressed him on the type of flight plan, "Were you going IFR on that?" the pilot said "yes," even though he was not instrument rated. If the pilot would have said "no," surely this briefer would have then said, "VFR is not recommended." But the briefer was allowed to think that this was a proposed IFR flight. That had an influence on the way he answered the question, "Okay, doesn't look like anything serious moving in before noon or so, does it?" The meaning of the word *serious* is different when describing VFR and IFR. To an IFR pilot the existence of clouds is understood, so the word *serious* means conditions of ice, turbulence, or storms. The briefer had no reports or forecasts that would indicate severe IFR weather.

The word *serious* to a VFR pilot is different. Any low clouds would be serious to a VFR flight. This pilot was good at deception. He had obviously done this before. Then, at the end of the conversation when a flight plan is usually filed, he backed out with an excuse: "I'm not sure yet whether I'm going. I gotta call a guy." If a pilot has such poor judgment that he must mislead the FSS briefer, the very person who can help, then he is an accident looking for a time and place to happen.

The pilot took off at 6:58 a.m. The last that was ever heard of him was when he responded to the takeoff clearance. Five minutes before the takeoff, Dodge City issued their hourly report of the weather. The area around the Dodge City airport had a measured ceiling of 500 feet overcast and a visibility of 12 miles. The information was in the system that told of the IFR conditions near the pilot's destination, but the pilot never again accessed the system.

There is evidence that suggests that this pilot thought nothing of flying near or in the clouds while VFR. During the investigation of this event, the pilot's wife told an accident investigator that her husband was capable of flying in the clouds. She had been with him on two other flights when he climbed and descended through the clouds. He probably anticipated flying just under or maybe in the clouds on this flight. That may have been why he did not ask any questions about the low ceilings in the first place. He may have believed that he was just fine staying outside the system and the rules. He had done so many times before and would do so again.

His decision to take off was flawed from the beginning. The decision was based on overconfidence and misunderstandings. It was determined that the pilot must have been following Highway 54, which goes almost directly between Wichita and Greensburg (FIG. 12-1). Within 20 minutes after departure, the pilot passed near the Kingman airport. The elevation of the ground had risen from about 1,300 feet in Wichita to 1,600 feet at Kingman. A few minutes after this, the Dodge City weather observer saw things changing rapidly and issued a Special Observation that reported the ceiling now at 400 feet overcast and four miles visibility with fog. This information was now in the system.

The pilot was at a point of decision even if he did not know it. Options: Call for the latest weather information in the face of lowering clouds or say nothing and continue on.

The pilot flew on as the clouds came down and the ground came up. North of Kingman is the Hutchinson VOR. The chart lists the Wichita FSS as a parent facility for this facility. The VOR information box indicates that the Wichita FSS will listen on 122.1 and respond on the VOR frequency of 116.8. The pilot could have easily accessed the weather information. If he had known of the weather and recognized it as dangerous, he could have made the decision to return to Wichita or land at Kingman. He did not talk to anyone but flew on in silence.

Forty minutes after takeoff, he would have flown over the Pratt Airport. South of

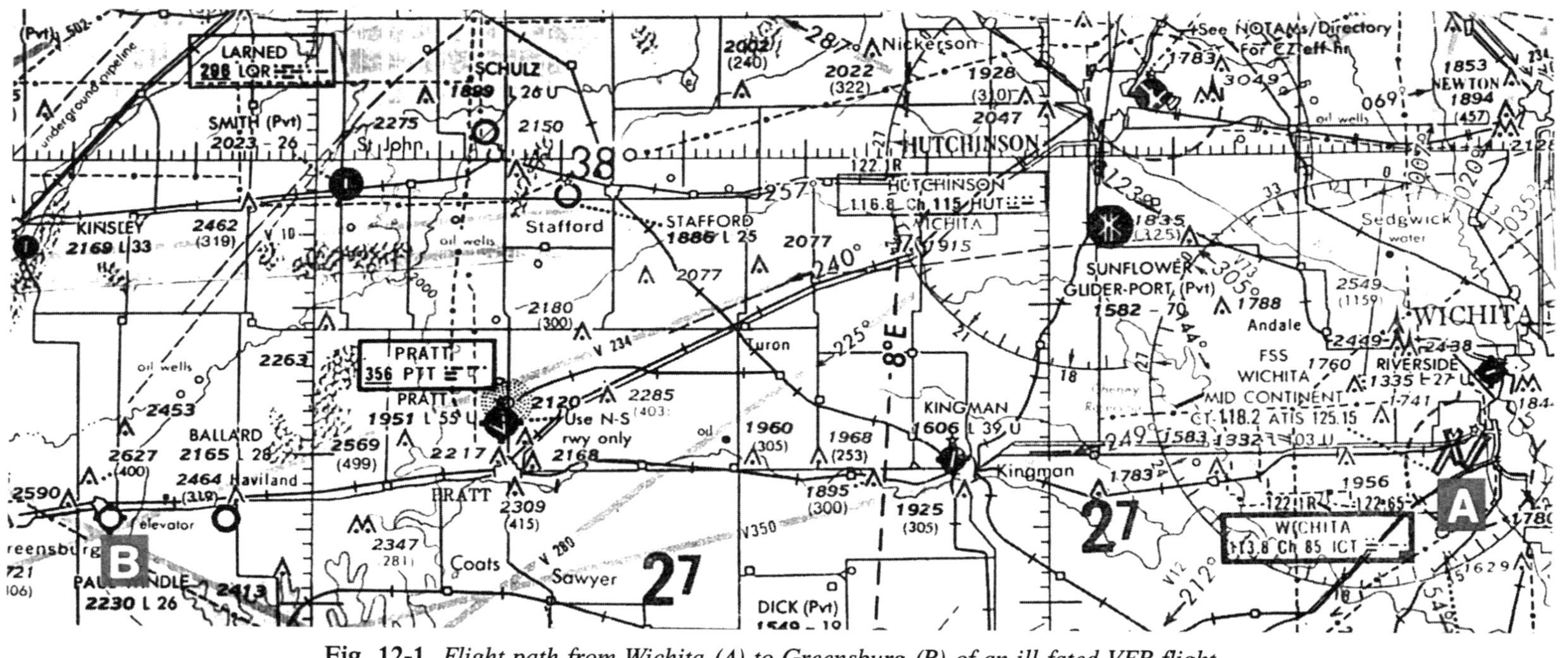

Fig. 12-1. *Flight path from Wichita (A) to Greensburg (B) of an ill-fated VFR flight.*

Pratt is the Anthony VOR. This VOR offered another link with the Wichita Flight Service Station. North of Pratt is the Great Bend RCO. The chart indicates that the Russell FSS is the parent facility for Great Bend. These two facilities provided excellent opportunities to receive weather information that could have influenced a decision to turn around or land at Pratt.

Again a point of decision was ignored. With a safe alternative directly under the airplane in the form of an airport, he still did not seek advice or information. He was now probably afraid of being "caught."

Then a witness saw the airplane pass. The person said he saw an airplane flying under the clouds. The airplane was so low that it was below the top of a tower. The tower is indicated on the chart with an AGL altitude of 319 feet. Five minutes after this sighting, the airplane crashed into a field and the pilot was killed.

All the opportunities for decision making ran out. The pilot's overconfidence and pride were stronger than his judgment.

In order to make good decisions, a pilot must be receptive to all possibilities, especially the possibility that a 180-degree turn should be made. Knowledge is strength. For whatever reason, this pilot decided not to be as knowledgeable about the weather conditions as he could have been. His lack of understanding and poor judgment never allowed him to make good decisions. The pilot had several opportunities to break the chain, but he never realized a chain was forming until it was too late.

HASTE MAKES WRECKAGE

Bad decision chains are not limited to low-time and inexperienced pilots. Even pilots who know better fall victim.

The experienced pilot of a Cessna Citation found himself behind schedule one morning. He had previously called in an IFR flight plan for a proposed takeoff from Mountain View Airport in Mountain View, Missouri. He called the Flight Service Station from home and told the briefer that he would be ready for takeoff in 15 minutes. It was 9:15 a.m. He accepted a void time clearance for 9:30 over the telephone when he was not even at the airport yet.

This certainly was a poor decision. The pilot, faced with a tight schedule, came to a crossroads and made a decision that set him up for real trouble. Every other decision that was made from this point on was predicated by the fact that a void time clearance had to be met. We do not know what pressures drove this pilot to make such a decision, but it was made.

He drove to the airport, arriving with only 10 minutes before his clearance would be void. He loaded two passengers into the Citation. To this point the pilot had not received any weather briefing for the flight, even though the weather at the airport was 100 feet overcast and less than one mile visibility. The pilot had less than five minutes to complete the Before Starting Engines, Starting Engines, Before Taxi, Before Takeoff, and Takeoff checklists. It was determined that these checks could not have been performed with the accuracy required within that length of time.

The pilot faced another point of decision. He knew from his training how important it is to carefully prepare an airplane for flight. The pilot right here could have seen things going the wrong way and stopped the chain. He would not have made the void time, but another telephone call to FSS could have extended the time.

It was determined that the time between engine start and takeoff was only two minutes. Unfortunately, the gyro instruments in that airplane take a minimum of three minutes, depending on temperature, to spin up to a speed that will provide correct indications.

This was yet another opportunity to say, "Enough is enough." Knowing that the instruments had not begun working properly, he could have waited. But he was in a hurry; he had to go. Later the chief pilot of the company, who was not on the flight, said that the pilot's side HSI normally took longer to spin up than did the HSI on the co-pilot's side. The NTSB concluded that the pilot might have been using a combination of incorrect information from his HSI and at the same time looking across the cockpit at the co-pilot's HSI. This would have forced him into an abnormal scan of the instruments. Knowing this ahead of time, the pilot should have seen that an improper preflight, rushing through the checklists, and improper instrument readings could only lead to trouble. The chain had three recognizable links in it, any one of which could have been broken with a good decision.

The airplane took off into the IFR conditions. Following the false instrument indications, the pilot gradually rolled the airplane into a 90-degree bank with the nose 30 degrees low. The flight only lasted one and a half minutes. The plane struck the ground at a high rate of speed only 1.75 miles from the runway. All aboard were killed.

NO BALANCING OF RISK OR THE AIRPLANE

Bad decisions led to an accident of a Part 135 flight in Alaska. Pilots are taught about weight and balance almost from the first lesson. Weight and balance knowledge is required on the Private Pilot and Recreational Pilot check rides. Finding experienced ATPs who disregard weight and balance calculations is unusual. But here again, good pilots make bad decisions.

Two pilots were flying a deHavilland DHC-6, better known as a Twin Otter. The flight originated at Bethel, Alaska, where the plane took on three passengers and 1,633 pounds of cargo. The flight took off and flew its first leg to Chevak without incident. At Chevak the two passengers got off and five other passengers got on. 950 pounds of cargo was unloaded and 902 pounds was reloaded and placed in the aft baggage compartment. The pilots unloaded and loaded the airplane themselves.

The pilots, who had firsthand knowledge of the airplane's loading, failed to evaluate how the change in weight would affect the stability of the airplane. The airplane took off again, this time for Scammon Bay. The airplane was still within the weight-and-balance limitations, but nobody knew that for sure.

The landing at Scammon Bay was described by passengers later as being shallow with high engine power. This should have been a clue to the pilots. At Scammon Bay

278 pounds of mail was removed from the nose compartment, leaving the nose empty, and 191 pounds was removed from the cabin. Everything in the aft compartment remained the same.

The simplest example of weight and balance is a teeter-totter. A diagram of this is in most elementary flight textbooks. When the board is in balance, any change in weight will affect the balance. The weight in the nose of the airplane was balancing the weight in the rear. With the nose compartment now empty, the board could not balance. It is like when one kid steps off the teeter-totter while the other kid is in mid-air. The kid comes crashing down. A decision opportunity is passing the pilots by unnoticed.

One pilot stayed in the cockpit with one engine running while the unloading took place. The airplane took off one more time, this time bound for Hooper Bay. The passengers said later that the airplane came off the ground earlier than before and that the pilot flew low over the runway for a time before making a normal climb. The flight to Hooper Bay was smooth and in VFR conditions at all times.

The approach to Hooper Bay was made from a right base to runway 13. The passengers said that the approach seemed to be higher than normal, based on other landings in the Twin Otter. Then the nose of the plane suddenly pitched up and the plane descended rapidly. The passengers could see and hear what was going on in the cockpit. When the nose pitched up, the pilot in the left seat was heard to say, "I said more power ****, more power!" The pilots "frantically" moved levers after the nose pitched up.

The pilot's opportunities for decisions had run out. They were blind to all the signs. The airplane tried to tell them on takeoff, but they were apparently unaware.

The airplane crashed short of the runway. The two pilots and six passengers were seriously hurt, but all survived. The pilots allowed a chain to form. The links of the chain had to do with the loading and unloading of cargo. The airplane was not overweight but out of balance. Each cargo stop and each change in cargo position moved the center of gravity (CG) farther and farther aft.

There is no leeway for an aft CG. If the airplane should stall with an aft CG, it is against the laws of physics for the plane to recover. Some pilots feel that with great pilot skills a recovery can be made, but they are wrong. An aft CG will not automatically cause a stall; but if the pilot allows the plane to stall, what happens next is no surprise. With an aft CG, a stall recovery is impossible. These two pilots can attest to that fact.

At each stop these pilots had the opportunity to check the balance of the airplane, but for whatever reason they decided against it.

A LATE DECISION IS A BAD DECISION

The pilot and co-pilot of a small business jet planned an IFR flight from Augusta, Georgia, to Bluefield, West Virginia. The weather at Bluefield was 600 scattered and 800 broken. The visibility was four with fog, and the temperature was 32°. The plane took off with three passengers aboard and was routine until within 35 miles of

Bluefield. The Atlanta air route traffic controller updated the weather from Bluefield for the pilots: ". . . weather at Bluefield, measured 700 overcast, visibility one mile with fog and snow . . . they advise that snow plows are on the runway and they need about 10 or 15 minutes warning before you get there." The crew acknowledged the information. The crew asked for and was granted a frequency change to talk firsthand with the FSS. The FSS gave the crew essentially the same information as the center did but included, "braking action [on the runway] reported poor by a Beech 99."

This report was key. The airplane these pilots were flying was faster and heavier than a Beech 99. The aircraft operating manual that was onboard the airplane contained performance data that showed that a safe landing was not possible on the Bluefield runway under these braking conditions.

This brought the pilots to a point of decision. Being familiar with the airplane, the crew should have known that this landing was dangerous and started considering an alternate. No decision was made at this point, however, and they continued inbound.

The crew was then told to report to Roanoke Approach control, and subsequently Roanoke cleared the flight for an ILS runway 23 approach. The pilot intersected the Localizer and was advised that the visibility was now three quarters of a mile with snow and ice on the runway. The airplane descended on the approach and broke into the clear. The crew then attempted to make a circling approach to runway 05. A witness saw the airplane on the circle approach and reported that the plane re-entered the clouds. The crew made a missed approach and asked to try the ILS one more time. They were cleared for another try and this approach was made to straight-in minimums. Everything looked normal until after the airplane touched down. The airplane did not decelerate past the terminal building. The airplane continued down the runway, apparently braking but to no avail.

Then with only 1,200 feet of runway remaining, FSS personnel heard a substantial increase in the engines' thrust. Just as the airplane reached the end of the runway, the pilot attempted rotation for lift-off. It was too late; the aircraft struck the Localizer antennas and crashed. All five occupants of the airplane were killed in the post-crash fire.

This accident is a little different than the ones discussed before. The chain of events that led to this accident happened quickly. The pilots did not ask for the NOTAMs for Bluefield prior to takeoff. If they had, they would have known about the runway conditions earlier. Still, they knew about the snow and ice on the runway before the approach. They apparently did not consider the folly of a landing on the snow-covered runway enough to divert to another airport. It is unknown why a circling approach was attempted on the first ILS. When the pilot did finally touch down, there was a moment of indecision. On the runway the decision to make the landing a touch-and-go instead of a full-stop was a good one. The pilot did not make a bad decision, but he did make a late decision. Time and runway went past before he saw that something had to be done. Sometimes in flying a situation can sweep the pilot away. In a situation such as this the lack of thorough planning leads to indecision. Not making a decision can be as costly as making a bad decision.

THE BOSS SAID, "LET'S GO!"

The pilot of a Beech 65 multi-engine airplane waited at Houston's William P. Hobby airport for a flight to Dallas Love Field. The president of the company he worked for was in a meeting in Houston but wanted to jump back in the airplane after the meeting and be home in Dallas that night. The pilot checked all the weather for the trip and taxied the airplane to the Sky Travel service ramp. The pilot requested that fuel be loaded on the airplane but was told by the lineman that they were temporarily out of fuel.

The pilot filed a flight plan for the trip but did not ask for a weather briefing. IFR conditions existed along the route of flight. The pilot believed that fuel would be available shortly and was waiting for the fuel truck when the president of the company and the chairman of the board drove up.

The lineman overheard the president ask the pilot if they were ready to leave. The pilot replied, "We are waiting on fuel." The president then asked the pilot if there was enough fuel on board to get to Dallas, and the pilot said there was enough. The president then said, "Well, lets go!" The two men loaded their baggage and climbed in. Soon the airplane took off.

Point of Decision: Never let non-pilots make air safety decisions, especially when dealing with IFR conditions. Options: Explain to the president the extra safety involved with filling the tanks, or say he is the boss, "Lets go!"

The airplane was flying in instrument conditions when the pilot reported in to Houston center by saying, "with you level at eight thousand." Thirty minutes later the airplane disappeared from the radar screen. All attempts to contact the airplane failed.

At this very moment several people living near Madisonville, Texas, witnessed the end of the story. They heard an airplane in the clouds making erratic power changes. One second the engines were "wide open," the next they were almost silent. The airplane then appeared from beneath the clouds, but it was not in one piece. In fact, it was in many pieces. There were no wings or tail attached to the fuselage prior to impact with the ground. All occupants were killed.

The investigation revealed the accident chain. First, the pilot was not current to use his instrument rating, and he had no instrument training in multi-engine airplanes. This link left the pilot vulnerable. The lack of currency alone did not cause the accident; it was only one piece to the puzzle.

Next, the pilot let pressures from the boss make his decision for him. It is hard to say no to the man that signs your paycheck. The employees of a company might be experts at what they do, but they are not pilots. The president of the company probably thought of fuel requirements in automotive terms. The tank does not have to be full if all you need to do is drive around the corner. The investigation revealed that there was enough gas on board to get to Dallas but that the main tanks had run dry. The auxiliary tanks of this airplane do not feed the main tanks but go directly to the engine when directed by the fuel selector valves.

The theory is that the airplane's main tanks started to run out and that this caused the engine to run rough or even to stop. This distracted the pilot from the primary job of flying the airplane. By the time the pilot got the tanks switched and the engines running, the airplane was in an unusual attitude. The pilot, not proficient in instrument conditions and untrained on multi-engine IFR operations, could not recover. In fact, his efforts to return the airplane to straight-and-level flight only made the problem worse. He must have been spatially disoriented and literally tore the airplane apart in the air with the wild gyrations that followed.

The fact that they did not fill the main tanks before takeoff did not alone cause the accident. The fact that the pilot was not instrument-current did not alone cause the accident. The fact that the pilot had no IFR multi-engine training did not alone cause the accident. The fact that the president was in a hurry did not alone cause the accident. But taken together, these factors linked the chain of disaster.

"DON'T WORRY ABOUT THAT 20¢ PIECE OF EQUIPMENT!"

Airline pilots are not immune to being caught up in a bad decision chain either. One of the most gripping accidents involving pilot decision making or the lack thereof is the case of Eastern Airlines flight 401. In December of 1972, three veteran pilots flew a perfectly good L-1011 into the Florida Everglades and killed 99 people.

The flight was on approach to runway 9L at Miami International. There was no moon and the night was dark, but the flight was in VFR conditions. The Cockpit Voice Recorder picked up the conversation in the cockpit of the ill-fated flight.

While inbound the pilots placed the landing gear lever in the down position. Only two of the three lights became illuminated. The nose gear light was dark. The Captain of the flight told Miami that they had a problem with the nose gear and that they would break off the approach and try to fix it. The controller gave the plane a heading of 360 degrees, which would be the first leg of a pattern back around to reintercept the approach.

All three pilots were convinced that the gear was down and that the problem was actually a burned-out light. For several minutes all three pilots could be heard talking about replacing the burned-out bulb with one that was known to work. The problem was that they could not take out the bad light. It had jammed, but all three pilots took their turn trying to pull it out. During this time the co-pilot said, "Do you want me to fly, Doug?" The Captain must not have heard the question because he said abruptly, "What altitude are we assigned to?" The assigned altitude was 2,000 and so the pilot placed the airplane on auto-pilot to hold that altitude while they fixed the problem.

Many decision points were passing them by. First, nobody had taken charge of the situation. Nobody had delegated authority. All three pilots should not have been working on the same problem; somebody must fly the airplane. Next, if the nose gear was not down, a landing on the two main landing gears was an option that could have been considered and planned for. Third, the nose gear position could be verified without the light by looking in the wheel well and seeing if index marks were lined up. Finally, the Captain did ask the Second Officer to go back and check the index lines. He said,

"Don't worry about that 20¢ piece of equipment," referring to the burned out light.

Then on the Cockpit Voice Recorder the clear sound of the auto-pilot disengage horn is heard. The auto-pilot was somehow tripped off but nobody heard the horn. Everyone was now following a path where outside facts were missed. Nobody was aware that the airplane was starting a slow descent. Again the Captain said, "Go check that damn nose wheel!" And the First Officer said, "It is always something, and we were on schedule, too!"

At this point, the air traffic controllers see by way of the altitude-reporting transponder that the airplane is low. The controller says, "How are things coming along out there, 401?" This request is so vague that the crew does not realize that the controller is concerned about the plane's altitude. If the controller had said, "Eastern 401, climb immediately," maybe the pilots would have woken up. But as it turned out, the controller's vague request was just another link in the chain.

The pilots had made so many bad judgments in handling the problem that they had totally removed themselves from flying the airplane. Nobody was watching the instruments or knew the status of the airplane. The plane had flown over the everglades now where there were no lights to give the pilots perspective. Finally, the First Officer said, "Hey, there is something wrong with the altitude. We're still at 2,000, right!" The next sound heard on the tape is the sound of impact.

If the pilots in each of these accidents had been able to step back from the scene and view it objectively as we have done, their mistakes would have been easy to see. The accidents would not have taken place. Each pilot reached a point of decision and did not realize a decision was called for or ignored that fact. Pilots have a way of placing blinders on their head. The pilots did not see risk factors that were presented to them and therefore they did not act to stop a progression of deadly events. Only pilots can prevent "pilot error." The best prevention is good decision-making skills.

13
Career Decisions

IN THE EARLY 1970S MY FIRST FLIGHT INSTRUCTOR TOOK ME ASIDE. HE said, "Your progress in the airplane is coming along fine, but I don't want you to get the wrong idea. You will never get a job doing this!" Over the years I proved him wrong, but it was the market, not me, that changed. There was a time when the fascination of flight was reserved for pleasure flying only. Today, however, the possibility of using that fascination of flight as a tool for career advancement is great.

With airlines hiring, many people are considering making flight a career who never would have when it was just for fun. There are still many pilots who fly just for fun. They will be career private pilots, and there is nothing wrong with that. But more and more pilots are catching the career-flying fever. Flying an airplane as a career is a big challenge. Like all decisions the more that is known about a situation, the better the final decision that is made. There are plenty of good books on how to get a commercial pilot certificate, but this chapter deals with what can be done with it.

Three factors have come together that have allowed the market to become pilot-friendly. The first factor was Airline Deregulation. The law was passed in 1978 and changed the way the airlines and the government do business. Since the passing of the law, airline companies are on their own to sink or swim. Before the law, the government widely subsidized airlines if they began to sink just so airline service to some areas would continue. Airlines soon discovered that many markets could not be sustained without the subsidy payments and pulled out. The major airlines withdrew to the more profitable routes, and many markets were left stranded. Before long, smaller commuter airlines came to the rescue of the stranded markets and began to generate profits again. The profits were possible because airplanes that more fit the market were used. Before the law, Boeing 727s would fly half empty to a small town without fear of losing money. Now, a 19-passenger turboprop flies the route using a smaller economy of scale. Over 500 commuter airlines were started to fill in the gaps left by deregulation. Many of these companies have already gone out of business, leaving only the airlines that did a better job of cost control or affiliation remaining.

For years, overnight cargo airlines have used the "hub-and-spoke" method of transportation. The idea is simple. Flights filled with packages from all over the nation converge on a single airport. The packages are then unloaded, sorted, and placed on a different plane. All the planes then take off and return to where they came from. This means that if a package is sent from San Diego to Los Angeles, it must do so by going to Memphis first (if Memphis is the hub airport). Everything works great. The packages do not complain about having to go to Memphis first, and the customers don't know the difference. This is much more economical than having flights between every city that have package delivery service.

The savings were seen by the passenger-carrying airlines as well. Now, passengers are treated like packages. The difference is that passengers have to sort themselves at the airports to assure that they get on the correct airplane. The major airlines have established hubs but cannot afford all the spokes. Commuter airlines fill this need.

If a passenger buys an airline ticket on a major airline from Chicago to Wichita Falls, Texas, he will not actually be flown on airplanes that are owned by the major airline for the entire trip. The trip will begin with a leg from Chicago to Dallas/Ft. Worth on a large transport jetliner: a Boeing 757. Once in Dallas, the passenger will be guided to an airline gate that is at the far end of the concourse. At the gate awaits a small turboprop. The turboprop has new paint on it that makes it roughly resemble the major carrier. The trip then continues to Wichita Falls. The passenger's ticket only has the two-letter identification code of the major carrier. This is possible because the major carrier has made an agreement with the small commuter. For the small airline's part, they provide a service over a short distance and feed the hub of the major carrier. The large airline books unsuspecting passengers on the small airline's flights as if they are all the same and allows the small airline to use the large airline's colors. The large airline can then advertise expanded service at no cost to them, and the small airline is funneled business they might not otherwise receive. To the prospective career pilot, this is great. The commuter airlines have become a little more financially stable over the years, and they are hiring.

Who are the airlines hiring? This brings up the second factor that has changed the market: the supply of military pilots. For years the only way to work for the airlines was to fly military first. This allowed the individual to log large amounts of flight time in large airplanes. After a military obligation was fulfilled, the pilot would simply change uniforms and begin with the airlines. The military finally got wise to this situation. They were losing millions in retraining costs, while already-trained pilots walked out the door.

The military began paying better and offering incentives for pilots to extend their military obligations. The plan worked. According to the Future Aviation Professionals of America (FAPA), the tide turned in 1985. Every year prior to 1985, military pilots were hired more often than civilian-trained pilots by the major airlines. After 1985 it has been the other way around.

I visited a Naval base recently and talked with the young pilot of a P-3 Orion sub-chaser. I asked him if he had ever considered leaving the Navy to fly for the airlines. He said he thought about it every day, but he figured it would take a five-year investment with the airlines to make the same money the Navy was paying. He had a wife and children and was not willing to take the gamble. "In the long run, I would make more money and move my family less with the airlines, but the Navy has got me where they want me," he said. I feel he represents the position of many military pilots.

When less military pilots come out, more opportunities exist for civilian pilots. The need for pilots with commuters went up at the same time the supply of pilots went down. Free market forces then drove down the requirements for flying with the airlines. Today less flight time is needed to get started. Pilots can wear eyeglasses and fly for the airlines as long as they can pass a first-class medical exam. Before, a four-year degree was always required; now, some airlines advertise that a high school diploma is enough for them.

The final factor is retirement. Airline pilots are forced to retire when they reach the age of 60. Many airline pilots today were trained under the old GI Bill, following the Korean War. These pilots are reaching the age of 60 in a large block. Estimates reach 2,000 pilot job openings a year through the 90s due to retirement alone. It is a great time to become a career pilot.

Most people consider a person who has passed the commercial pilot check ride to be a full-fledged career pilot. This is not the case, however. There are very few things that a pilot can do with a new commercial pilot certificate. What is allowed is outlined in FAR part 135.1. The specific operations that are allowed for airplanes are:

1. Flight instruction.
2. Nonstop sightseeing flights within 25 miles.
3. Ferry flights.
4. Aerial work including—
   a. Crop dusting.
   b. Banner towing.
   c. Aerial photography.
   d. Fire fighting.
   e. Pipeline/Powerline patrol.
5. Carrying parachute jumpers within 25 miles.

Missing from the list is any mention of carrying passengers on trips for money. Carrying passengers for money is reserved for Air Taxi and Air Carrier operations. How is a pilot supposed to bridge the gap from hopeful to career pilot? How do pilots climb the aviation career ladder?

First, get the best training that can be found. Since the airlines started hiring, flight schools have sprung up everywhere. Train at a school that has an excellent reputation for training pilots, not just for having people pass tests. Ask how many school graduates have jobs in the industry and what those jobs are. Consider combining aviation and college together. The University Aerospace Association publishes a catalog of all colleges and universities that offer aviation courses and degrees. College courses are usually more intense and cover more ground than is the case with a single instructor and student one on one. If two pilots are invited to interview with an airline and both have identical trainability, flight time, medical certificate, and pilot certificates, the pilot with college experience will get the job.

THE "INTERNSHIP" OF AVIATION

With pilot certificates in hand, new commercial pilots begin the "internship" of aviation. The first rung of the ladder is flight instructor. Student flight instruction is the first one on the Part 135 list, and since many people are learning to fly, there are more opportunities to be an instructor than anything else on the list. It is a sad commentary on the industry, but the people who are depended upon to train the future pilots are underpaid and underappreciated. The CFI might get four or five hours of flight time per day, but to get that much he must be present at the airport about 12 hours a day.

The old flight instructors who have seen it all and lived it all are a dying breed. Today the industry forces the profession of flight instruction to be made up of transients. Now, if a pilot has been instructing for three years or more, he is an old-timer. Nobody can afford to be a flight instructor for long even if he desires to do so. Flight instructors get compensated in three ways. The first way is in the form of money. The second way is in the form of flight time. The last way is in the form of self-satisfaction in a job well done. That last way is hard to cash in. The flight instructor is hoping that the flight time acquired will be able to buy him a step onto the next higher rung on the ladder.

The next rung is the jump to a part 135 Air Taxi and Commercial Operator job. The part 135 regulations have no minimum time above commercial pilot for the job of Second in Command, but very few operators hire pilots with ink still wet on their commercial certificate. Air Taxi operators are not flight schools; it is extremely rare that they will take on a low-time commercial pilot and bring him along. They would rather hire someone who already has the flight time and for whom they don't have to provide. The part 135 pilot in command flight-time requirement for VFR flights is 500 hours, but this is not very practical either. No company will assign a job that must get done to a pilot who can't fly when the weather is below VFR minimums. To really be considered for employment, pilots should shoot to meet the pilot in command minimums for IFR flight: 1,200 hours.

Every company has its own seniority list. Pilots with only 1,200 hours start at the bottom. The bottom of this pile usually means contract flying and usually at night.

These jobs produce plenty of flight time but they are grueling. They fly older, "ragged-out" flying trucks full of other people's business. These flights have a poor overall safety record. They fly in just about any weather because packages, spare parts, and canceled bank checks do not complain about turbulence and lightning. Many of these companies are run on a shoestring. The bottom line, not safety, can easily become the driving force. Coming from an environment of flight instructors, where safety is preached, this world is a real eye-opener.

A friend of mine was once caught on the back side of a squall line with a load of urgent bank papers. He called the operations office of the company and said he would not be able to complete the delivery because of the weather. He was told that he should make the flight anyway or tomorrow night they would have somebody in his place who would! The goal here is to survive this rung on the ladder with enough quality time to move on.

It is a common practice for pilots desperate for flight time to "ride along" on these flights. If you ride, beware. Riders on cargo flights are not covered on insurance. If anything should happen on the flight, you (or your estate) will have no legal rights and the company will claim you were a stowaway.

The next step up is Charter or Air taxi. Charter airplanes at least look better than cargo planes because they must impress the customers. These airplanes usually come with two engines. This is important because the jump to the airlines won't come without at least 300 to 500 hours in twins. The pilots can also "burn kerosene" for the first time on this rung. The flight time for a charter pilot can be sporadic and the schedule unbelievable. Charter pilots carry beepers that run their lives. There are many who have stopped here on this rung. For a pilot who sticks with a good company, the pay can be good and the equipment flown can be excellent.

The next rung on the ladder depends on personal preference and opportunity. The options are commuter airlines or corporate flying. Flying for a corporation can be a great job. At the top of this pyramid are pricey business jets (FIG. 13-1). A pilot knows he has arrived when his seat is forward of the nose wheel. Still, some do not consider this a top rung because the pilots are occasionally seen in the airport men's room cleaning out the coffee pots.

The airlines are the top rung. Yet, a pilot's first airline job is the bottom of still another ladder to climb. The commuter airlines are counting on the fact that young pilots will do just about anything to wear their uniform and fly their planes (FIG. 13-2), so the starting salaries are low. In many cities, sanitation workers bring home more cash than first-year pilots. But after the first "probation" year, the money will start to flow a little faster.

Many young pilots get hired by a commuter airline and let their guard down a little. They enjoy the new schedule and the prestige of airline pilot. But if a pilot's final goal is the major airlines, the time spent with the commuters is just another internship. The commuters are not actually a "farm team" for the majors yet, but it is moving in that direction. Choosing a commuter should be the same as choosing a flight school. What can the commuter airline do for me in the short run? Does the

Fig. 13-1. *Airplanes are as common in American business as computers, expense accounts, and fax machines.*

Fig. 13-2

commuter have a good record with the pilots, passengers, and banks? Young pilots who have spent lots of money, waited while student pilots soloed, and flown canceled checks at night are eager to move ahead. It is easy to jump at the first thing that presents itself. But avoid the temptations and be selective! The company chosen to fly with will be the biggest decision of a career. Like every aeronautical decision made, best results require judgment. Judgment springs from knowledge, skill, and experience. People who can make good decisions make great pilots!

14
The Final Decision

"IF YOU ARE LOOKING FOR PERFECT SAFETY [NO RISK], YOU'LL DO WELL TO sit on a fence and watch the birds. But if you really wish to learn you must mount a machine and become acquainted with its tricks by actual trial." Wilbur Wright made this statement in 1902, but it speaks to the pilots of today. The phrase, ". . . if you really wish to learn . . ." stands out. Pilots must want to become the best pilots they can be. Pilots must be eager to learn and never become stale.

In the final analysis, a pilot's attitude will determine whether or not he exercises good judgment. All the information in the world is of no use until someone decides to use it. The safe pilot decides to go the extra mile in preparation, study, and planning. The safe pilot has situational awareness and makes one good decision after another, based on the situation at hand.

Aviation has become too busy, congested, and demanding for it to ever be considered just a hobby. If you fly, you must remain motivated to learn new things, keep proficient, and form opinions on issues. Apathy is a killer.

I challenge you to become passionate about flying. Today's system requires all pilots to be sharp. The margin of safety is only there because there are pilots and controllers out there right now exercising good judgment. Aviation is far too vast for anybody to ever get overconfident. Even the job-worn and world-weary pilots will tell you that they learn something new every flight. The learning never stops.

The more you understand and apply, the better decisions you will ultimately make. The final decision is yours!

Appendix
Pilot Personality Survey

Take the Pilot Personality Survey and see how your personality traits compare to those of the pilot personality as discussed in chapter 1.

1. Circle your age group.
   20 or under   21 to 25   26 to 30   31 to 40
   41 to 50   51 to 60   61 and older

2. Circle one.
   Male   Female

3. Pilot certificates held. (circle one)
   Student   Private   Private with IFR rating   Commercial
   Flight instructor   Airline transport

4. Flight time. (circle one)
   0 to 40 hours   41 to 100 hours   101 to 200 hours
   200 to 500 hours   500 to 2,000 hours   2,001 and more

5. Years interested in Aviation. (circle one)
   1 year   2 to 5 years   5 to 10 years   more than 10 years

6. Which activity would you rather participate in? (circle one)
   golf   Chess   Windsurfing   Aerobics

7. What was your favorite subject in High School? (circle one)

   Math   English   Science   Home Econ or Shop

8. If you were reincarnated and came back as an animal, which one would you want to be? (circle one)

   House Cat   Shark   Bald Eagle

9. What would be your choice of vacations? (circle one)

   Wildlife safari in Africa   Touring historic Europe

   Sail around the world solo

10. Which business would you most likely invest in? (circle one)

    US Government   Playboy Magazine   IBM

11. What describes you best? (circle one)

    Cautious   Contemplative   Compulsive   Courteous

12. If you could be one of the following heroes, who would you choose?(circle one)

    Albert Einstein   Chuck Yeager   Michael Jackson

13. Which challenge would you most likely want to accept? (put an X in blank of your selection)

    _____ Relief pitcher coming in during the 9th inning of the seventh game of the World Series. Your team is ahead 1-0. There are two outs and a man on third base.

    _____ You are on the 18th green of the Masters Golf Tournament. You have a one-shot lead and face a tricky 10-foot putt for par.

    _____ You are on the "Let's Make A Deal" show and must choose between $100 cash or what is behind door number 1.

14. What person would you most likely want to be? (circle one)

    Donald Trump   Ted Kennedy   Lee Iacoca   Ronald Reagan

15. What movie appeals to you the most? (circle one)

    Top Gun   Dirty Dancing   Batman   E.T.

16. When you go to the laundromat to do your clothes you—(put an X on the blank of what best describes your actions)

    _____ Neatly fold your clothes as they come out of the dryer

    _____ Return to the dryer 30 minutes after the clothes have finished drying

    _____ Throw your clothes in a basket and fold them later

    _____ Never fold them

17. When you buy groceries for your home or apartment you—(put an X on the blank of what best describes your actions)

    _____ Make a list of items you need before you go shopping

    _____ Go shopping only when you are hungry and you buy just what you feel like having at that time

    _____ Plan a week's worth of meals, make a list, and then go shopping

    _____ Live on whatever you can buy at fast food stores and vending machines

18. When it comes to being on time, people who know you would probably say—(circle one)

    You're always late They can set their watches by you

19. When it comes to "dumb" accidents you—(circle one)

    Pretty careful You have your share

    You are "accident prone"

20. What (or who) would you think is the funniest? (circle one)

    A pie in the face gag A really clever political monologue

    David Letterman Roseanne Barr

21. How many GOOD friends do you have? (circle one)

    One 2 or 3 More than 5 None

22. You are a great—(circle one)

    Listener Liar Partier Playboy Networker

23. What is your attitude about people you know? (circle one)

    Friendships are extremely important Never completely trust anyone

    Only trust your closest friends

24. It is 3AM and you are stopped at a red light (that may be stuck). What would you do? (circle one)

    Look both ways and go   Wait for it to change to Green

    Call the police to report a broken traffic light

25. When you were growing up your parents—(circle one)

    Showered you with love & praise   Were mere tools to get what you wanted

    Gave you lots of things but not praise & respect

26. You like to play games—(circle one)

    Alone   With a partner   As part of a team

27. What do you want? (circle one)

    Nothing more than what is earned or owed

    What others have: jobs, money, sex

    Whatever I can get, anyway I can get it

    More than what my close friends have

    Nothing

28. Which statement is true about you? (circle one)

    You are pretty good at sports   You are best at Math or English

    You are good at crossword puzzles   Your mood changes with environment

29. If you start a task you—(circle one)

    Cannot stop until you finish   Work until something else comes up

    Stop for the slightest excuse

30. When traveling by car you—(circle one)

    Like to do the driving   You don't care who drives

31. You are most accused of forgetting—(circle one)

    Where you put things   Faces   Names, phone numbers, birthdays

32. What describes you best? (circle one)

    I am spontaneous   I am set in my ways   I am fun to be with

    I am the best at anything I do

33. In your family are you—(circle one)

    The oldest child   In the middle   The youngest

34. Is your girlfriend or boyfriend, wife, or husband—(circle one)
The oldest child in their family   Middle child   Youngest child

35. I seldom drive slower than the speed limit—(circle one)
TRUE   FALSE

36. I have a morning routine that I follow the same way everyday (shower, shave, brush my teeth, etc.) (circle one)
TRUE   FALSE

37. If I had my choice, I would drive a— (circle one)
4-Wheel Jeep   Convertible sports car
Station wagon   Van

38. I own or would like to have a radar detector for my car (circle one)
TRUE   FALSE

39. The world would be better off if everyone was more like me (circle one)
TRUE   FALSE

40. If I were king, I would jail anyone who drives 10 mph under the speed limit or who turns without signaling (circle one)
TRUE   FALSE

41. When I am driving my car and see a hitchhiker I—(circle one)
Drive past and never consider picking him up
Drive past but feel guilty that I didn't pick him up
Give him a ride

42. You are flying with another pilot who has the same pilot certificates as you and about the same flight time as you. If the other pilot corrects you on something you will—(circle one)
Listen and try to learn something
Listen but never invite him flying again
Politely ignore him
Argue that what you did was better than what was suggested

43. If you see someone make a mistake while flying, you will—(circle one)
Say nothing   Quietly mention it to the person
Tell everyone you see about another's mistake

44. When you feel strongly about something, you will—(circle one)
    Keep it to yourself and say nothing
    Push to have others see it your way

45. With friends I would rather—(circle one)
    Listen as some tells about their last solo cross country
    Tell others about your last trip to a busy controlled airport

46a. Which would you rather do? (circle one)
    Work on an assignment that had strict guidelines and all you had to do was simply follow directions
    Work on an assignment that gave you a lot of freedom to explore the topic

46b. What situation would you most likely enjoy? (circle one)
    A situation in which you had total control and authority
    A situation in which another person is in charge and you must take directions from that person

46c. The job you would most enjoy would be one where—(circle one)
    You do something different every day and do more thinking than actual physical labor
    You do the same thing every day and enjoy the fact that it provides security with no surprises

47. Filling out a complete navigation log, weight & balance form, and consulting many performance charts is—(circle one)
    Essential for a safe flight
    Good practice but not necessary on every flight
    Good for beginner but later unnecessary
    A waste of valuable time

48. If the person who lives next door to you complained that your music was too loud, you would—(circle one)
    Turn the music down
    Tell the person if he/she doesn't like it they can move
    Ignore the person

49. What would give you the most pride? (circle one)
    Completing a difficult task, even when it takes 100% effort

Wasting an afternoon because you had nothing better to do

Getting a good grade, but knowing you did not give your best

50. A pilot is best described as—(circle one)

    A romamtic hero   Just another person doing a job

    A thrill seeker   An over achiever

51. A pilot is—(circle one)

    A person with above average talents who could excel in any field

    A person with average drive who thinks flying is as good a way to make a living as anything else

52. A person should get into flying because—(circle one)

    It is fun   It can lead to big bucks

    It's not what everybody does   It's a way to beat the 55 mph speed limit

53. When a flight instructor gives you some criticism about something you did during a flight, you—(circle one)

    Listen and try to learn something new every time

    Feel he/she is just being picky and what you are doing is really all right; it's just not perfect

54. When in flight training, your major objective is to—(circle one)

    Know enough to pass the next check ride

    Learn everything there is to learn

    Impress the instructor or examiner

55. After you get your private pilot certificate, what would you want to have happen? (circle one)

    TV news in your home town interview you about your success

    Nothing

    Show your certificate to friends who are not pilots

56. Why are you in flight training? (circle one)

    I want a high paying career

    Flying suits my personality

    My father (or other relative) is a pilot, so I have to be

    I want a big challenge to see if I can measure up

Index

A

C

D

J

K

L

M

N

O

P

R

S

T

U

V

W

Y